THEM+US

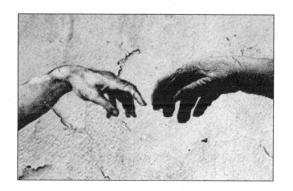

THEM AND US

HOW NEANDERTHAL PREDATION
CREATED MODERN HUMANS

DANNY VENDRAMINI

kardoorairpress

National Library of Australia Cataloguing-in-Publication entry
Vendramini, Danny, 1948-
Them and Us : how Neanderthal predation created modern humans
Includes index, bibliography
ISBN: 978 0 908244 77 5 (pbk.)
1. Anthropology – Predation (Biology) – Human evolution – Neanderthals – Human beings
304

Published in Australia by Kardoorair Press
PO Box 478, Armidale, NSW 2350, Australia
www.kardoorair.com.au

Designed and typeset by Helen Forlong
WordWitches, Sydney, Australia
www.wordwitches.com
Typeset in Garamond 11.5 pt

Author photograph: Josie Vendramini

Printed and bound in Australia by Ligare Book Printers

Cover images: Arturo Balseiro, Dharma Estudio

To my father, who said, "Be intuitive."

And to Rosie, who said, "Be rigorous."

ACKNOWLEDGEMENTS

Science is a collaborative pursuit and I am indebted to the authors of the 800 papers and academic sources I've quoted in this book. Without their bricks, there would be no house. In particular, my thanks to Tord Kjellstrom, Iain Davidson, Johan M G van der Dennen, Coral Wynter, Erik Trinkaus, Svante Pääbo, Heather Smith, John Shea, Tony McMichael, Paul Mellars, Susan Antón, David Pearce, Erella Hovers, and Michael Kaplan. Likewise, I'm especially indebted to my daughters Josie and Bella, Emily Walker, Bernard Shirley, Keith Johnson, Ned Walker, Andrew Bell, Tom Markham and my publisher Tony Bennett for their invaluable editorial input and advice.

My thanks also to Arturo Balseiro, Creative Director of Dharma Estudio, for his forensic reconstructions of a Neanderthal and to Helen Forlong from WordWitches for her scholarly editing and fabulous book design. Above all, my thanks and appreciation to my wife, muse, mentor and lifelong editor, Rosie Scott.

ILLUSTRATIONS

To reproduce the forensic reconstruction illustrations of the 'La Ferrassie' Neanderthal in Chapter 8 and on the covers, refer to our website for conditions.

WWW.THEMANDUS.ORG

For extra information, coloured illustrations and other material, visit the *Them and Us* website.

CONTENTS

PREFACE

I've always loved movies about mythic heroes battling the forces of evil, but in the 1970s, when I heard that George Lucas had based *Star Wars* on ancient hero myths, my lifelong fascination with mythology really took off.

In 1999, inspired by American anthropologist Joseph Campbell's work on universal myths, I started researching a book on the relationship between myths and movies. I wanted to explore why widely disparate cultures, often with no contact with one another, somehow came up with virtually identical mythic stories. From ancient Mesopotamia to modern Manhattan, from Amazonian Indians to American matrons, humans appeared so viscerally attracted to the same mythic themes—good and evil, sex and violence, heroes, quests, perilous journeys, dragons and other monsters—it was as if they had been hardwired into our genes.

I wanted to include one chapter in the book to explain exactly how these heroic tales came to be so universal that audiences around the world all responded in much the same way. But when I went to the literature I couldn't find a satisfactory biological explanation. Yes, there was Jung's theory of the collective unconscious—but for my purposes, that appeared too steeped in a quasi-spiritual ethos to provide a scientifically valid explanation.

I eventually realised there was a serious gap in the biological model— something missing—which I found so intriguing that I put the book aside. Instead, I began researching how humans and other animals acquire new instincts, innate behaviours and emotions.

Six years later, the British journal *Medical Hypothesis* published the results of my research, "Noncoding DNA and the Teem theory of inheritance, emotions and innate behaviour". The paper presented a radical new theory of the evolution of behaviour to explain how animals acquired new instincts and emotions. Its central proposition was that high intensity emotional experiences (usually caused by traumatic events like predator attacks, accidents and natural disasters) can, under certain circumstances, be permanently encoded into an area of an animal's genome called nonprotein-coding DNA. This is the part that is usually dismissed as 'junk DNA'.

It soon became apparent that 'Teem theory' was a kind of master key that could open other doors, for instance, explaining how humans acquired the repository of innate behaviours and emotions we call human nature. When I applied Teem theory to what had transformed humans from stone-age African hominids into fully modern humans, why we look and act the way we do, and even why we're obsessed with sex and violence and good and evil, it proposed a single simple explanation that was both extraordinary and unexpected.

The result is a unified theory of human origins called Neanderthal Predation theory (or NP theory) which is based on a fundamental reassessment of Neanderthal behavioural ecology. Exciting new evidence reveals Neanderthals weren't docile omnivores, but savage, cannibalistic carnivores—top flight predators—who hunted, killed and cannibalised our archaic ancestors in the Middle East for 50,000 years. What's more, Neanderthals were also sexual predators, who raided human camps to rape, and abduct young females, leaving a trail of half-cast 'inbreds'.

This multi-faceted predation eventually drove our ancestors to the brink of extinction. Genetic evidence reveals that at one stage our entire ancestral population was reduced to as few as 50 people.

The only humans to survive the predation were those born with mutations for 'survivalist adaptations'—modern human traits like language capacity, Machiavellian intelligence, coalition building, creativity, risk-taking and aggression. These traits effectively transformed them from a prey species to a virulent new hunter species—*Homo sapiens*.

Armed with these new attributes, the first modern humans systematically exterminated their former predators, firstly in the Middle East and then in a blitzkrieg invasion of Europe. They then spread out to colonise the world. Guided by an innate sense of *them and us*, hyper-aggressive men killed anyone who looked or behaved even remotely like a Neanderthal, including hybrids and other humans. It was this lethal process of artificial selection that gradually unified human physiology and behaviour.

It's a fairly radical theory, but its strength lies in its predictions and ability to explain aspects of human evolution, physiology and behaviour that have frustrated philosophers, biologists and anthropologists for centuries.

The book has been written for a general readership which has an interest in how we got here. I've included 'boxes' to explain peripheral subjects and there's a glossary of ancillary terms at the end. But to help academics evaluate the theory, I've also included my references—all 800 of them.

Because the evolutionary events I am investigating happened so long ago, some aspects of the scenario I propose are speculative. For instance, I speculate on the psychological impact that Neanderthal predation had on our ancestors, how the menfolk felt seeing their women abducted and raped. I do this because the psychology of ancestral humans had a direct bearing on our evolution and needs to be considered as part of a holistic theory.

For some scholars, though, the use of speculation and the imagination are anathema—but historically there has always been a legitimate place for the imagination in science. A scientific model can be subjected to rational debate and analysis only once it exists in a tangible form. The day before Einstein conceived his theory of relativity, there was nothing to think about. It existed in a netherworld beyond deductive reasoning, and required an act of imagination to bring it into existence.

Einstein is famously quoted as saying, "Imagination is more important than knowledge" and he explains, "For while knowledge defines all we currently know and understand, imagination points to all we might yet discover and create."

For radical, big-idea science, imagination isn't just ancillary to the scientific process, it is an indispensable ingredient.

With human evolution, it could be argued that the reluctance of academics to imagine alternative evolutionary scenarios, or to encourage lateral thinking beyond the narrow pathways of orthodoxy, has hampered progress of this field.

While imagination played a role in the formulation of NP theory, the resulting evolutionary scenario has, of course, been subjected to an exhaustive six-year process of scientific scrutiny and verification which involved sifting through 3000 scientific papers and other pieces of evidence. Ultimately, the theory's credibility rests on the rigour of this process.

1   MYSTERIOUS ORIGINS

what we don't know

We humans are such a clever species. Our spaceships have landed on the moon and Mars. We have discovered life forms ten kilometres underground and in deep-sea fumaroles. Our geneticists have sequenced over 200 genomes, while our astronomers have discovered earth-like planets on the edge of space-time. We've speculated on the extinction of the dinosaurs, and now physicists at the Large Hadron Collider are close to unravelling the secrets of quantum mechanics.

And yet, when it comes to ourselves, there's an awful lot we don't understand. The brain for example. And how we became human.

Science writer Carl Zimmer wrote in 2003 that, "what we don't know about our evolution vastly outweighs what we do know."

Three main aspects of human evolution continue to frustrate scientists:

- The abrupt transformation—from African hominid to modern human about 46,000 years ago
- Physiology—why, despite sharing 99 percent of our protein-coding genes with chimps, do we look so different?
- Human nature—where did all the unique behaviours that distinguish us from other primates come from?

Let's begin with the mysterious speciation event that suddenly created modern humans. "Few topics in palaeoanthropology", Cambridge University Professor of Archaeology and Human Evolution Paul Mellars observed in 2005, "have generated more recent debate than the nature and causes of the remarkable transformation in human behavioural patterns that marked the transition from the Middle to the Upper Palaeolithic era in Europe."[3]

MIDDLE PALAEOLITHIC AND UPPER PALAEOLITHIC

These terms refer to different stages of human evolution. The *Middle Palaeolithic* denotes archaic humans and hominids, a period before art, culture, symbolic language etc.—in short, the time before we were 'us'. *Upper Palaeolithic* refers to the new 'smart' *homo sapiens*—with a more sophisticated tool kit, representational art, symbolic language and creativity.

Although archaic hominids like *Homo heidelbergensis* had brains as big as ours 600,000 years ago, they never produced art, culture, complex language, symbolic thinking or any of the other tangible indicators of human capacity. This flowering of modern humanity has been described as 'the human revolution', the 'dawn of human culture', and the 'explosion of human capacity', but there is still no agreement on what precipitated it or why.

It is a commonly held misconception that the Upper Palaeolithic

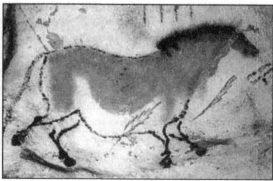

Excavated from a Middle Stone Age cave in South Africa, the 77,000 year-old block of red ochre (left) has been described as the earliest discovered art work. However, true representational art, like the magnificent horse from the Lascaux cave in France (right), did not appear until around 30,000 years ago.

revolution began in Africa. What the latest evidence shows is that a few isolated early examples of modern human behaviour did appear in Africa as early as 300,000 years ago[4] including what may be an example of 77,000 year old art[5] (*see previous page*). But none of these isolated flowerings of Initial Upper Palaeolithic culture ever 'took off' on a grand scale across the continent, much less across the globe. While a few isolated tribes made shell beads, others did not. While most of them fashioned crude tools, a small number made more efficient ones. And a few appeared to have used ochre (presumably for decoration) while others did not.

In November 2008, geologist Zenobia Jacobs, from the University of Wollongong in Australia, reported in the journal *Science* that two such Initial Upper Palaeolithic cultures flourished for only a few thousand years before disappearing.[6] One group (the *Still Bay culture*) emerged around 72,000 years ago but vanished about 1000 years later. The second (the *Howieson's Poort culture*) emerged about 65,000 years ago but lasted only 5000 years.

Jacobs notes that, "this burst of innovation ended about 60,000 years ago, returning to a further 30,000 years of relatively crude stone-age technology."[7]

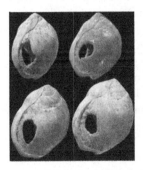

Making shell beads like these from the Blombos cave in South Africa is generally considered a sign of modern behaviour, but the people who made them disappeared about 60,000 years ago.
Photo: Chris Henshilwood and Francesco d'Errico.

The fact that these early African Upper Palaeolithic cultures were sporadic and short-lived came as a surprise to many anthropologists because it was assumed that Upper Palaeolithic culture would have spread like wildfire as a result of an increase in hunting and gathering yields. This turned out not to be the case. Data from both the Middle and Upper Palaeolithic reveal quite convincingly that there was actually no significant difference in hunting effectiveness between the two eras.[8,9,10]

This may seem odd because Upper Palaeolithic culture is now so indispensable to our modern lives that we can't imagine life without it. Yet we need to remember that archaic humans had survived more than

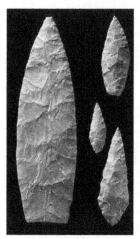

six million years (since diverging from the primate order)[11] without Upper Palaeolithic culture.

That is not to say the transition to the Upper Palaeolithic didn't result in minor increases in survival and reproductive rates. But while the acquisition of some Upper Palaeolithic behaviours in Africa may have been advantageous, or convenient, or simply pleasurable—and the tools they made more beautiful, like the 71,000 year-old spear points from Still Bay (*left*)—ultimately these behaviours were not so crucial for survival that everyone had to make the transition.

As world authority on the Middle to Upper Palaeolithic transition Ofer Bar-Yosef from Harvard University explains, the isolated occurrences of African Upper Palaeolithic culture "ultimately had no impact on the general trend of human evolution".[12] In effect, these sporadic occurrences of Upper Palaeolithic culture did not spread throughout Africa because they were not essential to survival in that region.

So where did the real Upper Palaeolithic revolution begin? Where did the *founder group* first emerge that was to become today's global population of humans? The archaeological evidence tells us that our founders came from an area in western Eurasia called the Mediterranean Levant (*see map opposite*), comprising present-day Israel, Lebanon, Syria, Palestine, the Sinai Peninsula and Jordan. It was these African immigrants, now living in the Levant, who made the transition to an Upper Palaeolithic culture and it was this specific culture that then dispersed across the globe.

This seminal transition occurred around 46,000 to 47,000 years ago.[13] It was then that a selection of Upper Palaeolithic behaviours suddenly appeared in a population of Middle Palaeolithic people living at Tachtit Boker, in present-day Israel. Within a few thousand years, this vibrant new Upper Palaeolithic culture had spread to Europe, Africa and Asia.[14,15,16,17,18,19,20]

This places the Mediterranean Levant at the geographical epicentre of humanity—the starting point for humanity's global colonisation of the planet.

The speed of the Upper Palaeolithic revolution in the Levant was also breathtaking. Anthropologists Ofer Bar-Yosef and Bernard Vandermeersch:

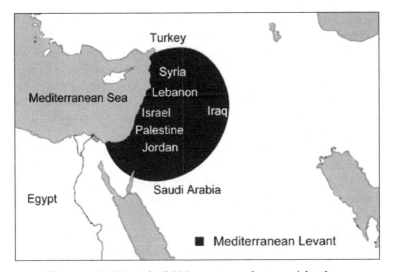

Between 40,000 and 45,000 years ago the material culture
of western Eurasia changed more than it had during the
previous million years. This efflorescence of technological
and artistic creativity signifies the emergence of the first
culture that observers today would recognise as distinctly
human, marked as it was by unceasing invention and variety.
During that brief period of 5,000 or so years, the stone tool
kit, unchanged in its essential form for ages, suddenly began
to differentiate wildly from century to century and from
region to region... Why it happened and why it happened
when it did constitute two of the greatest outstanding
problems in paleoanthropology.[21]

These are not the only outstanding problems. The abrupt metamorpho-
sis of primitive hominids into modern humans that occurred in the Levant is particularly puzzling given that their ancestors in that region and
elsewhere had survived for six million years without art, creativity, high
intelligence, civilisation or most of the other attributes of 21st century
humans. If they had survived without language for all that time, why did
they suddenly acquire it (as many researchers now believe) only about
50,000 to 100,000 years ago?[22,23]

Then there are all the peripheral questions. Were Neanderthals and
early humans one species? Did they socialise? Did they interbreed? These
issues are still being hotly debated, while the big question—why did

Neanderthals die out?—generates dozens of theories but no consensus.

Human physiology is the second big puzzle.

Although we share 99 percent of our protein-coding genes with chimpanzees, the difference in appearance continues to intrigue biologists. Why are women the only primate species to have visibly protuberant breasts, even when they're not pregnant or lactating?[24] It's not that their breasts are full of milk-producing tissue. They are mostly composed of fat. And when obvious signs of ovulation are the norm among female primates (allowing males to know when they're receptive and fertile), it seems *maladaptive* for women to evolve 'hidden ovulation'—making it impossible for men to know when they're fertile.[25] Likewise, it is still not understood why, at puberty, girls develop a layer of subcutaneous fat on the hips and buttocks, when no other primate does.

ADAPTIVE AND MALADAPTIVE

I try to avoid technical terms in this book, but 'adaptation' and 'adaptive' crop up so often and are so central to evolutionary biology that it may be helpful to define their meaning. An adaptation is any kind of inheritable trait, behaviour or feature that, for whatever reason, increases an organism's chances of surviving and reproducing in its current environment. The opposite of adaptive—when something reduces your chances of survival—is 'maladaptive' or deleterious.

Zoologist Desmond Morris highlights another paradox in *The Naked Ape*: "There are 193 species of monkeys and apes, 192 of them are covered with hair. The exception is a naked ape self-named *Homo sapiens*."[26]

The usual explanation for hairlessness is that it helped cool down our ancestors when they migrated from shady arboreal rainforests to the parched African savannah. But that doesn't explain why baboons, lions, camels, leopards, hyenas, tigers and gorillas—all from the hottest equatorial regions on the planet—have retained their body hair.

Equally puzzling is why only humans evolved flat faces, smooth skin, tumescent lips, a pronounced chin, clear eyes and protruding noses. We are also the only primate that is predominantly right-handed. And why is the human penis so much larger (relative to body size) than other apes?

The third major gap in our understanding of ourselves concerns our behaviour. The universal instincts, emotions and innate behavioural proclivities that comprise human nature are so different from those of every other species that it beggars belief. Why are we the only mammals to wear jewellery, play music, take drugs, make complex tools and weapons, cry tears, gossip and fear the dark? And why aren't any of the other 192 species of apes into body piercing, circumcision, clitoridectomy, tattooing, salsa, parachuting, or building intercontinental ballistic missiles?

"The enigma of war", according to evolutionary psychologist Steven Pinker, is that we still don't know "why people volunteer for an activity that has an excellent chance of getting them killed." It has been estimated that, in the last century alone, 203 million humans were killed by other humans.[28] William S Burroughs observed last century, "We are a war universe. War all the time. There may be other universes, but ours seems to be based on war and games."

Sexual violence is another fraught and enigmatic aspect of human nature. In the United States alone, according to the National Victim Center, 78 women are raped every hour, equating to 683,280 rapes each year. One in three American women will be sexually assaulted in their lifetime. Feminist historians and anthropologists argue this violence stems from an innate male fear and hostility towards women and their sexuality. American feminist Marilyn French does not mince words when she writes that it "cannot be an accident that everywhere on the globe one sex harms the other so massively that one questions the sanity of those waging the campaign: can a species survive when half of it systematically preys on the other?"[29]

Male violence towards women extends to their non-biological children. When Canadian psychology professors, Martin Daly and Margo Wilson investigated rates of fatal battering of Canadian children under five years of age between 1974 and 1990, they found a disturbing pattern—children under five were 120 times more likely to be fatally battered by a stepfather than a genetic father.[30]

Although we've barely scraped the surface of our behavioural oddities, it is clear we are a special species, hard-wired with many 'species-specific' behavioural proclivities that exert a subliminal influence on our decision making. They determine human preferences for specific facial features[31] and the kind of landscapes we prefer;[32,33,34] they compel us to watch the TV news and read newspapers; and they predispose young men to dangerous risk-taking behaviour.[35,36] Woman are inclined to adorn their bodies, be wary of strangers, and disdain excessive sweating, while men tend to speak for longer and interrupt more, are attracted to women with a specific hip-to-waist ratio,[37,38] and (famously) don't ask strangers for directions. What scientists have not resolved is precisely *why* we have accumulated this disparate assortment of behaviours.

what we don't know *can* hurt us

So, despite the claims of science, despite our own rationalisations, and notwithstanding the balmy reassurances of the church, there is a significant vacuum in the fields of human evolution, physiology, behaviour, psychology and history.

While these gaps may seem of little consequence, it may be argued that what we don't know diminishes our lives, and threatens the viability of the entire planet. Until we understand the evolutionary imperatives that subliminally drive universal human behaviours, xenophobia, superstition, sexism, war, racism, homicide, ecological vandalism, genocide and the nuclear arms race will continue to hold sway over humanity. Because the power of humans to affect planet Earth is unprecedented, understanding *why* is no longer an academic luxury—it is essential to our survival as a species. For these reasons, the assorted mysteries and paradoxes of humanity are incontestably the most important questions facing our generation.

the mother of all mutations?

To date, the most plausible explanation for the major evolutionary event that led to the abrupt emergence of *Homo sapiens* is the 'fortuitous mutation hypothesis' of American anthropologist Richard Klein. Klein suggests that a major genetic mutation occurred in the human lineage between about 50,000 and 40,000 years ago that created the 'fully modern' human brain.[39,40,41]

That the mutational process was crucial to the Upper Palaeolithic transition is axiomatic: after all, the qualities that make us human are all inheritable and therefore must be encoded in genes, which we know are subject to random mutations. The trouble is this transition would take more than a single mutation. Just to change the colour of the eye of a fruit fly requires mutations in 13 different genes.[42]

But even the complex genetic changes required to transform the face of a chimp into that of a human pale into insignificance compared to those required to convert a Middle Palaeolithic hominid brain into an Upper Palaeolithic modern human mind. Recent data from brain scans and molecular genetics studies reveal the neuronal modules that support human capacity, consciousness and other high level cerebral functions are numerous, variable and inordinately complex. For example, researchers at the University of Pennsylvania School of Medicine recently identified 282 separate genes in which a single point mutation (equivalent to one letter in an entire book) can result in mental retardation.[43] Given that general intelligence is only one of the many psychological aspects of human intelligence and cognition, the Upper Palaeolithic transition would have required mutations to thousands, if not millions, of individual nucleotides, involving unfathomably complex arrays of protein synthesis. To achieve the complexity of the human mind (described as the most complex system in the universe)[44] would require not one mutation, but innumerable advantageous mutations functioning in complex inter-connecting chromosomal arrays.

Another problem with Klein's model is that it doesn't accommodate the other behavioural and morphological features—from hidden ovulation to hairlessness—that are an indispensable part of modern humanity.

Finally, even if one individual is born with a favourable mutation, it doesn't mean that everyone else in the population will inherit it.[45,46,47,48] When a mutation or gene does spread to 100 percent of the population, it is called *fixation*, and the gene or mutation is said to be *fixed*. But that's no easy matter. To become fixed, a gene must be constantly and continually selected over multiple generations, and that usually only happens if it makes a strong contribution to *fitness*.[49] (Fitness does not mean being physically fit. Instead, it's a measure of an organism's ability to survive and successfully reproduce in its current environment, and refers ultimately to how many offspring an organism produces.)

Klein's hypothesis does not identify the environmental factors that rendered it necessary for these favourable mutations to keep being selected, generation after generation, until they achieved fixation in every human population—in every corner of the world.

heavy weather?

Another ecological factor that some researchers believe may have impact-ed on recent human evolution is climate change. And, yes, extreme cli-matic conditions and fluctuations (like those caused by droughts, floods, volcanic eruptions and asteroid strikes) can result in rapid evolutionary change, and even speciation events.[50,51,52,53,54] So did climate stress play a major role in human evolution? My review of the climatic evidence sug-gests there is only one plausible candidate—the massive Toba volcanic eruption in western Sumatra 73,000 years ago. Although it occurred in the southern hemisphere, Stanley Ambrose, from the University of Illinois, argues the six-year 'volcanic winter' that followed the eruption may have impacted on population densities in the northern hemisphere.[55,56]

Despite being seemingly plausible, Ambrose's theory has been challenged and rejected by a number of researchers on complex technical grounds.[57,58] Personally, I find it difficult to imagine what adaptations against atmospheric opacity, airborne dust and food shortage could have resulted in modern human physiology and behaviour. Even if the Toba event reduced the population size, that reduction would be across the board—unilateral and indiscriminate—so would not create any specific selection pressure. In other words, there would be no specific trait for natural selection to select for. How could a volcanic eruption create our love of music, or of fashion or sexual jealousy? Besides, there is a 26,000 year gap between the Toba event (73,000 years ago) and the appearance of the Upper Palaeolithic at Tachtit Boker 47,000 years ago.

Based on a review of marine oxygen-isotope data from deep-sea sediment cores, Stony Brook University anthropologist John Shea concludes, "the Middle Palaeolithic/UP transition in the Levant is not correlated with any major shift in the global oxygen-isotope record of climate change."[59]

The final nail in the argument that climate change triggered modern human behaviour came in November 2008. It was part of Zenobia Jacobs' landmark paper in *Science* that dated the rise and fall of the short-lived Howieson's Poort and Still Bay modern cultures in southern Africa. Jacobs' team studied ancient ice-core samples to find out what the climate was like when these two technologically innovative cultures first emerged. They were looking for any extreme climatic conditions or unusual environmental factors that may have been responsible for the appearance of these cultures. They found no correlation with any dramatic climate change.

The commentary in *Science* sums up their findings: "the rise of these industries does not appear to correlate with any known climatic changes, suggesting that these bursts of innovation can not be explained primarily by environmental factors."

Jacobs adds, "The cause of these two bursts of technological innovation, closely spaced yet separated in time, remains an enigma, as does the reason for their disappearance."[60]

So, if climate change did not play a part in the Upper Palaeolithic revolution, what else is left? Certainly no current theory explains how we acquired all our unique modern human features. Nothing explains the suddenness of the Upper Palaeolithic transition or why one instance of it (in the Mediterranean Levant) spread around the world while many other isolated examples of it did not. This suggests there is a need for a new conceptual framework—perhaps even something left field—to break the impasse. In the absence of a consensus, I put the case for a new theory of human origins.

what killed our ancestors?

In their efforts to unravel the evolutionary origins of humanity's abrupt emergence and its unique physical and behavioural features, anthropologists and archaeologists have traditionally focused on fossilised skeletal remains and artefacts. These include bones, tools, weapons, art, textiles and habitats—physical evidence that can be examined, tested, dated and quantified. But by far the most detailed scrutiny has been directed at the fossilised skeletons of our ancestors, exhumed from ancient sites.

Even though skeletal remains receive the most attention in journals and scientific conferences, I suggest it is not our bones that set us apart. After all, human adults have on average 206 bones, the same number as chimpanzees—they've just changed shape and size slightly over the eons. What really separates us from the other primates are *soft tissue features*—our faces, smooth skin, breasts, buttocks, noses, and hairlessness—and our behaviour. But because these features are not preserved in the fossil record and don't leave physical artefacts, they have been largely excluded from the debate on human evolution.

I think this is unfortunate. When you look at these soft tissue features in isolation, plus all the behaviours and emotions that do not fossilise, they might strike you as relatively minor. Insignificant even. Biologists call them *microevolutionary* features, in contrast to *macroevolutionary* features.

MICROEVOLUTION AND MACROEVOLUTION

In the twenties, the Russian entomologist Lurii Filipchenko divided evolution into two categories: *microevolution* and *macroevolution*. The terms—borrowed from the Greek words *micro*: small and *macro*: large—distinguish small-scale, incremental microevolution (such as a mutation that changes the colour of a pupil) from the more dramatic changes of macroevolution (such as when one species transforms into a new one).

But add them all up and these seemingly minor behaviours and physical features represent an example of *macroevolution*—a major (and rare) evolutionary event that results in the creation of a completely new species. Collectively, these small traits are what define humans as a unique species.

Understanding why these nonfossilised soft tissue features and behaviours evolved in the first place, and how they contributed to survival in the ancestral environment is, I believe, essential to revealing why *Homo sapiens* emerged as a new species.

Clearly these features evolved by *natural selection*—the evolutionary process co-discovered by Charles Darwin and Alfred Wallace—and somehow contributed to survival in the prehistoric environment. In other words, something in their environment made it necessary for early humans to evolve all those soft tissue features.

Charles Darwin (left) gets most of the credit for discovering natural selection, but Alfred Wallace (right) simultaneously arrived at an identical view.

The way an animal's environment appears to demand a new feature is called *selection pressure*. It happens when something in the environment reduces survival rates, usually by prematurely killing off certain animals. This makes it more likely that new traits which help an animal survive this premature death will be selected. For example, by killing off the animals that need lots of water, a drought can create selection pressure—for animals that need less water. This kind of selection pressure created camels. Constant bushfires can create selection pressure for animals that can burrow underground to escape the heat. If there is too much salt in a lake, it can create selection pressure for fish that can tolerate salt. And so on.

In theory, the more animals killed by an environmental factor before they can reproduce, the stronger the selection pressure will be for adaptations to mitigate it.

Interestingly, selection pressure can have a dramatic effect on the appearance of survivors. For instance, selection pressure generated by toothed predators gave the turtle its distinctive thick shell. Similarly, polar bears have a thick fur coat because the freezing arctic climate generated selection pressure for thermal protection.

the mysterious 'factor X'

So, what environmental factors and circumstances in the Levant could have generated selection pressure for humans to acquire all those new soft tissue features? For example, if hairiness is the default state among land mammals, and all other primate species have retained their body hair (including those living in hot, tropical habitats) what particular environmental factor (or factors) made it necessary for our ancestors to lose theirs? What killed off all the hairy hominids and left only the hairless ones?

The challenge is to identify the specific environmental factor—'factor X'. What caused women with flat chests to die out and ancestral males with small primate-sized penises to become extinct, so that only well-endowed men remained? And why was it deleterious to have a flat nose like other primates, so that all our flat-nosed ancestors went the way of the dodo? These are questions that go to the heart of the matter.

the levantine epicentre

The focus of my enquiry turned to the Mediterranean Levant because that is where Upper Palaeolithic behaviours first appeared before they dispersed across the world. The Levant was the geographical epicentre of humanity, so this is where factor X must have been most intense. This is where something in the environment killed off Middle Palaeolithic hominids, so that only Upper Palaeolithic humans survived.

Here is another exciting clue in our evolutionary detective story. Something happened in the Levant that did not happen anywhere else. Some localised environmental factor made it imperative for archaic humans to acquire the accoutrements of modern humans. And, whatever it was, it was absent in Africa and Asia.

But it wasn't just the magnitude of the transition in the Levant that was unprecedented. So too was its speed, and this provides another clue. Natural selection is nearly always a grindingly slow process that achieves results only incrementally over thousands or even millions of generations.[61,62] This did not happen in the Levant. Steven Kuhn and his colleagues from the University of Arizona report the spread of Upper Palaeolithic ornament technologies (modern tools, art, etc.) was "essentially simultaneous" on three continents.[63] What was it about the Levantine environment that made it so imperative for Middle Palaeolithic humans to suddenly become Upper Palaeolithic humans? Why the urgency?

Cognitive capacity, art, complex language, organisation, culture, music, dance and other Upper Palaeolithic behaviours that distinguish modern humans appeared only 46,000 years ago.[64,65,66] If mysterious environmental conditions caused all these behaviours to materialise virtually overnight, did they cause our distinctive physical features to emerge as well: hairlessness, hidden ovulation, rounded breasts and buttocks, full lips, clear eyes, and prominent noses?

This raises the possibility that both the physical and behavioural features that define us as human may have occurred in response to selection pressure generated by unprecedented environmental circumstances— factor X—that occurred in the Levant, but nowhere else. The identification of factor X—something that killed off most of the archaic humans, so that only those that looked and behaved like modern humans survived— becomes paramount in solving the human origins puzzle.

The magnitude and sheer evolutionary potency of factor X is itself a vital clue. Only singular and exceptional forces could create a new species so quickly. What could be so deleterious, so lethal, that only those few individuals who looked and behaved like modern humans could survive?

You may think that identifying that single, highly potent environmental factor would be difficult. But it soon became clear to me there was only one environmental dynamic powerful enough to cause a speciation event in such a short time. Only one environmental factor could direct natural selection to confer art, spoken language, organisation, symbolism, long-term episodic memory, forward thinking, exceptional intelligence and innumerable other uniquely human cognitive traits on one primate species, while the other 192 species remained unaffected. And only one selection criterion could radically alter the visual appearance of humans to make them look so different from every other primate. That single factor is *predation*—the timeless dance of death between predator and prey.

OUT OF AFRICA
INTO THE FRYING PAN

man the hunted

The conflict between the need for food and becoming food has made predation one of the most pervasive and influential ecological mechanisms in the animal kingdom—the sharpest instrument in natural selection's toolbox.[67,68,69] Predation generates competition, not only between individuals, but also between species. And competition, as we know from Darwin, is the fuel that drives the natural selection engine.

Predation has been fundamental to the evolution of major adaptations like the cobra's venom, the leopard's stealth and the eagle's aerial agility. It created insects that look like leaves, frogs with poisonous skin and fish that can change colour to match their background. It transformed massive terrestrial dinosaurs into petite flying birds and dog-sized mammals into blue whales. Predation gave sharks their optimum aerodynamic shape, porcupines their spines and skunks their terrible smell. It bestowed phenomenal sprint speed on cheetahs, equipped bees with their stings and rhinos with their thick skin.

Nowhere in nature do we see natural selection resulting in so much unbridled creativity as in predator and anti-predator adaptations. It goes beyond the ingenious techniques of camouflage mimicry we see in the insect world. The special colours and markings that warn off predators are equally ingenious. Predation produced complex strategies, elaborate traps and the sweetest perfumes to lure unsuspecting victims to their deaths. What could be more inventive than the Angler Fish dangling a tiny fishing rod from its head, complete with wriggling bait in its mouth to catch unsuspecting prey?

Given that selection pressure generated by predation has been indispensable to the evolution of a wide range of animals, from snails to whales, it is not unreasonable to suggest that—given the right ecological conditions—predation could result in archaic stone-age hominids transforming into fully modern humans.

But here's the rub. There are two sides to predation dynamics— predator and prey—and although the idea of 'man the hunter'[70,71,72] is deeply embedded in anthropological thinking,[73] the general view of most researchers is that evolutionary scenarios based on humans as predators do not adequately explain our unique evolutionary trajectory.[74,75,76]

While we're accustomed to seeing ourselves as the pre-eminent predator on the planet—residing at the top of the food chain—this view has seriously compromised our ability to think impartially about our lowly origins. My interpretation of the evidence suggests the abrupt transition from Middle Palaeolithic to Upper Palaeolithic, our unique physical appearance and our distinctive behaviour are consistent only with the view that humans evolved—for a period of time at least—as a species of prey.

In other words, the defining physiological, behavioural and emotional characteristics of *Homo sapiens* may be the adaptations of a prey species exposed to systemic long-term predation by a single predator.

My hypothesis argues that, although we are currently one of the few species on Earth to have no natural dietary predator, this was not always the case. It suggests that, like almost all the other 1.5 million animal species on the planet, we too were shaped by the ecological consequences of predation.

and the killer is...

The next step in the hypothesis is to identify the significant predators in our evolutionary history. A number of suspects immediately spring to mind—lions and leopards would probably top the list. During our African sojourn these feline predators undoubtedly took their toll on ancestral hominid populations. So too did snakes, rhinos, elephants, bears, buffalo and any one of the 400 other species known to kill humans.[77] And although *arachnophobia* is one of the most common human phobias (and we certainly have evolved instinctive 'brush away' reflexes to deal with spiders and other creepy crawlies), spiders did not fundamentally reshape us as a species. Nor did lions, although they probably played a part in chasing our ancestors out of Africa.

My examination of the archaeological evidence from the Levant, plus the latest genetic data from both ancient DNA (extracted from fossilised bones) and from the human genome, lends itself to only one plausible interpretation—that the principal predators of archaic humans were Neanderthals (*Homo neanderthalensis*).

neanderthal predation theory

Neanderthal predation theory (NP theory) argues that Neanderthal predation was the single macroevolutionary factor that transformed archaic hominids into modern humans and that, without it, we would still be a docile stone-age hominid. Everything that defines what humans are today is due directly or indirectly to Neanderthal predation. Just as we have inherited a fear of spiders from our prehistoric ancestors, modern humans have also inherited a primordial dread of Neanderthals—and this daily affects all our lives.

The core hypothesis of Neanderthal predation theory proposes that from at least 100,000 years ago until around 48,000 years ago, in the East Mediterranean Levant, Neanderthals systematically abducted, raped, hunted and devoured archaic humans to the edge of extinction— generating selection pressure for defensive changes in human physiology and behaviour. The resulting strategic adaptations created modern humans. All the major biosystems that make us human—high intelligence, spoken language, art, hairlessness, our distinctive faces—are derived from Neanderthal predation.

neighbours from hell

Obviously, for predation to have occurred, Neanderthals and Middle Palaeolithic humans must have been living in the same place at the same time, long enough for Neanderthals to have altered the trajectory of human evolution. So the first tenet of NP theory, and the first of its predictions, is that archaic humans and Neanderthals lived within the same geographical and chronological context for at least a few thousand years. This prediction can also be used as the first test of the hypothesis.

The Mediterranean Levant during the Late Pleistocene provides the earliest and best evidence of contemporaneous cohabitation. The long stretch of land on the eastern edge of the Mediterranean Sea called the Levant has often been described as a biogeographical 'corridor' between western Eurasia and Africa through which African migrations transited for millions of years.[78]

LATE PLEISTOCENE

The Late Pleistocene stage of the Pleistocene epoch dates from around 126,000 years ago to around 10,000 years ago. That stage is followed by the Holocene which continues to the present.

Flint artefacts retrieved from Yiron, in northern Israel, provide the earliest evidence of hominids living in the Levant. At 2,400,000 years old, Yiron is the earliest hominid site outside Africa.[79] The earliest actual skeletal remains from the area are represented by a fragmentary 200,000 year old hominid excavated at the Mugharet-el-Zuttiyeh cave, in Israel. The paucity of the remains makes identification problematical, but they are thought to be that of an early Neanderthal.[80,81]

Based on recent dating of Middle Palaeolithic shell beads from the Skhul cave on the slopes of Mt Carmel, in Israel, anatomically modern humans were living in the Levant from between 135,000 to 100,000 years ago[82,83,84] and possibly much earlier.

Fossils from the nearby Qafzeh cave tell us they were still there 85,000 years ago.[85]

THE SKHUL-QAFZEH PEOPLE

Because the earliest anatomically modern, Middle Palaeolithic people discovered in the Levant came from two adjoining caves on Mt Carmel (Qafzeh *left*) and (Skhul *right*) the term 'Skhul-Qafzeh humans' can be used to describe these ancestors.

While their skeletons were much the same as ours, behaviourally the Skhul and Qafzeh people were still Middle Palaeolithic stone-age hominids, although the shell artefacts found in the Skhul cave suggest they were at least on the cusp of a transition to a more advanced culture—even if their tools were still primitive. As to what they looked like: although their skeletons were relatively modern, it's impossible to say if they outwardly resembled modern humans or some other primate—in all likelihood, they were something in between.

The supposed migration route for the Skhul-Qafzeh humans was through the Great Rift Valley in eastern Africa, along the Nile corridor

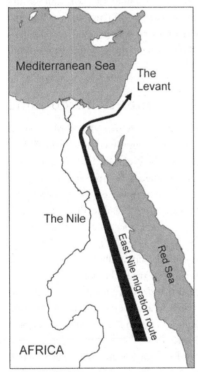

(between the Red Sea and the Nile) and into the Levant (*left*).[86,87] At the time, the Levant was part of a major migration route for animal species from northeast Africa and southwest Asia.[88,89] For early humans living in the Levant this provided an abundance of prey species, including boar, mountain gazelle, red deer, ibex and aurochs.[90]

Today, that area of the Middle East has a typical Mediterranean climate, with long dry summers and cool humid winters.[91] Judging from pollen records obtained from marine cores, the climate in the Late Pleistocene was cooler, more humid, and punctuated by periods of drought.[92] With the climate relatively stable and food plentiful, the African migrants appear to have adapted well to their new environment. The coastal regions of the Levant had permanent supplies of fresh water and its mountains were riddled with limestone caves (including the Skhul and Qafzeh caves) which the humans occupied as permanent sites. Also, its woodlands were among the richest habitats in western Eurasia,[93,94] and the Mediterranean Sea was close enough to harvest shellfish to supplement their diet.

In these favourable conditions, their Middle Palaeolithic technology—

although rudimentary by our standards—was sufficient for the Skhul-
Qafzeh humans to prosper for thousands of years.

All good things must come to an end, and one day a group of these
archaic humans came face-to-face with a strange and very different group
of hominids they had never seen before—Eurasian Neanderthals who
had moved into the Levant from Europe.

This encounter may be the most important single event in human
history.

Ostensibly, it was simply two sibling species meeting for the first time.
But from a broader evolutionary perspective, that encounter represents
the introduction of a major new environmental stressor that would
fundamentally impact on early human ecology. On that day, what was
to become an interminable selection pressure was exerted for the first
time—a pressure that has continued to reshape and redefine humankind
up to the present.

meet the cousins

It is thought that some Neanderthals had been forced out of Eastern
Europe by one of the periodic ice ages that engulfed the region. Whatever the circumstances of their migration, the Neanderthals from Europe
that occupied the Levant gradually developed a few physical variations.
To distinguish this sub-species from the parental European population
(often called *classic* Neanderthals) the Levantine Neanderthals are usually
referred to as *Eurasian Neanderthals*, or *Near Eastern Neanderthals*. In this
book, I use the former.

Eurasian Neanderthals are represented principally by fossil material
found at a number of caves in the Levant—Amud, Kebara and Tabun—
all in Israel. On the basis of dates from both early modern human and
Neanderthal sites at Mt Carmel, there is an overwhelming weight of
evidence that Skhul-Qafzeh humans and Eurasian Neanderthals occupied
the same area of the Levant at the same time.[95,96,97,98,99,100,101,102,103]

As to the important question of how long this coexistence lasted,
the imprecision of dates derived from thermoluminescence dating
technology and uncertainties relating to provenance make it difficult to
say for certain.[104]

One particular problem is the possible *interstratification* of stratigraphic
levels relating to one of the Levant hominids (known as Tabun C1).
Normally in an archaeological dig, the lower down you go, the older the
material is. But sometimes, because of earthquakes, floods, landslides and

other natural phenomena, the levels (and the archaeological material in them) get jumbled and, occasionally, even reversed. This interstratification can make dating difficult.

If the famous Tabun C1 Neanderthal (which was dated at 171,000 years old) comes from Level C, as suggested by archaeologist Nira Alperson and her team,[105] it would indicate Skhul-Qafzeh humans and Neanderthals shared the Levant for at least 70,000 years.

Based on excavations at Geula Cave, Israel, plus the Skhul and Qafzeh fossils, Chilean physical anthropologist Baruch Arensburg suggests a 100,000-year geographic overlap between humans and Eurasian Neanderthals from Tabun, Kebara and Amud.[106] Other scholars date the Levantine overlap at 90,000 years,[107] while several other teams argue the two species coexisted on the eastern shores of the Mediterranean for 65,000 years.[108, 109, 110]

In all likelihood, throughout this period, there were multiple 'trickle' migrations into the area by both Neanderthals and early humans, driven by climatic variability and parallel migrations of fauna into the region from Africa.[111] Ofer Bar-Yosef argues at least one migration of European Neanderthals into the Levant was precipitated by the rapid onset of glacial conditions in eastern Europe and western Asia 75,000 years ago.[112]

While estimates for the length of time both species shared the Levant vary, everyone agrees they did so for many thousands of years. I conservatively estimate Neanderthal cohabitation with the Skhul-Qafzeh

Tabun cave on the slopes of Mt Carmel in Israel, occupied successively by archaic humans, Neanderthals and modern humans. From a Darwinian perspective, this is the real Garden of Eden. Photo: Rotem Hofman

people in the Levant occurred between 100,000 to 50,000 years ago, providing a 50,000-year period of potential Neanderthal predation.

On the basis of 20 years per generation, 50,000 years represents 2500 generations. At 25 years per generation, that's still 2000 generations.

However, I will later argue that the *indirect* impact of Neanderthal predation continued right up to the Late Neolithic Period (a mere 2000 years ago) and even beyond, which would add another 45,000 years of evolutionary pressure. At 20 years per generation, that's 4750 generations of humans that were subject to selective pressures generated directly or indirectly by Neanderthal predation. Considering that only 100 generations have lived since the time of the Romans and ancient Greeks, 4750 generations is more than enough time for a macroevolutionary event to occur.

competition—natural selection on steroids

When it first became evident that humans and Neanderthals had lived in the same region for over 50,000 years, there was a great deal of heated debate as researchers struggled to understand the implications of such a lengthy cohabitation.

Erik Trinkaus and Pat Shipman describe it in *The Neanderthals*:

> This new twist pointed up a fundamental problem that had been there all along, overshadowed by the problems of chronology and phylogeny. It was awkward, if not downright contorted, to try to explain how two groups of humans [*sapiens* and Neanderthals] occupied the same region—either alternately or simultaneously—using the same set of tools to exploit the same plants and animals over a period of fifty thousand years and yet remained anatomically and genetically separate.[113]

But cohabitation of the same ecological niche also has another consequence—it generates *competition*—that great driving force of evolution. Without it, evolution grinds to a snail's pace.

Competition from Neanderthals provides another vital clue—motive. NP theory draws on this maxim to argue that the competition Neanderthals introduced with their colonisation of the Levant kick-started a burst of evolutionary activity among the Skhul-Qafzeh humans that would eventually transform them into a new species. In effect,

Es Skhul cave (cave of the baby goats) on Mt Carmel was home to some of the earliest modern humans. This is where the modern human journey really began.

competition with Eurasian Neanderthals became the catalyst that created modern humans.

Here, though, the competition wasn't between two physiologically different species. It was between sibling species—species that were similar in general appearance and occupied the same ecological niche. This upped the ante, and also complicated things.

There is general agreement among palaeontologists that, because both species had similar needs for food and shelter, from the day Neanderthals arrived in the Levant they would be competing against the local humans for the same resources,[114,115,116] the same cave sites, fresh water, fruit trees, ochre and flint. But the fossil evidence also tells us they were rivals for something much more basic—they were hunting many of the same prey species.[117,118]

From the perspective of the Skhul-Qafzeh humans, the interloping Neanderthals suddenly disrupted the ecological homeostasis humans had enjoyed for at least 40,000 years—and probably considerably longer. From the Neanderthal perspective, the new Skhul-Qafzeh neighbours presented both a direct challenge—and an opportunity.

In *The Origin of Species*, Darwin observes that "competition will generally be most severe between those forms which are most nearly related to each other in habits, constitution, and structure."[119] He goes on to say that, in the struggle for existence:

> ...it is the most closely-allied forms,- varieties of the same species, and species of the same genus or of related genera,- which, from having nearly the same structure, constitution, and habits, generally come into the severest competition with each other; consequently, each new variety or species, during the progress of its formation, will generally press hardest on its nearest kindred, and tend to exterminate them.

The case for lethal inter-species competition is also suggested by Gause's law of competitive exclusion,[120] which states that two species with similar diet and ecological requirements cannot both indefinitely occupy the same environment. Something's got to give. Applied to the Levant, it predicts that Neanderthal encroachment into the Skhul-Qafzeh's habitat would cause ecological instability within the hominid niche.

This elemental evolutionary imperative to out-compete, exterminate or expel a competitor from a common territory pitted Neanderthals and humans against each other. And, clearly, the stakes were high. It was a struggle for survival, and the loser faced extinction.

This raises the most fundamental question: if both hominid species were trying to out-compete each other, who would win? This question encapsulates the most fundamental truths about our species and takes us to the second major tenet of NP theory.

NP theory is extrapolated from a simple premise—Neanderthals weren't the harmless hominids that many anthropologists have presumed them to be—but something else entirely. They were the pre-eminent European-Eurasian predator—what biologists call an *apex predator*—one with no rivals within their ecological niche. As such, they resided at the summit of the food chain.

This predicts that as the more powerfully-built hominid—who had evolved the predatory instincts, strength, ferocity and lethality to pursue and subdue a wide variety of large and dangerous prey over hundreds of thousands of years in the most demanding environments—Neanderthals would quickly assert a strategic dominance over the Levantine early humans.

It also argues that Neanderthal competition acted as an ecological catalyst that generated enormous selection pressure on the Skhul-Qafzeh humans which, in turn, drove evolutionary change.

These hypotheses claim that practically everything we know about Neanderthal evolutionary history (*phylogeny*), habitat, diet, hunting strategies, tool use, sexuality, territoriality and a host of other core factors—and how they affect behaviour (what scientists call *behavioural ecology*)—needs to be reassessed. Importantly, a fundamental reassessment of Eurasian Neanderthal and early human behaviour, physiology and ecology is also the best way to test these hypotheses.

PART I

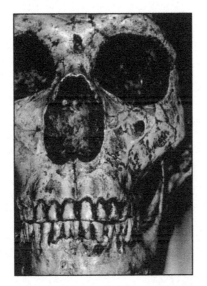

THEM

If modern humans are the result of inter-species competition then, clearly, we need to understand the nature of the competition. When we comprehend the ecological nuances of our competitors and the nature of the competition they generated, it will be immediately apparent who won and why—and what the evolutionary consequences were for both sides. The next four chapters take a new look at Neanderthal behaviour, physiology and ecology, based on the latest archaeological and genetic evidence.

3 THE PERFECT PREDATOR

shadowy figures

The study of Neanderthal behavioural ecology is a relatively new field and so far hasn't generated a great deal of interest among researchers. And yet, because species are products of their environment, a detailed study of the nuances of the Neanderthals' environment (as inferred from the archaeological and genetic evidence) may answer important questions about how they behaved, what they looked like and why they emerged as a separate species. The kinds of questions this discipline tries to answer include: Did Neanderthals interbreed with early humans? What did they look like? Why are Neanderthal genes so conspicuously absent in modern humans?[121,122] How smart were they? Then there's the big question: What caused their extinction—a subject that currently generates countless theories but no consensus.

But perhaps the most important objective of my reassessment of Neanderthal behavioural ecology is to shed some reflected light on human evolution. NP theory is actually a theory of *coevolution*—the synchronistic evolution of two sibling species living close to each other— so discovering how the environment shaped Neanderthals may also tell us how Neanderthals shaped humans.

Another objective of this reassessment is to correct what I believe to be a distorted anthropocentric bias that has inculcated western thought on all things Neanderthal. Instead of seeing Neanderthals for what they were, a unique and complex species inhabiting a particular ecological niche, it has been assumed they were essentially a mirror image of ourselves—albeit, not as smart. Perhaps, like children discovering they have a sibling they've never known, we harbour an unconscious longing for some kind of meaningful connection—a reunion of sorts—a sense that we're not alone in the universe. But this oversimplification robs us of the detail—the nuances which conceal the greatest truths. Neanderthals may be our doppelgangers but, until we stand them side by side with other primates and make the objective comparison, we'll never know for sure.

Although the reassessment is consistent with the latest archaeological findings and genetic data from extracted ancestral DNA, some aspects of it are speculative and rely in part on circumstantial evidence (which I will duly note). Fortunately, advances in palaeoecology and genetics over the last few years provide a solid support for the reassessment.

neanderthals 101

Neanderthals were a species of hominids who lived in Europe, western Asia and Britain (which was then a peninsula of northwest Europe, thanks to sea levels being 80 metres lower than today). It is believed they became extinct about 28,000 years ago, although some dates suggest they survived until 24,000 years ago.

NEANDERTHAL OR NEANDERTAL?

The word itself comes from *Neander Thal* (which means 'Neander Valley' in German) where the type specimen (Neanderthal 1) was discovered in 1856. With no 'th' sound Germans pronounce it Neandertal, while in English, Neanderthal, with the softer 'thal' has become widespread. Neanderthal is more commonly used today, but either word is acceptable.

Until recently, Neanderthals were thought to be the same species as us. But over the last decade, geneticists have extracted DNA from ancient Neanderthal bones which, when compared to human DNA, shows conclusively that although Neanderthals were members of the same genus as us—*homo*—they weren't human.[123,124,125] The DNA variation was enough to conclude that Neanderthals were a separate species.

Geneticists are divided about when Neanderthals split from the human

Skull cap from the Feldhofer Neanderthal (right) discovered near Düsseldorf in 1856. Although the third specimen found, it became the 'type specimen' and was dubbed Neanderthal 1.

ancestral tree. Estimates vary between 350,000,[126] 370,000,[127] 500,000[128] and 631,000 to 789,000 years ago.[129] In other words, for maybe half a million years, they were off on their own evolutionary trajectory—forged and shaped by the environments they inhabited during this period.

Although they were slightly shorter than the Skhul-Qafzeh humans, (which probably helped conserve energy in cold climates), the remains of a few tall Neanderthals have been found. In the 1960s, a Japanese expedition excavated an almost complete Neanderthal skeleton at Mt Carmel in Israel. What was extraordinary about this adult male (known as Amud 1) was that he was almost six feet tall—an exceptional height in those days—and ostensibly a giant who would have towered over early humans of the period.

Despite usually being slightly shorter, the average Neanderthal was much stockier, weighing about 25 percent more than a human. They were so heavily muscled, their skeletons had to develop extra thick bones and attachment points to take the strain. With massive barrel chests, arms like Arnold Schwarzenegger and legs like telegraph posts, it has been estimated Neanderthals were about six times stronger than modern humans.

"One of the most characteristic features of the Neanderthals," writes palaeoanthropologist Erik Trinkaus, "is the exaggerated massiveness of their trunk and limb bones. All of the preserved bones suggest a strength seldom attained by modern humans."[130]

James Shreeve, author of *The Neanderthal Enigma*, adds that, "a healthy Neanderthal male could lift an average NFL linebacker over his head and throw him through the goalposts."[131]

It wasn't just Neanderthal adults who were bigger, stronger and burlier than modern humans. Their children were too. "You should see some of the skeletons for these individuals," anthropologist John Shea told *Discovery News*. "The females were big and strong, while a 10-year-old kid must have had muscles comparable to those of today's weight lifters."[132]

On the basis of their stone weapons and tools, preserved remains

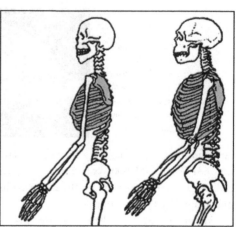

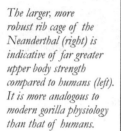

The larger, more robust rib cage of the Neanderthal (right) is indicative of far greater upper body strength compared to humans (left). It is more analogous to modern gorilla physiology than that of humans.

of the animals they hunted, and the way they processed carcasses, it is now generally agreed that Late Pleistocene Neanderthals were skilled hunters rather than opportunistic scavengers.[133,134,135,136] A great deal of research, particularly over the last decade, has recognised the cognitive and behavioural complexity of Neanderthals.[137,138,139,140,141] As one study of Neanderthal hunting techniques concludes, "although Neanderthals and modern humans differed in salient ways, the vast behavioural and cognitive gulf that was once thought to exist between them has now narrowed considerably."[142]

a creature of the cold

Although Eurasian Neanderthals and Levantine early humans inherited similar features from common primate and hominid ancestors, the different geological and climatic ecosystems they inhabited for hundreds of thousands of years gradually selected for physical and behavioural differences. We know the coastal environment of the Levant during the Late Pleistocene resembled the African savannah, with over a hundred different varieties of edible plants, so it is not surprising that Levantine humans retained the adaptations they had acquired in Africa over the preceding six million years. That included their omnivorous diet and a preference for savannah habitats.

In contrast, Neanderthals evolved in ice-age Europe, the only hominid species to evolve in a climate of seasonally lethal cold.[143] During their half-million-year occupation of Europe, they gradually acquired a range of physical and behavioural adaptations to protect themselves against the cold. One of the main adaptations to the periglacial environment, which has been described as one of the harshest and most inhospitable habitats ever occupied by hominids,[144] was the adoption of a high protein animal meat diet. Steve Kuhn and Mary Stiner, from the University of Arizona, say that few plants could survive in that cold climate and that those that did were not nutritious enough, or required too much effort to collect and process relative to their low nutritional yields.[145]

Because of their considerable weight and energy expenditure, not to mention the need to maintain body temperature within functional levels, Neanderthals had to regularly find and consume enormous amounts of protein which was converted to body heat. It has been estimated the average Neanderthal consumed about 1.85 kg (4.1 lbs) of fat-rich meat every day.[146] That's equivalent to the meat in 16 McDonald's Quarter Pounders. Early Neanderthal scholars assumed they were simply dumb cavemen who probably scavenged most of their meat from other animals, but we now know this was not the case. In fact, there are no exclusive mammalian scavengers. That is because the time and energy it takes to scavenge enough food is simply too high compared to hunting. And most predators vigorously defend their kills, so a scavenger is always at risk from being injured or killed.[147]

All this leads to the conclusion that Neanderthals were not scavengers. As Erik Trinkaus explains, "Neanderthals were not randomly wandering around the landscape, stumbling on an animal they could kill or a carcass they could scavenge."[148]

Only fresh meat could provide Neanderthals with the high protein, energy-rich diet they needed to maintain their large body mass and energy expenditure. Because fishing wasn't practised in the Middle Palaeolithic,[149] and there is no evidence of Neanderthal fishing technology, the only way they could have obtained a constant supply of fresh meat was by hunting terrestrial prey.

Just as modern Inuit residing in glacial habitats have adopted a high protein diet of animal flesh, European Neanderthals abandoned the omnivorous diet of their African ancestors for a carnivorous diet of animal flesh. Such a fundamental switch in their diet would create a substantial ecological divide between the Neanderthals and humans. When European Neanderthals abandoned their hunter-gatherer lifestyle and became hunters, their whole evolution was focused on becoming better hunters. And that, I suggest, had profound implications for human evolution.

a taste for flesh

You might think it would be virtually impossible to tell what your average Neanderthal ate for breakfast or dinner 100,000 years ago but that is not so. Researchers have discovered that the chemical composition of animal bones is affected by what they eat. When geneticists began analysing isotopes of bone collagen in Neanderthal bone specimens, they found that the Neanderthal diet consisted almost entirely of meat.[150,151,152] In one French study, calcium ratios extracted from 40 Saint-Césaire Neanderthal samples revealed the Neanderthal diet was composed of about 97 percent (in weight) of meat.[153] These and similar findings are summarised by English palaeoanthropologist Paul Pettitt who concludes that Neanderthals ate "meat for breakfast, lunch and tea".[154]

By comparison, even though our African ancestors who migrated into the Levant were hunter-gatherers, the reality is that they were not so much hunters as gatherers. The fossil evidence tells us that early humans resolutely maintained their African omnivorous diet, which consisted mostly of gathered food—berries, roots, tubers, fruit, nuts and plants. In fact, the majority of their energy intake was supplied by uncultivated fruits and vegetables.[155] Analysis of Middle Palaeolithic human remains shows that archaic humans had only limited hunting abilities, captured only small to medium-sized or weak game, avoided dangerous prey and supplemented their diet by scavenging.[156,157,158,159,160] Even today, modern hunter-gatherers such as the !Kung people of the Kalahari Desert obtain only 33 percent of their daily energy intake from hunted animals.[161]

Although diet may seem an inconsequential matter in the great panoply of events and circumstances that led to the evolution of our species, in reality, how a species evolved its unique diet and acquired the adaptations to maintain it successfully has far-reaching evolutionary consequences.

the top of the food chain

Social predators (predators that hunt cooperatively in packs) use their own claws, talons, teeth, stings, poisons and beaks to disable and kill prey. Neanderthals represent the rare example of a predator intelligent enough to hunt collectively *and* use complex weapons.

Ample evidence exists to show that Neanderthals and their Middle Pleistocene European predecessors were practised in using stone-tipped wooden spears to hunt prey.[162,163,164] In Lehringen, Germany, the broken tip of a Neanderthal spear was found still embedded in the ribs of an elephant skeleton, while at Umm el Tlel in Syria, a Neanderthal spear point was recovered from the cervical vertebra of a horse.[165]

Neanderthals did not hunt rabbits, rats, hedgehogs and other small game. We know from the bones littering their caves that Neanderthals were using their flint-tipped thrusting spears to bring down the largest and most dangerous species in Europe—woolly mammoths, giant cave bears, woolly rhinos, bison, wild boar, wolves, antelope and even cave lions.

Back then, these animals were considerably larger than their modern-day equivalents. The Eurasian cave lion stood 1.5m tall at the shoulder, about as tall as a Neanderthal. The animals the Neanderthals were attempting to kill were among the largest and most dangerous on earth. We must presume they mustered up the courage to hunt them because there was no alternative. Only these large mammals provided enough of the high protein meat they needed to survive. If they couldn't bring them down, they would starve.

The wild animals that roamed the glacial tundras of ice-age Europe not only fed and fuelled Neanderthals, they moulded them. Their ferocity, their will to live, their own acquired lethality raised the bar and forced Neanderthals to become tougher, smarter and more aggressive. These wild beasts helped transform Neanderthals from a docile African hominid to the fiercest European predator.

While courage does not fossilise, we need to at least briefly consider how important it was to Neanderthal survival. The major animals Neanderthals hunted were physically larger, stronger and tougher than them. Some were predators themselves. What courage would it take to attack a towering mammoth, or a cave lion, or a woolly rhino, approaching close enough to stab it repeatedly with a stone-tipped spear—while it was desperately flaying with its horns, teeth, talons or claws—and to keep attacking until the thrashing beast was finally stilled?

Courage was not the only essential attribute. Natural selection also favoured the smartest individuals—the ones who survived because they could fashion weapons and use them to gain a strategic advantage, to outwit and out-manoeuvre animals ten times heavier.

Just as wolves, lions, hyenas and other carnivorous pack-pursuit predators evolved specialised sensory, behavioural and physiological adaptations that increased capture rates and improved killing efficiency, so too would Neanderthals acquire and hone similar predatory adaptations. In other words, hunters evolve to become more efficient and lethal. They acquire increasingly refined adaptations to locate, stalk, track, capture and kill their preferred prey—whatever it is. Being a predator defines its own evolutionary path.

High intelligence, guile, cunning and stealth only emerge at the pointy end of natural selection—the dangerous prey that killed off thousands of early Neanderthal hunters gradually shaped them to be the best predators they could be—relentless, stoical, ingenious, duplicitous and able to detect and interpret the tell-tale signs and scents of their quarry. Gradually, the gored, gutted, torn-apart, trampled-on individuals who lost their lives in the hunt gave way to a new breed of super-smart, hyper-aggressive killers.

A final line of evidence that Neanderthals evolved as a predator species is the thickness of their skulls. These were unusually chunky—at least compared to those of early humans. This chunkiness is called postcranial hyper-robusticity and has been interpreted by Valerius Geist, from the University of Calgary, as an adaptation to close-quarter hunting confrontations with large mammals.[166] It is another one of those things that gets selected—over time only the thick-skulled Neanderthals survived. Just as over time the demands of predation bestowed on Neanderthals their massive trunk and limb bones and their exceptional strength.[167]

An accepted method of testing scientific theories is to generate predictions from the theory and test them empirically. If Neanderthals were carnivorous predators engaged exclusively in hunting large, dangerous animals, this generates several predictions that can be tested. For a start, life at the top of the food chain would not have been easy, so Neanderthals would suffer more physical injuries than early hunter-gathering humans. This violent lifestyle would also mean that they did not live as long as humans. Both these propositions are corroborated by a plethora of scientific evidence.[168,169,170,171]

Judging by the high frequency of bone fractures in Neanderthals,[172,173] their close-quarter encounters exacted a heavy toll in physical injuries. In his study of trauma injuries among Neanderthals, Erik Trinkaus found that almost every adult Neanderthal skeleton ever examined reveals some evidence of skeletal trauma.[174] In one examination of 17 Neanderthal remains, Trinkaus found 27 skeletal wounds. And there would have been many more soft tissue injuries that were not preserved. While some of these injuries may have come from interpersonal violence,[175,] others must have been suffered in the course of predatory encounters.

On the basis of microscopic and chemical analysis of their bones, scientists have been able to estimate how old each Neanderthal was when they died. From this data, it has been established that Neanderthals rarely lived beyond the age of 40, which is considerably less than Upper Palaeolithic modern humans.[176] Life at the top of the food chain was incredibly tough.

A picture begins to emerge of Neanderthals, not as the popularly portrayed dim-witted scavengers, but as cunning, formidable predators—two-legged, big-brained versions of lions and sabre-toothed tigers—and, like other top-level carnivores, possessing specialised hunting strategies to maximise their killing efficiency. John Shea provides an apt conclusion: "Once seen as dull-witted cavemen, new evidence indicates Neanderthals were intelligent, adaptable, and highly effective predators."[177] Elsewhere, the Stony Brook University anthropologist describes them as the "superpredators of the Ice Age".[178]

For a species that evolved in the frigid wastelands of ice-age Europe and survived that punishing environment for 500,000 years, being tough, stoical, resilient and aggressive was part of a tried and tested survival strategy. These attributes are the hallmarks of a top flight predator which, in conjunction with their amazing predatory prowess, allowed the Neanderthals to claim the position at the apex of the food chain. In Europe, Neanderthals became the perfect predator. And when some of them migrated to the Levant (to become the Eurasian Neanderthals) they brought with them all their predatory skills and attitudes—the whole gambit of their ferocious lethality.

4

THE LEAN MEAN KILLING MACHINE

tastes like chicken

Despite a great deal of recent evidence showing Neanderthals ate only meat, the behavioural implications of an exclusively carnivorous diet have been largely ignored by anthroplogists. This may well be anthropomorphic reticence—we don't like to think of our sister species as callous killers. Or perhaps it simply conjures up an unpalatable association with predators like lions and wolves—predators we instinctively fear. Whatever the reason for this, it seems strange, as the findings are an important and exciting new line of evidence with the potential to reveal new insights into Neanderthals. Why? Because what an animal eats—and how it obtains its food—says a great deal about the kind of species it is.

Analysis of animal bones and teeth that litter Neanderthal caves not only shows they were carnivores, but that they were trying to extract maximum nutritional sustenance from every carcass. "They weren't just eating steaks off these animals," Erik Trinkaus reports, "they were eating everything that was edible. They were smashing up the skulls and eating brains. They were eating tongues."[179]

Moreover, evidence from a number of European Neanderthal sites reveals cut marks on Neanderthal bones. These marks, and the way the bones have been cracked open to extract the marrow, has been interpreted as evidence of cannibalism. Neanderthal sites where cannibalism has been reported include Krapina[180] and Vindija[181] in Croatia; Marillac,[182] Combe Grenal,[183] Macassargues[184] and Les Pradelles[185] in France; and Zafarraya[186] in Spain. While some of these findings have been questioned, recent unambiguous forensic evidence of cannibalism from several new European excavations has come to light.

In northern Spain the El Sidrón Neanderthal cave has surrendered the bones of eight Neanderthals that bear the unmistakable slashing and butchering marks caused by cannibals wielding hand axes, saw-toothed knives and scrapers to cut up and deflesh the bodies.[187] The research team, led by palaeoanthropologist Antonio Rosas, reported that leg and arm joints had been dismembered, long bones smashed to extract marrow and, in a few cases, the skulls deftly skinned with flint blades. The victims were of all ages—four adults, two teenagers, a child and a baby. Once the bones were processed, they were treated the same as the other animal bones—scattered indiscriminately around the cave.

At the Moula-Guercy rock shelter, in Ardèche, France, three Neanderthal victims of cannibalism have been unearthed.[188] Defleshing and disarticulation involved cutting their arms off at the shoulders and elbows, hacking off the thigh muscles, severing the Achilles' tendon on one individual, slicing the temporalis muscle on the side of the skull on another two, and cutting out the tongue of the youngest. The bones—except the hand and foot bones—were then cracked open on a hammerstone to extract the nutrient rich marrow.

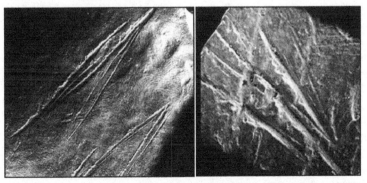

The evidence of cannibalism: at Moula-Guercy, in France, Neanderthals used a flint knife to fillet the temporalis (chewing) muscle from the side of the skull.
Photo: A Defleur *Science* 286:130

Interestingly, although the Moula-Guercy Neanderthals were fire-makers, and simple hearths were found in the cave, the cannibalised bones reveal few signs of cooking. Either they preferred to eat the flesh raw or else they hacked it from the bone before roasting it. In either case, once the bones had given up all their nutritional value they were, like the El Sidrón bones, tossed onto a scrap heap along with those of other animals.

"The Neanderthal bones", writes Karoline Lukaschek in her doctoral thesis *The History of Cannibalism*, "were mingled with those of the deer and scattered throughout the cave. Both types of bones appear to have been littered across the cave floor rather than buried. If the deer were butchered for food, then the Neanderthals were, too."[189]

The Krapina rock shelter in Croatia is arguably the largest Neanderthal site ever discovered. As many as 800 fossilised Neanderthal bones have been discovered there, representing about 80 individuals. Although the way some of these bones have been hacked and scratched has long been suspected to be the result of cannibalism, until recently not everyone agreed. That was until 2005, when the bones were re-examined by a team from the British Museum using the latest high-tech digital-imaging microscopes.

Jill Cook and her team confirm that many of the bones had cut marks, percussion pits from hammerstone strikes, striations, crushed spongy bone and abrasion patterns consistent with dismemberment and defleshing. Cuts were made to the pelvic and leg bones which had been stripped of their flesh and rubbed with an abrasive to remove the fat and gristle. Some of the skulls had their ears lopped off, their tongues cut out, their lower jaws removed, and the skin on their heads peeled off.[190] Again, the bones were dumped with those of other butchered animals.

Collectively, the findings from El Sidrón in Spain, Moula-Guercy in France, and Krapina in Croatia prove beyond doubt what Croatian palaeontologist Dragutin Gorjanović-Kramberger asserted over a 100 years ago[191]—Neanderthals, at least periodically, practised cannibalism.

The evidence of Neanderthal cannibalism in Europe is consistent with the discovery that their European ancestors were also cannibals. Excavations at the Gran Dolina cave, near Atapuerca, in northern Spain have revealed unambiguous evidence of cannibalism going back 780,000 years, by *Homo antecessor*, hominids who are thought to be direct ancestors of Neanderthals.[192]

Whether Neanderthal cannibalism was dietary (for food) or ritualistic (for religious or quasi-religious reasons) is impossible to say for sure. But it is not difficult to see that dietary cannibalism would be a highly adaptive survival strategy during times of food shortage, providing a much needed extra source of protein. On the other hand, ritual cannibalism involves an appreciation of religious and spiritual concepts, symbolism and ritualised ceremonies that would require complex symbolic intelligence. So far, this has been associated only with fully Upper Palaeolithic cultures rather than Middle Palaeolithic hominids.

The logical question that follows on from this is, did European Neanderthals also eat archaic humans in Europe? The answer of course is no, simply because Middle Palaeolithic humans did not live in Europe. Indeed, there is no evidence that archaic humans ever entered Europe during the entire 500,000 years of Neanderthal occupation. I will argue later that this was because the Neanderthals vigorously defended their territory against all intruders. It was only much later (towards the end of the Neanderthal occupation) that Upper Palaeolithic humans (Cro-Magnons) armed with high-tech weapons finally managed to enter Europe.

This brings us to the question of cannibalism in the Levant by Eurasian Neanderthals. From the solid evidence of Neanderthal cannibalism in Europe it is highly likely that Eurasian Neanderthals also ate each other in the Levant, even though evidence from cannibalised bones has not yet been uncovered in that region. This lack of evidence is hardly surprising— in Europe, 500 Neanderthal sites have been discovered which had been occupied for half a million years. In the Levant only a handful have been uncovered and these had been occupied sporadically for less than 60,000 years. Also, cannibalised bones were less likely to be preserved in the Levant because of the warmer climate. The icy climate of Europe was much more conducive to the preservation of fossilised bones.

it's all just meat

The recent corroboration of Neanderthal cannibalism lends itself to an intriguing new theory—the possibility that Eurasian Neanderthals also cannibalised Skhul-Qafzeh humans. From an adaptationist perspective, it makes sense that for a carnivore predator like a Neanderthal, no edible, economically procurable species would be off the menu.

If recovered animal bones reveal that Neanderthals were trying to extract every last morsel, and if they hunted every large animal in their territory—even formidable ones like mammoths, bears and lions— then, in the absence of cultural, moral and religious constraints against cannibalism (which to date have only been attributed to fully modern humans), we need to seriously consider whether they also hunted and ate Skhul-Qafzeh humans.

This does not necessarily mean Neanderthals hunted the Levantine humans as a priority. After all, their ancestors in Europe had acquired a preference for deer, horse, mammoth and other herbivores, so the Eurasian Neanderthals probably maintained that preference—under normal conditions. What can be inferred though, is that the Levant human population (which has been estimated to number between 5000–10,000 individuals)[193] would have provided Eurasian Neanderthals with an additional food source that could be exploited as required, particularly when their preferred prey was scarce or seasonally unavailable.

Even though cannibalism has been observed in over 1300 animal species,[194] including chimpanzees,[195,196] for a few scholars the idea that Neanderthals would want to hunt humans for food is anathema. Over the last decade, Neanderthals have increasingly been perceived as gentle, humane cousins, displaying almost the same intellectual and emotional proclivities and sensitivities as modern humans.

This is due in part to the suggestion that Neanderthals may have demonstrated symbolic thinking, including playing musical instruments and burying their dead with flowers. For example, several researchers have claimed that a fragment of a cave bear's femur with two holes, from Divje Babe in Slovenia, is a 'Neanderthal flute'.[197,198]

In 2006, Iain Morley, from Cambridge University, conducted a detailed microscopic analysis of the Divje Babe bone (*right*). He discovered that, although the bone looks like a flute, it shows evidence of gnawing by a carnivore along its entire length. Also, the size and shape of the holes are the same as the canine teeth of brown bears and cave bears. He concludes that the bone is "the product of a number of stages of carnivore activity, and there is no need to invoke any hominin agency in the creation of the object".[199]

What is so convincing about Morley's argument is that under a microscope, on the underside of the bone, the indentations of the carnivore's bottom teeth are clearly visible, directly opposite the so-called 'flute holes'.

A second case is the alleged burial with flowers of the *Shanidar IV Neanderthal*, which one researcher has interpreted as a ritual burial by symbolic people.[200] This made quite an impact in the media at the time and created an image of Neanderthals as the gentle hippies of the Pleistocene. But this too has been disputed. Anthropologist Jeffrey Sommer concludes in the *Cambridge Archaeological Journal* that the flower pollen found in the grave was more likely to have been brought there by rats that had burrowed into the grave.[201]

Because cannibalism raises such emotive issues, it is worth emphasising that, from a purely Darwinian perspective, eating archaic humans wouldn't involve the negative connotations normally associated with murder or cannibalism. Judging by other predators, killing for food isn't personal. Nor is it motivated by homicidal rage, insanity or even anger. A lion has no personal animosity towards the antelope it brings down. There may be the excitement of the hunt, the suspense of stalking a prey for hours or even days, the exhilaration of the chase and the satisfaction of a clean kill—but ultimately, it's not personal.

Primatologist and anthropologist Richard Wrangham, from Harvard University, who has studied social predators in Africa, says that they don't show obvious signs of excitement when killing a prey,[202] and Johan van der Dennen, from the University of Groningen in the Netherlands, notes that social carnivores don't play with or taunt their prey, preferring instead to dispatch them quickly with a fatal bite.[203] Ultimately, within the context of food procurement in the endless winter of the European Stone Age, cannibalism would often be a question of survival of the fittest. It was all just meat.

The reluctance to attribute the ferocity and viciousness of modern feline and canine predators to Neanderthals has delayed the resolution of the Neanderthal problem. Ferocity and brutality are key prerequisites of predation which, in turn, is widely acknowledged to be an important driver of physical evolution.[204,205,206] Predacious behaviour is among the most important single determinants of a species' evolution, creating specific demands on an animal's physiology and behaviour. If a species' raison d'être is killing, then killing guides its evolution.

family feuds

While dietary cannibalism would be one reason why Neanderthals hunted early humans, it would not be the only reason. Another factor that may have played a role in the Levant is *intraguild predation*—the killing and consumption of an intermediate predator by a top predator from the same guild,[207] for example, the killing of cheetahs by lions.[208]

Intraguild predation is a widespread phenomenon among mammalian carnivores,[209] but it is unusual in that the top predator does not always eat the middle predator it kills. Of 21 reported cases of intraguild predation in one study,[210] the top predator ate the middle predator in only ten cases. For example, spotted hyenas always ate the cheetahs they killed, but lions weren't observed eating any cheetahs. This has prompted several researchers in the field to maintain that the evolutionary function of intraguild predation might be to reduce competition for a shared prey resource.[211,212]

With intraguild predation being a common occurrence among mammalian land-based predators that have been around for at least three hundred million years, its evolutionary origins clearly go back far enough to apply to Neanderthal-human interactions in the Levant. If all the modern social carnivore species practise intraguild predation, then it is appropriate to suggest that Neanderthals also practised it on early humans.

coalitionary killing

Apart from killing animals for food, lethal violence is rare among mammals. When it occurs, though, it is usually between individuals.[213] But a rarer form of lethal violence has also been observed among wild animals—*coalitionary killing*—which is characterised by lethal violence between groups, or violence directed by a group towards an individual. Coalitionary killing has been observed among spotted hyenas,[214] wolves,[215] lions[216] and cheetahs[217]—all social predators—but is most common among chimpanzees and humans.[218]

Among populations of chimps which have been studied in their natural habitat, there have been countless cases of violence observed. A primatologist at Sydney's Taronga Park Zoo told me, "the chimps are the most dangerous animals we have at the zoo. We never ever go into their enclosure." I have witnessed a number of outbursts of aggression in the Taronga troop, characterised by quick vicious attacks, lots of blood-curdling shrieking, high-speed chases and the use of branches as weapons. Then it's over and the females go in to comfort the victims.

Despite this, no lethal case of violence by a single individual has ever been reported, either in a zoo or in the wild. All the fatal attacks have been by groups (or coalitions). Victims sometimes include members of the same group, but more likely they're members of neighbouring communities. Usually, a group assault lasts a minimum of 10 minutes, during which the attackers hold down the victim and continue to bite, strike, tear and drag until the victim is killed or immobilised.[219]

A graphic example of coalitionary killing by captive chimpanzees was observed at the Arnhem Zoo in the Netherlands in 1980. Primatologist Frans de Waal, who spent several years observing what at the time was the world's largest captive colony of chimpanzees, reported that on 12 September the males' sleeping quarters "turned red with blood".[220] On that night, two chimps (Nikkie and Yeröen) ganged up on the alpha male (Luit) and inflicted such injuries (including tearing off his testicles and several of his fingers and toes) that he died the following day.

While it may be an unpalatable concept, Eurasian Neanderthals were social carnivores, so coalitionary killing would be part of their genetic make-up, simply another string to their adaptationist bow.

lethal raiding

Lethal raiding is yet another form of deadly group behaviour. It describes the intrusion by a group of predators into a neighbouring territory, specifically to conduct a surprise attack, cause casualties, and retreat to the home territory.[221] Like coalitionary killing, lethal raiding is the exclusive preserve of social predators. Wolves, lions and spotted hyenas have been observed making lethal raids into neighbouring territories[222,223] but, again, chimpanzee and human males are by far the most frequent exponents of lethal raiding.

Lethal raiding is perplexing because field studies consistently show the raids are not escalations of current conflicts, acts of self defence, or aimed at poaching food from a neighbour's territory.[224] In all observed cases of chimpanzee raiding, the males encroach in unusual silence, in single file, into a neighbouring territory until they locate and capture a vulnerable individual who is then mercilessly attacked and, in most cases, killed.

Richard Wrangham says, "lethal raids indicate an appetite for hunting and killing rivals that is akin to predation."[225] Based on her own observations of chimps at Tanzania's Gombe Stream National Park, Jane Goodall argues that killing is the sole objective of lethal raiding.[226]

Although many theories try to explain coalitionary killing, lethal raiding and intergroup aggression among chimpanzees (see Johan van der Dennen, for an excellent review),[227] to date no consensus has emerged. One suggestion is that lethal raiding and coalitionary killing in contemporary chimpanzees is derived from an innate hostility towards outsiders—a primate form of xenophobia.

Another theory is that it represents an extreme form of sexual competition, aimed at killing rival males and gaining access to sexually mature females from neighbouring communities.[228,229,230] This fits with the fact that lethal raiding is almost exclusively carried out by males,[231,232] and that ten out of eleven victims of lethal raiding by chimpanzees at Gombe National Park were males.[233] It also seems significant that male raiding parties of wild chimpanzees at Gombe were observed violently 'kidnapping' females, resulting in prolonged fighting and skirmishes lasting several days.[234,235] These females eventually joined the raiders' community.

When it comes to the body count, however, chimps pale into insignificance compared to humans. Throughout recorded history, humans living in small tribes have shown themselves to be masters of both lethal raiding and coalitionary killing. And judging by well-observed accounts of modern hunter-gatherer groups, the pattern of violence is surprisingly similar to that of chimpanzees. For example, the Yanomamö people of Central Brazil undertake commando-style incursions deep into their neighbours' territory, attacking unsuspecting villages, killing whoever they can as quickly as they can, then beating a hasty retreat before the villagers can organise a proper defence.[236,237,238]

The similarity to human patterns of intergroup aggression and warfare are so striking that most researchers in the field believe they represent a direct continuity between modern human violence and primate aggression, going back five to six million years to common ancestors.[239, 240, 241,242,243]

In *The Origins of War* Keith Otterbein draws on the evidence of warfare among primates, prehistoric hominids, early agriculturists, and contemporary hunter-gatherer societies to show that coalitionary killings and intergroup warfare by males have been a ubiquitous feature of our species for over five million years.[244]

If we draw an evolutionary link between the violent tendencies of our closest (surviving) relative and our own, then it is necessary to include Neanderthals in that link. They are as closely related to chimps as humans are, and even more closely related to humans than chimps. If coalitionary violence and lethal raiding are a significant feature of chimpanzee and human societies, then they were almost certainly present in Neanderthal society.

In Europe, where the original and largest population of Neanderthals lived in isolation, European Neanderthals could only have directed lethal raiding, coalitionary killing and cannibalism against other European Neanderthals, who were obviously a formidable and well-armed adversary. Raiders faced the risk of being injured or even killed during incursions.

But in the Levant, I suggest, Skhul-Qafzeh humans represented a less aggressive, more docile, but nevertheless sexually compatible option—not to mention an alternative supply of fresh meat during times of food stress. They represented a 'soft' target for aggressive Eurasian Neanderthals. This—and the margin of safety it provided—would have encouraged lethal raiding against Levantine early humans.

It is not difficult to see that a group of aggressive Neanderthal males, faced with the decision of which troop to attack—a neighbouring group of heavily armed Eurasian Neanderthals, or a group of timid Skhul-Qafzehs—would opt to attack the human camp. How terrifying this must have been for our primitive ancestors—when the Neanderthals came with spears and stone knives, to terrorise and kill the men and kidnap the young girls and women. Such traumatic experiences would become indelibly encoded into their communal psyche, to leave them scarred for life.

If the portrayal of Neanderthals as a proficient spear-wielding apex predator-carnivore is accurate, then lethal raiding and coalitionary killing by Eurasian Neanderthals would result in significantly more casualties than an equivalent raid by modern chimps (who do not use sophisticated weapons), or even by Middle Palaeolithic humans.

turf wars

Were Neanderthals territorial? And, if so, what are the behavioural implications? Modern humans certainly are.[245] A cursory glance at an atlas reveals humans pegging out national boundaries, signposting them with flags and a common language, and defending the borders of their villages, cities, states and countries against all invaders, often with their lives.

While territoriality—the use of physical force, threat, or advertisement to defend an area—is a feature of human society, it is also prevalent among chimpanzees.[246,247] Male chimps regularly patrol the borders of their territory and intruders are usually attacked and, in some cases, killed. For primatologists, one of the most intriguing aspects of chimpanzee territoriality is just how violent they are towards intruders from neighbouring communities.[248, 249] Jane Goodall makes the point:

> In the chimpanzee, territoriality functions not only to repel intruders from the home range, but sometimes to injure or eliminate them; not only to defend the existing home range and its resources, but to enlarge it opportunistically at the expense of weaker neighbours; not only to protect

the female resources of a community, but to actively and aggressively recruit new sexual partners from neighbouring social groups.[250]

Chimpanzee territory size is thought to be directly correlated to their survival—the larger the territory, the more food and other resources it contains.[251] So we might reasonably conclude that if both humans and chimpanzees are aggressively territorial, then so too were Neanderthals.

We can also look at Neanderthal territoriality from another perspective. Several scholars have pointed out that because modern social carnivores like chimps, lions and hyenas have similar group dynamics, dominance hierarchies, land tenure systems and cooperative hunting techniques, they can be used to infer behaviour in early hominids.[252,253] The reasoning goes that, as social carnivores, Neanderthals probably evolved similar territorial imperatives as those of modern social carnivore species because the evolutionary constraints are similar.

Ecological studies show that territoriality is common in all modern social carnivores, particularly in lions, hyenas, wolves and chimpanzees and, not surprisingly, involves extreme violence.[254] What is perhaps surprising is that of all the social carnivores, chimpanzees are the most violent.[255,256]

This raises the likelihood that, as social carnivores, populations of Eurasian Neanderthals defended their territory aggressively, and probably expanded it by replacing other groups of Neanderthals and Skhul-Qafzeh humans.

Yet another, more direct insight into possible Neanderthal territoriality comes from Oxford University archaeologist Sarah Milliken's comprehensive 2007 study of Neanderthals in Italy. She writes:

> At Falce del Viaggio in the northern part of the Murge, high quality chert [a flint-like stone] was procured from the Gargano promontory, 70 km to the north, while at sites located 90 km to the south, chert was procured from the Basilicata Apennines, 70 km to the west. The absence of Gargano chert at the southern sites, and of Basilicata Apennines chert at Falce del Viaggio, suggests that the sites in these areas were part of two completely separate Neanderthal territories.[257]

Several other lines of evidence reveal that Neanderthals occupied forest areas, both in the Levant and in Europe. While in Europe forests provided some protection against icy winds and near-lethal wind chill, they were also home to some of their favourite prey, such as deer. Forests may have also suited their hunting style, where they could use the cover of trees to get close enough to ambush their prey. Again, in the Levant, archaeological assemblages reveal Neanderthals mostly hunted woodland species,[258] suggesting they occupied the inland mountains and forests, while humans resided in the flat coastal lowlands.[259] This evidence supports the premise that each species occupied its own well-defined separate territory.

It seems telling that, although Middle Palaeolithic humans colonised all areas of the Levant (before the Neanderthals arrived), there is no evidence they ever colonised Europe.[260] Was that because Europe was Neanderthal territory? Did humans try to push into Europe? And were they repelled by a determined species hell-bent on protecting their territory? Richard Klein believes this may have been the case—that Middle Palaeolithic humans did not colonise Europe because they couldn't compete against the Neanderthals.[261] This adds credence to the model that Neanderthals were a formidable and hostile adversary who poached territory from the Levantine early humans and tenaciously defended it.

The prospect of Neanderthal territoriality broadens the concept of 'them and us' to include 'theirs and ours'. Territory, with all its direct connotations to resource procurement and survival, provided yet another arena of conflict between the two competing species. In practical terms it meant that, when on hunting and gathering expeditions, Skhul-Qafzehs had to be careful not to stray inadvertently into Neanderthal territory or they risked being attacked and seriously injured, if not killed. No matter how lost they were, the last thing a group of Levantine hunters could afford to do was ask a stranger for directions.

In summary, it is reasonable to conclude that coalitionary killing, lethal raiding, dietary predation and aggressive territoriality would have resulted in the reduction of the Skhul-Qafzeh population in the Levant. And this in turn, could have serious long-term evolutionary implications. But there was one more reason that Eurasian Neanderthals were attracted to the Levantine humans, and this was arguably the most important reason of all—sex.

5

YOU SEXY BEAST

x-rated neanderthals

What was Neanderthal sex like? Did they copulate in public like chimpanzees, gorillas and bonobos or did they shy away like modern humans? Did Neanderthal females sport fulsome breasts and curvaceous hour-glass figures? And what about love? Did Neanderthal couples stare into each other's eyes over a smouldering camp fire, fall hopelessly in love and spend the rest of their lives together raising cute little Neanderthal babies? The truth is, researchers know almost nothing about Neanderthal sexuality. And that's mainly because sexuality is mostly about interpersonal behaviour and soft tissue physiology, neither of which are preserved in the fossil record.

Even if we know little about Neanderthal sexuality, we know a great deal about human sexuality, and the single most striking aspect of it is that it is unique in the primate order. Humans are the only primates to experience romantic love and to bond for life, the only ones to have breasts, rounded buttocks, multiple orgasms, pendulous penises and pubic hair. So, if humans are the only primates that are predisposed to monogamy, sexual modesty, private copulation and to regarding incestuous relations as taboo, we cannot automatically assume Neanderthals followed suit.

For example, we have many other features that are unique which we know Neanderthals did not share. Our exceptional intelligence, for example, and our creativity, art, music, culture, memory, language and consciousness. To assume Neanderthals shared our unique sexuality when they shared none of our other unique features is simply anthropomorphic speculation and at odds with Darwinian theory. Natural selection tells us that species don't arbitrarily acquire macroevolutionary features like a radical new sexuality. This kind of big-ticket item emerges only in response to extreme, concerted and prolonged evolutionary circumstances.

In the absence of any exceptional evolutionary conditions that may have caused Neanderthal sexuality to spiral off onto the same atypical trajectory as ours, we can conclude that the Neanderthal mating system remained essentially primate in nature. After all, the primate mating system had been tried and tested by natural selection over millions of years.

This also integrates with the view of a number of researchers that reproductive strategies of early hominids were similar to those of modern chimpanzees.[262,263] From this, a more parsimonious picture begins to emerge of the Neanderthal mating system.

This new view suggests that Neanderthal sexuality was mechanistically regulated by developmental, hormonal and neurological cues, just as nonhuman primate sexuality is today.[264] At the biological centre of this kind of rigid mating system is the female ovulation cycle. When a sexually mature Neanderthal female came into oestrus, a cocktail of hormones (primarily oestrogen and progesterone) would cause her genitalia to swell, and the increased blood flow would turn the anogenital region a pinkish-purple colour. This colourful and conspicuous display would trigger hormonal responses in Neanderthal males that stimulated sexual arousal and mating behaviour, just as it does in all nonhuman primates.[265, 266]

Just to make sure the boys got the message, females in heat would rub their genitals provocatively and present their swollen rumps to the males. But ultimately, the big guns were the array of sexual scents, pheromones and discharges that modern primates still use to attract males. They include axillary steroids, vaginal aliphatic acids, and stimulators of the vomeronasal organ, the small nodule in the nose that chemically detects pheromones. Even today, although modern humans have lost much of their pheromonal receptivity, tests show that men find the smell of women's bodies more pleasant and sexually attractive when they are ovulating.[267]

At the same time, testosterone and other sex hormones would send the adult males into a frenzy of aggressive competition with each other. These status contests are aimed at intimidating rivals and gaining priority

At Sydney's Taronga Zoo, a male chimp inspects a female's swollen genitalia, then mounts her briefly. NP theory argues that Neanderthals followed this model.

access to prime age females. In chimpanzee society, the most aggressive, dominant male ends up siring about 50 percent of the offspring of a troop,[268] so there would be heated competition to assume the mantle of alpha male. Following the ancestral tradition, Neanderthal females would observe these combative contests with great interest, holding off until the dominance hierarchy had been established and then copulating with the highest ranking male first, before evaluating other suitors, just as chimps do today.

We also know from field studies of chimpanzees that, once the alpha male has claimed his prize, he attempts to guard the female until her sexual swellings subside to prevent other males copulating with her. Sometimes males form coalitions to guard a female, at other times the alpha male will shadow a female night and day to fend off attempts by determined, but less dominant males to access her.

treat 'em mean, keep 'em keen

Judging by modern primates, status contests and the intimidation of males (including human males) were not the only weapons in the Neanderthals' sexual arsenal. Barbara Smuts, a professor of psychology and anthropology at the University of Michigan, studied baboons and chimps in the wild in the 1970s. During that time, she witnessed many attacks by male chimps and baboons against females in oestrus and has proposed that intimidation and coercion are widespread tactics in securing females. Smuts reported that her research on olive baboons in Kenya, "showed that, on average, each pregnant or lactating female was attacked by an adult male about once a week and seriously injured about once a year. Estrous females were the target of even more aggression."

In *Apes of Wrath*, Smuts discusses the function of male sexual violence:

> I saw in Gombe, a male chimpanzee even attacks an estrous female days before he tries to mate with her. Goodall thinks that a male uses such aggression to train a female to fear him so that she will be more likely to surrender to his subsequent sexual advances. Similarly, male hamadryas baboons, who form small harems by kidnapping child brides, maintain a tight rein over their females through threats and intimidation. If, when another male is nearby, a hamadryas female strays even a few feet from her mate, he shoots her a threatening stare and raises his brows. She usually responds by rushing to his side; if not, he bites the back of her neck. The neck bite is ritualized—the male does not actually sink his razor-sharp canines into her flesh— but the threat of injury is clear. By repeating this behavior hundreds of times, the male lays claim to particular females months or even years before mating with them. When a female comes into estrus, she solicits sex only from her harem master, and other males rarely challenge his sexual rights to her.[269]

Applied to the Levant, this introduces the probability of Neanderthals using threats, coercion and sexual violence against females to obtain mating opportunities.

when 'no' meant nothing

No discussion of Neanderthal sexual aggression would be complete without consideration of the ultimate expression of male sexual aggression. Although rape is rare among mammalian species, according to Richard Wrangham, "rape occurs much more commonly among the great apes than among most animals".[270] Jane Goodall has observed male chimps raping females at Gombe,[271] captive gorillas are known to rape females,[272] and in one troop of orang-utans, a massive 86 percent of sub-adult male copulations were rapes.[273] And it needs hardly be emphasised that rape occurs in all known human cultures.[274] In one American survey, 13 percent of women over the age of 18 reported being raped at least once.[275] Another survey of 930 women from San Francisco concludes that 24 percent of American women will experience a completed rape at some time in their lives, and almost half will be victims of attempted rape.[276]

Given that chimp, gorilla, human and orang-utan males all periodically rape females (including one reliable account of an orang-utan raping a female human)[277] it seems probable that Neanderthal males periodically raped their own females.

When it came to the sex act itself, if Neanderthal copulation was triggered by hormonal responses to visual and pheromonal cues, it would be highly motivated but perfunctory and mechanistic, just like chimpanzee and bonobo sex is today.[278] And if chimpanzees and bonobos copulate with alacrity with multiple partners, and don't fall in love or form lasting pair bonds,[279] then in all probability Neanderthals didn't either.

From a purely Darwinian perspective, the objective of this tried-and-tested primate mating system was simply to ensure the fittest, strongest, healthiest males passed on their genes. Aggressive male competition served that purpose.

the levantine club scene

So what about humans? Did the Skhul-Qafzeh sexual system follow the primate model, or had it already morphed into the more complex love-based sexuality we're familiar with today? This is a vitally important question because the answer has a direct bearing on human evolution. If both the Skhul-Qafzeh humans and the Eurasian Neanderthals adhered to the same ancestral primate mating system, then it raises the possibility that the two species were sexually compatible. And this would be very significant.

At issue is—when did modern human sexuality diverge from its primate homologue to its present form? Did the Skhul-Qafzeh humans fall in love, avoid sex in public, indulge in fore-play and form life-long pair bonds, or did the males battle it out to claim the females with the biggest rumps?

While the archaeological evidence is silent on this matter, we can still make some informed guesses. For example, it's known that modern human skeletal anatomy evolved into its present form only about 150,000 years ago. We also know that modern human behaviour appeared only around 46,000 years ago. Because modern human sexuality is inexorably tied to these major physical and behavioural changes, it indicates that modern human sexuality and love are recent phenomena—connected with us becoming fully human. It means that 100,000 years ago, human sexuality almost certainly still adhered to the same primate mating system as Neanderthals.

This is corroborated by the law of homology which argues that both species acquired their sexual systems from recent common ancestors so would be similar. And, because mating systems are so fundamental to procreation and survival, they are highly conserved (they don't change much over time) which indicates that early human and Neanderthal mating behaviour did not diverge significantly over time. As sexually homologous sibling species, they would have the same sex hormones, the same developmental cues and be receptive to the same sexual advertisements. Having been pheromonally aroused by similar inducements, they would respond hormonally with similar behaviours. This means the genital tumescence, pheromonal scents and secretions produced by human females in oestrus almost certainly would have aroused and attracted Neanderthal males.

For these reasons, a number of researchers from different disciplines have argued that Neanderthals and Skhul-Qafzeh humans were sexually compatible and could produce fertile offspring.[280, 281,282]

Sure, primate species separated by time and geography tend to acquire minor differences in their sexual behaviour. For example, in addition to same-sex behaviour, both male and female bonobos regularly practise homosexuality, whereas chimpanzees mainly copulate with members of the opposite sex. But despite any superficial differences that accrued, Neanderthals and early humans were still sibling species descended from the same common ancestor as modern primates. This means that Neanderthal and Skhul-Qafzeh mating systems would bear a striking resemblance to modern primate mating systems, notwithstanding the chronological gap that separates them.

kicking sand in our faces

The doctrine of sexual homology provides us with an important evolutionary clue to understanding early human-Neanderthal interactions It opens the Pandora's Box situation of Neanderthal males directly competing against early human males for the same sexually mature females. And because sexual reproduction is one of the most powerful and highly motivated behaviours in the animal kingdom and the mainstay of vigorous (and occasionally lethal) competition between males, it predicts that competition for mating opportunities created and sustained a deep, antagonistic conflict between the two sibling species.

The issue of Neanderthal and Skhul-Qafzeh males competing for the same fertile human females takes us to the nub of an intriguing evolutionary conundrum. It also brings to the fore what I suggest is the one major difference between the species—the degree and ferocity of Neanderthal male competition and sexual violence.

As proficient hunters and skilled fighters—armed with flint-tipped spears, clubs and knives—Neanderthal males would turn sexual competition on its head and raise the sexual/survival stakes considerably. Male sexual competition is largely informed by physical aggression, intimidation of rivals and coercion of prospective female mates. An alpha Neanderthal in the throes of a testosterone-charged sexual frenzy would present a formidable and determined adversary, and woe betide anyone who stood between him and any female he wanted.

Because pheromonal scents produced by ovulating modern human females can be detected over great distances, and at extremely low concentrations (less than one ten millionth of a gram), there would always have been the possibility that sexually aroused Neanderthal males would come sniffing around the human camps. There the sight of females with swollen, brightly coloured genitalia, and emitting pungent sexual aromas, would cause a flood of testosterone in the males that would precipitate a panoply of intimidating behaviours. We know this from studies of adult male chimpanzees in the Kibale National Park in Uganda by field researchers Martin Muller and Richard Wrangham, who found that levels of the male hormone testosterone peaked when females' genitalia was at its maximum tumescence and colouration and these peaks corresponded with the highest level of male aggression.[283]

Just as raiding groups of male chimps attempt to dominate, drive off and, in some cases, kill males from different troops to establish alpha status and gain access to their females, so too it is likely that

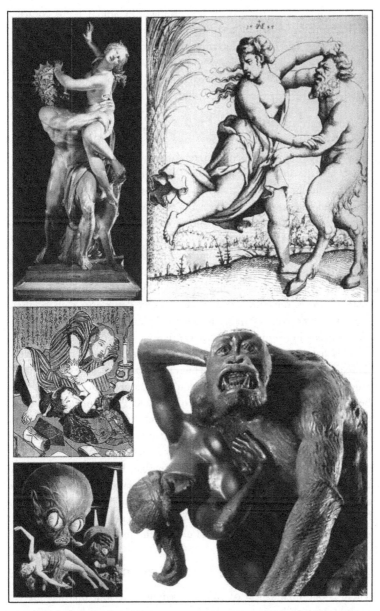

World mythologies are full of tales of abduction and rape by half-human, half-animal creatures, aliens and other sexual predators. NP theory suggests this is an expression of innate fears acquired as a result of Neanderthal sexual predation.

Neanderthal males engaged the human males in similar status contests. Fuelled by hefty doses of testosterone, males from both species would be aggressive and equally determined to claim any available female, and this raises the question—who won these status contests? To answer that, we need only review the nature of the competition the Neanderthals faced.

in the blue corner...

How well did the early Skhul-Qafzeh humans shape up as competitors? When sexually aroused Neanderthal males raided a human camp, growling demonically, brandishing spears, attacking the males and abducting the young females, how did our ancestors fare? Were they well-matched adversaries, using similar weapons and tools to battle it out? Not quite. As we've seen, the Skhul-Qafzeh people did not hunt large, dangerous prey. Instead, they maintained their omnivorous African diet which consisted mainly of plant foods, supplemented by small game. Because Levantine humans retained aspects of the vegetarian diet inherited from their primate ancestors, they never joined the exclusive carnivore's club. So there was no evolutionary imperative to acquire the full range of predator adaptations needed to support exclusive carnivory.

This has led a number of researchers to the view that the archaic humans who evolved in Africa and migrated to the Levant were, by nature, a timid and cautious species.[284] If you're not a predator, then you must be prey—to any one of the dozens of predators known to have stalked the African savannah. As zoologist John Paul Scott argues, timidity and a wariness of potential dangers were essential behavioural adaptations for surviving in the predator-infested world of prehistoric Africa. [285]

So, although Neanderthals and humans had both optimally adapted to their original environments (Europe and Africa respectively), when the competition hotted up there can be little doubt the predatory adaptations Neanderthals acquired in Europe would provide them with a clear competitive advantage over the Skhul-Qafzeh humans.

she's leaving home, bye bye

There is one final aspect of primate mating behaviour that may have a bearing on early human sexuality. Incest increases the risk of congenital birth defects and impacts on longevity,[286] forcing animal species, including primates, to acquire adaptations to discourage incest. The main method among primates is the dispersal of sexually mature females from the birth (or natal) group to new communities.[287,288] Among common chimpanzees, for example, males tend to remain in the natal group while between 50 to 90 percent of chimp females move to neighbouring communities.[289] This exchange injects fresh genes into both groups.[290] Researchers have also noted that female chimps regularly sneak off to mate covertly with males from outside groups. Genetic analysis of paternity in three wild chimpanzee communities in West Africa found males from outside the troop fathered about seven percent of all the infants.[291] At Gombe, Jane Goodall observed that about 13 percent of female copulations were with males from outside the troop,[292] while at Taï it was one percent.[293]

Obviously, early human society had some form of incest avoidance protocol and if it originally subscribed to the primate model, then prior to the appearance of Neanderthals in their territory some sexually mature Skhul-Qafzeh females would have normally dispersed to other human groups.

Once Neanderthals moved into the Levant, Skhul-Qafzeh females would come under pressure to repress this instinctive behaviour as intergroup transfer became more problematical and dangerous. It was not just that females would be too afraid of Neanderthals or repulsed by their behaviour to voluntarily have sex with them. In all likelihood, human males would have taken a dim view of any female caught 'sleeping with the enemy'.

the cat among the pigeons

This analysis indicates that human sexuality became the focus of a vicious and destabilising interspecies competition that not only imbued human sexuality with angst, but also threatened the viability of the entire Skhul-Qafzeh population. At the psychological level, while we cannot say for certain how the Skhul-Qafzeh females responded to Neanderthal abductions and rape, we know from research on rape in modern human societies that between 37 and 57 percent of women who experience rape suffer post-traumatic stress disorder. This is higher than the rates of post-traumatic stress disorder for other crimes against women, including burglary, robbery and aggravated assault.[294]

As to the emotional/psychological impact this violent sexual competition had on Levantine males, we might reasonably hazard a guess that their powerlessness to prevent the loss of their fertile young females only added to the frustration and anxiety they already felt.

Of course, natural selection doesn't give a toss about fairness—or maintaining a level playing field. It would be of no consequence that Neanderthals made cuckolds of an entire species, nor that their competitive edge rendered aspects of the Skhul-Qafzeh mating system maladaptive. Natural selection was not concerned that this deleterious form of sexual predation exposed a vulnerability that would have profound evolutionary consequences for the Skhul-Qafzeh people. And for us. The only thing that mattered was that intimidation, abduction and rape allowed Neanderthals to access a new source of fertile females—something that was highly adaptive because it introduced fresh genes into their breeding population.

6 OUT IN THE COLD

a case of mistaken identity

The prevailing logic in the popular science media regarding the physical appearance of Neanderthals seems to be: if humans don't resemble other primates—then neither did Neanderthals. Even though the other 192 primate species don't look like us, we somehow assume that Neanderthals did. This premise is sometimes supported by the fact that human and Neanderthal skeletons are so superficially similar (they have the same bones in roughly the same places) their facial features must be similar too. But then again, human and chimp skeletons are also similar and yet their facial features are quite different.

It's not only the media that has perpetrated the anthropomorphic view that Neanderthals and humans were like two peas in a pod—scientists have too. In the pictorial 'evolution of man', ancient hominids like *Australopithecus,* and *Homo robustus* and *habilis* stand at one end of a monkey-human continuum, while Neanderthals stand proudly with early humans at the other end—a little hairier—but demonstrably human.

It has even been claimed that if you gave a Neanderthal a bath, a shave, a haircut and a new Armani suit, he could pass off unnoticed on the New York subway as yet another surly stockbroker.[295]

As recently as 2007, Professor of Biological Anthropology at Harvard University Daniel Lieberman was quoted as saying, "If a Neanderthal were to come along, we'd think he was kind of weird. But we might also wonder whether to admit him to Harvard."[296]

The Field Museum of Natural History in Chicago commissioned this reconstruction of a classic European Neanderthal (from La Chapelle-aux-Saints, in France) to illustrate just how modern-looking these guys were. Graphic adapted from J H McGregor.

There is no scientific evidence to support this contention. Anthropologist Judith Berman, who has carried out a detailed study of the perception of prehistoric hominids in both the media and science, makes the point that the familiar iconography of the 'cave man' has its origins not in science or hard evidence, but in medieval European art,[297] and has simply continued, driven by anthropomorphism, into modern popular culture.

As soon as an objective evolutionary perspective is applied to the Neanderthals' external appearance, it becomes obvious that what they looked like was determined by natural selection. Ecology, which includes the physical environment and the behaviours required to survive in that particular environment, is what determines an animal's appearance. Only by disregarding our anthropomorphic bias and concentrating on examining the relationship between Neanderthals and the environment in which they evolved, can we create an accurate identikit picture of a Neanderthal.

the environmental factor

Neanderthals evolved in ice-age Europe, and survived in that ice-box environment for hundreds of thousands of years only because they managed to adapt biologically to the cold. Having argued that climate played a pivotal role in Neanderthal behaviour (by forcing them to adopt the carnivorous diet that segued into a predatory lifestyle), we must expect that the climate would also have affected their physiology.

Cold-climate Neanderthal adaptations are thought to include novel features like short limbs,[298] the shape of the femur and pelvis,[299,300] large noses, and compact torsos—all of which are thought to minimise heat loss.[301,302] The same stocky build is evident in people (like the Inuit) living in arctic regions today. Of course, the exceptionally cold temperatures of ice-age Europe would have created an extreme version in European Neanderthals—what anthropologist, Trenton Holliday from the University of Central Florida calls the 'hyperpolar' body shape.[303]

a hair-raising question

A cold-adapted gelada baboon

What Neanderthals looked like is defined by numerous features, but let's consider the 'big ticket' items—the major physical features that create the all-important first impression. The most noticeable, from a distance at least, would be the amount of body hair and its colour, raising the question—how hairy were they? Were they smooth-skinned and hairless like us, or covered with thick fur like other primates? And if so, what colour was their fur?

Today, every single warm blooded mammalian species living in a similar icy climate has acquired a thick coat of body fur to maintain their core body temperature. Most primates live in warm or tropical climates, but a few have taken up residence in very cold regions of the earth and this provides an opportunity to see how they have adapted to the cold. Not surprisingly, cold-adapted modern primates, such as Japanese macaques and gelada baboons, have not only acquired extra long, extra thick fur coats, but have also evolved an annual thicker 'winter coat' for when temperatures really plummet.

This indicates that the iconic view of Neanderthals—as almost as devoid of body hair as modern humans—is an anthropomorphic relic and needs to be re-examined. As part of my investigation, I re-examined the fossil and cave art evidence from Europe during the period of Neanderthal occupation. This revealed that every Late Pleistocene terrestrial mammal

Woolly mammoth, woolly rhinoceros, Eurasian cave lion, musk oxen, cave bear, and European bison all lived in Europe at the time of the Neanderthals, and all had long, dense fur coats.

species inhabiting Europe and the Middle East had long thick hairy coats to protect them from the cold.[304,305,306,307]

If all these animals acquired thick fur to insulate them against the freezing cold, it seems likely that Neanderthals did too.

The only thing standing between a hairless Neanderthal and a snap-frozen Neanderthal would be some form of cultural buffeting, such as clothing, fire or shelter. But Neanderthals made only simple fires and, apart from the odd wind break, did not build complex structures.[308] So far, significant improvements in clothing, pyrotechnology and shelter have been associated only with Upper Palaeolithic people,[309,310] but it is important to consider whether clothing—skinned from animals and fashioned into something resembling a loosely fitting garment—helped

Neanderthals survive the worst of the European winters. If so, did this lead to them discarding their ancestral primate fur?

But first, we must discard preconceptions derived from the countless pictorial representations of Neanderthals dressed in over-the-shoulder furs and loin cloths. These illustrations are mostly rooted in antiquated concepts of sexual modesty and fanciful imagination. There is no direct evidence that Neanderthals ever wore clothes. In fact, it is difficult to see why their unique cold-adaptive 'hyperpolar' body shape would be needed if they did. Australian anthropologist Ian Gilligan argues that clothing could not have been a major factor "as regular use of complex garments would result in a consistently warmer microenvironment for the body and hence a less cold-adapted physique".[311]

And what exactly is meant by *clothing*—or more precisely, the type of clothing required to keep someone alive in ice-age Europe? University of Durham archaeologist Mark White makes the point that to provide anything like the level of insulation necessary for survival:

> Neanderthal clothing would have needed to be more than the ragged loincloth, off-the-shoulder wrap or cape of popular depiction (the last of which would pin the arms inside, preventing effective action). Some form of tailoring would probably have been required,[[312]] but the Middle Palaeolithic has thus far yielded no evidence of needlecraft technology, which first appears in the Upper Palaeolithic.[313]

Having discarded the familiar picture of the burly Neanderthal in a loin cloth, our focus shifts to whether they could tailor the kind of closely fitting 'body suits' needed to survive. Ian Gilligan explains that :

> [Such] complex garments demand that the skins be carefully shaped by cutting, especially for the separate rectangular pieces that form cylinders to cover the limbs, and these need to be joined together in some way, usually by sewing. Where multiple layers are used, the inner garments must be carefully prepared, with finer cutting and sewing to achieve the necessary close fit.[314]

Complex garment manufacture requires needles to sew pieces together and, to date, no eyed needles have been recovered from Neanderthal sites, although some creationist web sites would have you believe otherwise.

Literally thousands of Neanderthal stone tools and pieces of bone and ivory have been found but, despite the fact that they fossilise well and are common in Upper Palaeolithic human sites, eyed needles have never been found at Neanderthal sites. While Donald Johanson and Blake Edgar note in *From Lucy to Language*, "there is no scrap of archaeological evidence for Neanderthal clothing",[316] this would not preclude Neanderthals throwing the odd fur over their shoulders or tossing a skin down on the cave floor to make a more comfortable nest. But the absence of sewing needles is telling and indicates that Neanderthals relied primarily on biological means rather than sewn garments to keep themselves warm.

A HUMAN UPPER PALAEOLITHIC NEEDLE

Several creationist web sites misquote Donald Johanson and Blake Edgar's book, *From Lucy to Language* to claim that Neanderthals used ivory needles 26,000 years ago. They even accompany this claim with a photo (left) of an ivory needle purportedly excavated from a Neanderthal site. This is nonsense. Eurasian Neanderthals did not carve bone or ivory. The needle shown is actually from Enlene, an Upper Palaeolithic human site in France.[315]

Photo: David Brill, courtesy Société Civile de Domaine de Pujol

But, even if Neanderthals could make thermal garments able to withstand the cold and wind chill of ice-age Europe, they also had to know how to maintain their effectiveness. For example, wet clothes can be extremely dangerous, and can increase heat loss by a factor of five.[317,318]

Another factor that may have a bearing on this question is that archaeological evidence reveals that when culturally insulated modern humans finally entered Europe, they were able to colonise the continent and Siberia as high as latitude 60° North. But significantly, European Neanderthals rarely strayed above 50° North. After an extensive survey of hominid and human colonisation of high latitudes, John Hoffecker, a research scientist from the University of Colorado at Boulder, concluded that the Neanderthal's northern expansion was halted by climate:

> Despite their special cold-adapted traits, the Neanderthal range of climate tolerance was limited compared to that of modern humans. They probably were unable to cope with average winter temperatures much below −10° C and were generally restricted to wooded terrain.[319]

Similarly, another survey of Pleistocene acclimatisation found that European Neanderthals avoided areas where the winter temperatures fell below -8° C, and preferred summer temperatures between 12° and 25° C.[320]

While there may be several reasons for this, it seems likely that while modern humans could live in sub -10° C temperatures because they had properly fitting tailored thermal garments, Neanderthals could not because they did not have clothes that could provide enough warmth. It also implies that -8° to -10°C was the absolute insulating limit of their body hair. Any colder than -10°C and their fur simply could not maintain their core body temperature. Without clothes, cold stress (hyperthermia) was like a brick wall that stopped them in their tracks.

The cold factor may also explain why Neanderthals essentially lived in forests which sheltered them from the icy winds that swept across the open savannahs.

All this leads to the hypothesis that Neanderthals not only retained the ancestral primate body hair they acquired in Africa, but that in periglacial Europe their hair increased in length, thickness and density in order to aid thermoregulation and heat retention. And, if the thick body fur of these primate ancestors was bolstered by a seasonal 'winter coat' to provide extra warmth in icy conditions, in summer the Neanderthals almost certainly moulted.

These conclusions redefine the Neanderthal appearance, suggesting it more closely resembled that of a tall, hairy ape than a modern human.

As to the colour of the Neanderthal fur, while it is impossible to say for certain, in 2007 Carles Lalueza-Fox and a group of geneticists amplified and sequenced part of a gene called MC1R (one of the genes thought to regulate skin colour) from two European Neanderthals. This revealed the MC1R was slightly different from the normal human form.[321] Although there is a possibility that the samples were contaminated (easy to do with samples of ancient DNA) the researchers believe the Neanderthal version of the gene may have been less effective than ours, so may have resulted in reduced pigmentation levels, "possibly even similar to the pale skin colour and/or red hair observed in modern humans".

Although these conclusions made for good press they are, of course, highly speculative, as genes are so complex it is virtually impossible to say what effect even one nucleotide substitution will have on protein synthesis. Besides, while fur and hair may be one colour, the underlying skin may be a different colour.

While it may seem appropriate to speculate that, because the fur of Neanderthals' three closest primate relatives (chimpanzees, bonobos and gorillas) is black, theirs would be black too, this doesn't necessarily follow. Other factors need to be considered as well.

The colour of the fur of many modern animals, including most primates, appears to be influenced to varying degrees by the need to hide from predators and prey.[322,323] Generally, mammals tend to assume the colours of their overall environment, a phenomena called *background matching*. It means that primates that live in desert environments or open grasslands tend to be a mottled brown colour, while those that reside in forest habitats tend to have darker fur.[324] Of course, this would not apply to Neanderthals if they were an apex predator.

Another consideration is climate. A few modern cold-climate, snow-dwelling mammals, such as the polar bear, have acquired an all-white coat as an aid to camouflage. However, Pleistocene Europe was not the Arctic and its climate, although cold, wasn't polar, so an all-white fur would probably prove maladaptive in the long term. All other bear species, including the ones that live in cold climates similar to that of the Neanderthals (like the Asiatic black bear, kodiak bear, Himalayan black bear, Formosan black bear, brown bear and the grizzly bear), have opted for dark-coloured fur, almost certainly because dark pigmentation absorbs solar radiation and converts it to heat[325]—an adaptive feature in ice-age Europe.

Ultimately, primates come in a striking range of fur and skin colours from white to jet black, and include brightly coloured features like the noses of male mandrills, the lurid chest patches of gelada baboons and the discombobulating red faces of the red uakari. Even closely related species sometimes display markedly different colours.[326] Given this, it is impossible to come to any definitive conclusion regarding Neanderthal colouration. Unless global warming dramatically reveals a deep-frozen Neanderthal (a la Ötzi the Neolithic 'iceman') we may never know for sure what colour their fur really was.

an ear to the ground

Another visually striking aspect of Neanderthals was their faces. Although they retained some ancestral primate elements, their features were also shaped by the glacial environment of ice-age Europe—so we need to examine them individually.

The ears of species that live in icy climates, like the arctic fox (left), have noticeably smaller ears than species like the fennec fox (right), that reside in tropical regions.

Chimps and bonobos have relatively large protruding ears and we might reasonably expect Neanderthals to have had the same. But ears tend to be strongly influenced by the particular environment an animal inhabits, so we need to consider whether climate may have impacted on the shape and size of Neanderthals' ears.

In hot tropical climates, some animals (like elephants) adopt large ears which act like a car radiator, cooling the blood pumping through them. Conversely, in environments where low winter temperatures and high wind chill are major factors, small ears get selected because they lose less body heat and are less susceptible to frost bite. Primates that live in Japan and other northern latitudes have small ears covered with fur—large ears would prove maladaptive in a glacial climate, creating selection pressure for small ears close to the head, covered by thick fur.

What are the behavioural implications of this? Well, polar bears have very small ears and therefore don't hear very well. This isn't a problem because polar bears rely on their exceptional sense of smell to locate prey up to 24 kilometres (15 miles) away. The same was probably true for Neanderthals. They most likely did not have particularly acute hearing but, if their sense of smell was as keen as the evidence suggests, they would not have needed it.

on the nose

When speculating on the appearance of the Neanderthal nose, anthropologists tend to take the all too familiar anthropomorphic view—their noses looked like ours, albeit larger and broader. The fact that the Neanderthal nose was bigger than ours is usually explained as an adaptation to cold climate—that a large nose would somehow warm the cold air—

but there is not the slightest evidence to support this contention. Some palaeoanthropologists, like Alfred Czarnetzki, argue the opposite is true—that large noses are adaptations to hot, humid regions.[327]

Marc Meyer and his colleagues from the University of Pennsylvania provide another opinion—that Neanderthal "nasal morphology may have a stronger association with masticatory or paramasticatory functions than with climate".[328] Robert Franciscus and Erik Trinkaus argue in the *American Journal of Physical Anthropology* that Neanderthals evolved their extra large noses as an adaptation to their active and strenuous lifestyle,[329] to get more air in and out of their lungs, more quickly. That seems somewhat counterintuitive as animals (including humans) breath through their mouths during peak physical exercise.

The absence of a consensus suggests the need for a fresh look at Neanderthal noses and, in particular, why they were so large.

The noses of the closest primate relatives of Neanderthals (gorillas (*left*), chimps, and bonobos) are broad and flat—nothing at all like ours. If you remove humans from the equation (because, as we will see later, we're a special case), the law of homology, or common descent, would say Neanderthals retained the ancestral primate nose—unless special ecological circumstances created selection pressure for something different.

Neanderthals evolved in glacial Europe and, if this icy environment appears to have influenced every other aspect of their physiology and behaviour, the question is: could the freezing climate also have influenced the shape of their noses? And the answer is, most certainly. A large protruding nose would be more prone to freezing—recent field observations of Finnish solders demonstrated that their noses and ears suffered the most from frostbite.[330] In glacial conditions like those experienced by Neanderthals, any appendages that stuck out—like lips or noses—were more susceptible to becoming frostbitten, so natural selection would most likely retain the flat ancestral nose (just as it opted for small ears) rather than adopting a protruding human-like nose.

The cold climate explains the flat nose. But it doesn't explain why their noses were so large. For that we need to consider another ecological constraint that may have affected the shape and size of the Neanderthal nose. My ecological review of Neanderthal physiology suggests they were nocturnal—they hunted at night.

7 NIGHT STALKERS

Predation forces carnivores to expend considerable amounts of time and energy hunting. Because most prey species are easier to catch at night when they're resting, the majority of mammalian land predators hunt nocturnally. Research has also shown that scents can be detected over greater distances at night—further encouragement for predators to hunt nocturnally.[331] Most of the hunting by lions in the Etosha National Park in the Serengeti, for example, takes place under cover of darkness.[332]

It is possible then that, in addition to daylight hunting, Neanderthals also adapted to nocturnal hunting during their European sojourn. This hypothesis, which has implications for both behaviour and physiology, can be examined by extracting several firm predictions from it and testing them empirically.

The first prediction of the nocturnality hypothesis is that, like other nocturnal hunters, Neanderthals would have acquired specialist physical and behavioural adaptations common to nocturnal predators. For a start, we would expect them to acquire specialist eyes able to locate prey under low-light conditions

Secondly, because nocturnal mammalian predators rely to a far greater extent on scent to locate and track prey than do daylight hunters, they tend to have more developed olfactory organs.[333] As there is a direct relationship between an animal's ability to smell and the size of its nose,[334] this predicts that Neanderthals acquired additional sensory detection receptors (called olfactory neurons) to detect and process scent molecules. Theoretically, this would result in a larger nose.

Ostensibly, this prediction seems almost impossible to prove because noses are made of soft tissue which does not normally fossilise. However, the size of the nose can also be measured by the nasal aperture in the skull, and even a cursory comparison (*below*) between a Neanderthal skull (*left*) and a modern human skull (*right*) graphically reveals that the Neanderthal nasal aperture is considerably larger than in humans. This raises an interesting new question. In other animals with a keen sense of smell, the extra olfactory neurons are housed in a protruding snout but, if Neanderthals retained a flat nose as an adaptation against frostbite, where were the extra olfactory neurons, membranes and epithelial tissue placed? Anatomically, there's only one viable option—they had to be accommodated internally, just behind the flat nose.

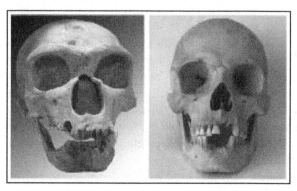

This provides a prediction that can be tested. It claims that the enlarged olfactory organ required by their nocturnal lifestyle would result in the midface area around the nose extending out to make room for the extra olfactory neurons, turbinal bones and epithelial tissue. It's what's called *midfacial prognathism*. In all likelihood, the tip of this 'snout' would have a patch of moist black hairless skin around the nostrils called a rhinarium which would increase sensitivity to smells.

These adaptations would create the impression of a kind of moist, protruding muzzle—like a dog's—quite different from the flat face of early humans. Obviously, while soft tissue features like noses don't fossilise, facial prognathism requires a forward projection of the skull, and skulls generally fossilise well. This allows the hypothesis to be tested by examining facial prognathism in Neanderthal skulls.

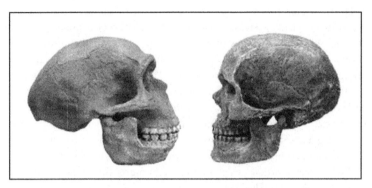

When you compare a Neanderthal skull side-on (*above left*) with that of a human (*above right*)—you are immediately struck by its distinct facial prognathism—and understand why it is sometimes referred to as the *Neanderthal snout*.[335,336] This forward projection of the midface is actually one of the defining characteristics of Neanderthal morphology—widely used by palaeontologists and archaeologists to identify Neanderthal specimens.

So far, the midfacial projection of Neanderthals has not been explained by any existing scientific theory. But because it is such a ubiquitous and distinctive feature of all Neanderthals, it must have been driven by strong selection forces. Nocturnality and a cold climate appears to explain why a large nose and facial prognathism would be adaptive.

The enormous flat primate nose and the exceptional sense of smell it afforded must surely have been one of the Neanderthals' most useful weapons, ideal for locating and tracking their prey—including humans. These bloodhound creatures could sniff out their quarry in the dark, hiding in bushes or concealed in tall grass. This kind of sensory acuity allowed them to climb to the very top of the food chain.

night vision

Around the world, a few species of modern primates have become nocturnal. All of them have acquired changes to their eyes and visual systems to increase retinal image brightness in low-light conditions.[337,338,339] Yale University's Timothy Goldsmith argues in 'Optimization, constraint, and history in the evolution of eyes'[340] that the evolution of primate colour vision was shaped by an extensive period of early mammalian nocturnality. Based on a comparison of primate visual systems, Callum Ross and Christopher Kirk from the University of Texas at Austin conclude that nocturnal visual predation was a major factor in the early evolution of the primate visual system.[341] The eyes of nocturnal primate predators are superbly adapted, allowing hunters to see, chase and capture prey in almost total darkness, aided by exceptional stereoscopic vision that can accurately judge distances in low light.[342,343]

To achieve these visual feats, nocturnal primates acquired larger pupils and corneas (relative to the focal length of the eye) than diurnal species of similar size. Not surprisingly, Christopher Kirk finds that to accommodate these larger eyes, nocturnal primates have evolved larger optical orbits (eye sockets) compared to species that are active during the day.[344]

So, if Neanderthals were nocturnal hunters, they would have had larger eyes than early humans.

Can this theory be scientifically tested? Yes, because large eyes need large eye sockets. Just as all nocturnal primate species have extra large eye sockets to accommodate their oversized eyes, Neanderthals' eye sockets could be expected to be significantly larger than those of humans (*below right*). And even a cursory review of a Neanderthal cranium (*below left*) reveals that they are.

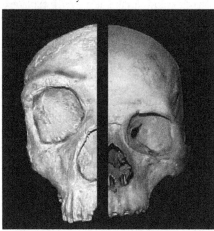

It was not just the odd Neanderthal who had these massive eye sockets. Every Neanderthal skull ever discovered has the same extra large eye sockets. To date, there is no explanation for this physiological novelty, which is hardly surprising given that nocturnality has not previously been considered in relation to Neanderthals.

snake eyes

If Neanderthal eyes did adapt to night vision, they would also have to somehow prevent damage to their super sensitive night vision retinas by strong sunlight. In glacial Europe during the Late Pleistocene, Neanderthals' eyes also had to cope with blinding sunlight reflected off snow. Unless Neanderthals invented sunglasses, their sensitive nocturnal retinas faced the risk of serious damage and even blindness.

Snow blindness would of course affect their hunting prowess so we might expect it to generate selection pressure for some ingenious Darwinian adaptation to get around the problem. One that is common in nocturnal animals is a unique multifocus lens that uses concentric zones of different focal lengths to improve focus in low light. However, as Swedish researchers Tim Malmström and Ronald Kröger from Lund University recently demonstrated, multifocus eyes do not function properly with round pupils. They need slit-shaped pupils, like the crocodile eye (*left*) to facilitate the use of the full diameter of the lens in low light.[345]

And as it turns out, one of the added benefits of slit-shaped pupils is that the iris muscles can be closed tighter (like drawing a curtain) so they can shut out more light than round pupils. It's not surprising then that most nocturnal predators have eyes with slit pupils. For predators, they're unquestionably the best eyes for the job—so there is a strong possibility that Neanderthals also had slit-shaped pupils.

As to whether the slit-shaped pupils may have been horizontally or vertically aligned, the fact that nocturnal primates like rhesus monkeys, prosimians and owl monkeys all have vertically aligned slit pupils is not a coincidence. It's because, when one of these animals squints, its horizontal eyelids close at right angles to the vertical slit pupils, blocking out considerably more light than if eyelid and pupil were both aligned horizontally. Given this, it is likely that Neanderthal pupils were also vertically aligned.

Like all nocturnal primates, this woolly lemur from Madagascar has evolved vertically aligned slit pupils to protect its eyes from strong sunlight.
© Photo: Matt Scandrett

brow ridges

The theory of Neanderthal nocturnality also appears to explain the evolutionary origins of one of the most distinctive and unique facial features of Neanderthals—their massive double-arched brow ridges. If their hyper-sensitive pupils were prone to damage from strong sunlight and reflected snow, then this would generate selection pressure for prominent overhanging bony ridges above each eye and bushy eye brows to shade the pupils from direct sunlight. As you can see from these drawings of the skull cap of Neanderthal 1, the bony ridge runs across the forehead just above the eyes, shading the pupils as well as any baseball cap.

eyes that glow in the dark

Another common nocturnal adaptation that would have affected the appearance of the Neanderthal eye is an optical feature called a *tapetum lucidum*. If you shine a torch at a cat's eyes in the dark, you will see its eyes glow ethereally. This effect is created by the *tapetum lucidum* (from the Latin, 'bright carpet'), a re- flective membrane beneath the retina that re- flects light back to intensify the image enter- ing the eye—ideal for low-light conditions.

Most nocturnal animals have a tapetum lucidum so it is probable that natural selection also bestowed it on Neanderthals. Imagine our Skhul-Qafzeh ancestors sitting around their campfire looking up to see a bunch of Neanderthals rushing out of the darkness, their eyes glowing maniacally with demonic light.

It is worth mentioning here that humans have uniquely clear eye whites or *sclera*—the pale outer part of the eyeball that surrounds the cornea. Every other primate has brown or reddish scleras, so it is likely that Neanderthals did too.

The Neanderthal nocturnality model makes another important prediction. Nocturnal creatures do not evolve specialised sensory organs

So many human cultures portray their demons, ogres and evil spirits with large bulbous eyes as to suggest this description is 'hardwired' into our genes. (From top left to right) Switzerland's 'Boog' (bogeyman), Japan, Thailand, Central Africa, Nigeria, Canada, Indonesia, China, Greece, New Zealand, Bali and Tibet.

The preoccupation with scary eyes also infuses popular western culture, as evidenced by this motley assortment of fictional movie villains, aliens and robots.

in isolation. They need modules in their brains able to process the images, sounds, scents and other sensory data coming from these enhanced organs. In the case of Neanderthals, this would have required the emergence of a larger visual cortex to process low-light visual images.

In primates, the primary visual cortex is located in an area of the brain called the occipital lobe at the back of the skull. In humans, this area is particularly developed to cope with the demands of our heavy reliance on visual imagery. It may be a coincidence, but one of the most pronounced features of Neanderthal cranial morphology is an unusual projection of the occipital lobe, precisely where the visual cortex is located. This bulge is known as the *Neanderthal bun*, and is conspicuously absent from the modern human skull. Although several theories have been put forward to explain the Neanderthal bun,[346,347,348] none has gained wide acceptance.

What we do know, is that the bun extends the Neanderthal brain case, creating a slightly larger brain than modern humans—1500cc compared to 1400cc in humans. It is possible that the Neanderthal bun may have evolved to accommodate an expanded visual cortex, necessitated by a nocturnal lifestyle.

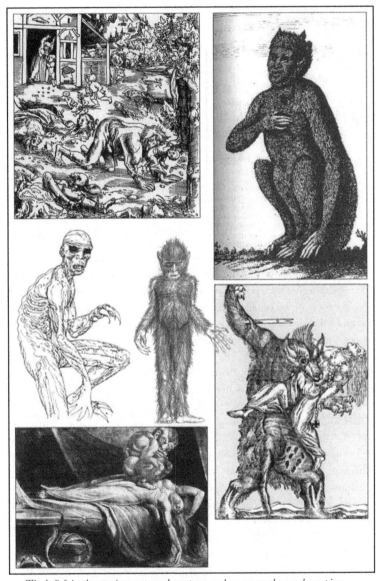

The belief in threatening nocturnal creatures such as werewolves and vampires remains widespread. Examples include (clockwise from top left) a 15th century English woodcut of a werewolf at work, a weretiger and a werewolf from Germany, a bug-eyed incubus crouching over his victim, a claw-handed wendigo from Algonquian mythology and the nocturnal tikoloshe from Zulu mythology.

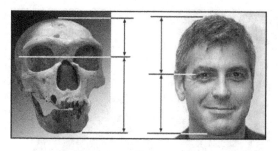

One feature of Neanderthal eyes needs to be noted—their position in the skull. The Neanderthal eyes followed the primate model, and were located much higher in their faces than modern humans, about where our forehead is, giving the impression that the top of their heads had been cut off.

talk of the devil

Speech is produced by soft tissues in the vocal tract which do not fossilise, so it's almost impossible to know exactly what Neanderthals sounded like. Or even whether they possessed a capacity for fully-articulate speech. But that hasn't stopped scientists and linguists from examining and measuring Neanderthal vocal tract bones and devising complex computer models to make some informed guesses. Although Neanderthals had a hyoid bone (which allows for more tongue movement) most researchers now seem to be of the opinion that the shape and size of the Neanderthal vocal tracts would not permit fully-articulate speech.

In a September 2008 paper presented to the American Association of Physical Anthropologists, researchers from Florida Atlantic University asked, 'Were Neanderthals tongue-tied?'[349] They used several methods to determine that the size and shape of the Neanderthal tongue was quite different from that of humans and concluded, "These results suggest that Neanderthals did not have the ability to produce quantally-based spoken language, leading us to conjecture that the answer to the question posed in the title must have been 'yes'."

At the same 2008 conference, delegates heard from a team of American scientists who had examined and compared the vocal tracts of Neanderthals with humans and chimpanzees. Their results indicate that the large Neanderthal nose would have affected the precision and clarity of their word formation. It also suggests Neanderthals had deep voices:

> A large nasal cavity would have decreased the intelligibility
> of vowel-like sounds, and the combination of a long face,

short neck, unequally-proportioned vocal tract and large nose make it highly unlikely that Neanderthals would have been able to produce quantal speech.[350]

From this and similar lines of research, we might conclude that vocally and linguistically, Neanderthals sit somewhere between higher apes and humans with voices possessing a deeper timbre than humans and lots of deep guttural sounds—but almost certainly no spoken language like ours.

8   THE CREATURE REVEALED

what they didn't look like

To arrive at a more accurate likeness of Neanderthals, we first have to abandon the anthropomorphic bias that has distorted our view for centuries. This won't be easy, as the view that Neanderthals looked like humans has been given a degree of scientific credibility by *forensic facial reconstructions*. This involves the use of computers or clay modelling to recreate people's faces from their skulls. In its correct context (reconstructing human faces) the process works extremely well. This is because we know what the soft tissue features ought to look like and where they're meant to go. The American forensic artist, Karen T Taylor is able to create an accurate reconstruction of a murder victim (*below*) because she

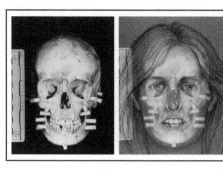

knows how thick human skin is, how large human eyeballs are, and what a human face looks like.

However, while facial reconstruction is also increasingly used by the media and museums to 'bring Neanderthals back to life', a growing number

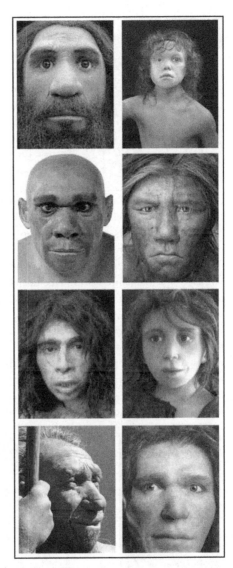

*A sample of computer-
generated and three-
dimensional models of
Neanderthals all reveal the
same anthropomorphic bias.
Most of them wouldn't look
out of place at a Saturday
rugby match.*

of scholars have come to the same opinion as myself—that this is the
most controversial technique in forensic anthropology.

The shortcomings are evident when you note that the skeletal features
of chimpanzee and human noses are virtually identical (they're both simply
cavities in the skull) and yet we have protruding noses and chimps have
flat noses. When it comes to guessing what kind of noses Neanderthals

had, most scientists simply assume they would have had protrudng noses like ours. The reality is that it's virtually impossible to say for certain what a primate's nose looks like from its nasal cavity. For example, the skull of a proboscis monkey (*left*) would not reveal its pendulous nose because it is composed of soft tissue which is not part of the skull.

Because the soft tissue facial features (skin, lips, ears, etc.) of nonhuman primates are so different from ours, human facial dimensions, organ shapes and textures would never be used to reconstruct a chimpanzee face. And yet Neanderthals have been anthropomorphised to such a degree that human facial data is consistently used to reconstruct Neanderthal faces. A typical example is the face displayed at the Allard Pierson Archaeological Museum in Amsterdam (*right*).

Photo : Michael D. O'Neill

It's not surprising then that almost all modern pictorial and three-dimensional representations of Neanderthals portray them as beetle-browed, large-nosed versions of modern humans—and often they're even clean shaven. Because we have noses that stick

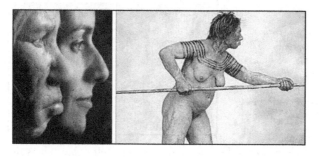

The October 2008 issue of National Geographic featured the latest forensic reconstruction—of a female Neanderthal—which took the anthropomorphic trend to new heights, showing her to all intents and purposes as unmistakably human, complete with body tattoos. Even the distinctive Neanderthal brow ridges have been de-emphasised. While this may sell lots of magazines, it is questionable science.

out, clear eyes, smooth skin and full lips, it has been supposed they had those too. And if humans can attend Harvard, so too can Neanderthals—although they'd need rich parents.

what they really looked like

Once the traditional anthropomorphic approach is put aside, and it is acknowledged that human physiology and behaviour are a one-off case, Neanderthal physiology can be seen in its correct evolutionary context. Neanderthals evolved from the same ancestors as gorillas, chimps and bonobos, who still look like classic primates after ten million years of evolution. Neanderthals almost certainly were not hairless or artistic. They didn't have Angelina Jolie lips, or clear white eyes, or even satin-smooth skin.

A more realistic Darwinian view argues that, unless powerful and persistent evolutionary forces rendered it absolutely necessary for survival to abandon their ancestral primate appearance, Neanderthals would have continued to look like tall, bipedal apes. After all, the core aspects of primate physiology had been tried, tested and continually refined by natural selection over at least ten million years.

I've nominated two major factors that caused Neanderthal physiology to diverge from primate orthodoxy: their predator lifestyle (including nocturnality) and the icy European climate they evolved in. In all other respects, the ancestral form would tend to prevail.

This review helps us to build up a more accurate identikit picture, revealing for the first time what the average Neanderthal really looked like. The one certainty is that there is not the slightest chance of mistaking one for a New York stockbroker—even dressed in an Armani suit.

From a distance, an approaching Neanderthal would instantly strike you as alien, resembling a tall, heavily muscled gorilla, rendered even more massive by its thick coat of extra long and thick fur. You would feel as if you have just come across the abominable snowman or bigfoot. As it approached, you would be struck by its large bulbous eyes with their vertically aligned slit pupils and brown scleras, shaded by prominent overhanging brow ridges and thick bushy eyebrows. Its eyes are also disturbing because they're so high up in the skull, about where your forehead is. The other striking feature of the face is that the middle area around the nose sticks out in a kind of dog-like muzzle. Its large broad flat nose, with slightly moist, black nostrils that twitch to sniff the air for tell-tale scents, occupies a disproportionate area.

The skin on the face and hands is tough, leathery and heavily wrinkled

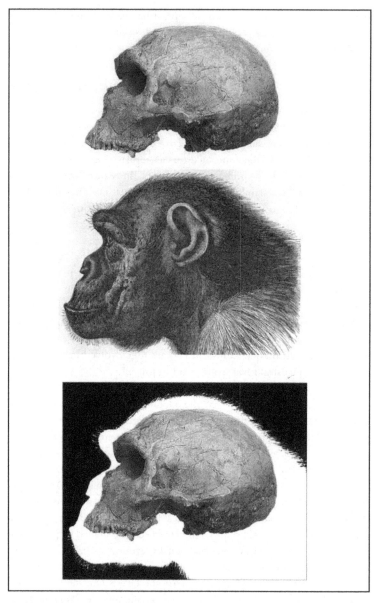

Neanderthals are depicted as looking like humans, but the European Neanderthal cranium (top) fits neatly into a chimp profile (bottom), suggesting Neanderthals looked more apelike than human.

A surprisingly accurate 1909 depiction of a Neanderthal by Frantisek Kupka for the Illustrated London News.

but, because of the enormous variation in skin colour among primates, it is impossible to say what colour its face is. The lips are so thin as to be practically nonexistent (which means that frostbite, sunburn and melanomas would not be a problem).

Its teeth are twice as large as human teeth but lack the large pointed canines of the big cats (indicating that this creature would not tear raw flesh from prey animals with its teeth but would use stone knives to cut it off). And (according to research conducted in 2008 by anthropologists Yoel Rak and William Hylander) its mouth can open unusually wide— much wider than human mouths—which would allow the Neanderthal to take extremely large bites, possibly as an adaptation to the size of the food it eats.[351] Finally, judging by the size of the jaw where the chewing muscles attach, the Neanderthal has a tremendous bite force.

Rather oddly, the creature doesn't have a well-defined chin. In fact, it's hard to discern a chin at all, as the slit mouth simply curves down to merge with the massive neck muscles. The same muscles snake around its neck to form a broad collar that runs up the side of its head, giving the impression it has no neck. It is these muscles that contribute to its enormous upper body strength.

As for its body, it is so heavily muscled, it makes a human body builder look weedy by comparison. Side on, the straighter, more inflexible spine, the stooped stance and lack of defined buttocks give it an unusual gait as it strides along. It doesn't walk like any human you've ever seen. All in all, this is a strange and fearsome creature indeed.

And to top it off, German researchers who re-examined two Neanderthal spines (from Kebara 2 and Shanidar 3) in 2008 reported that both individuals displayed kyphosis—they were hunchbacks. This was most unexpected and, what's more, their hunched backs weren't the result of injury, disease or old age. The authors, Jochen Weber and Carsten Matthias Pusch believe the condition was part of their natural anatomy.

Like modern primates, the skin of Neanderthals would have been tough, durable and heavily wrinkled—certainly not smooth like that of modern humans.

that's more like it

NP Theory can't say for certain exactly what Neanderthals looked like. Nobody can. Maybe one day, the frozen remains of an individual will be defrosted from its icy grave and we'll finally gaze on the face that really did launch a thousand ships. But, as the next best thing, I commissioned one of the world's best computer modellers to create a forensic reconstruction of an adult Neanderthal based on NP theory. Madrid-based digital sculptor Arturo Balseiro took up the challenge and, after many exchanges of emails, produced the extraordinary reconstructions displayed here.

To ensure accuracy, we scanned a high quality cranium cast of the La Ferrassie Neanderthal from France. The resulting pictures of the La Ferrassie adult male provide a far more accurate and nuanced portrait of the species than the current gallery of anthroporphic look-alikes you see in the popular press.

This was a very exciting process for me. As we watched the creature slowly emerge, we could tell from our own visceral reactions that we were on the right track, that the creature was triggering our innate Neanderthal responses. For the first time in 28,000 years, we were gazing into the eyes of our nemesis—the beast that had hunted our ancestors to the point of extinction.

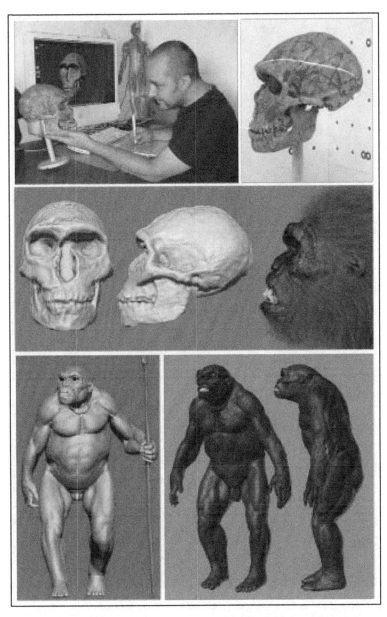

The forensic reconstruction of the La Ferrassie Neanderthal began with a computer scan of its skull. Digital sculptor Arturo Balseiro (pictured) then used NP theory to reconstruct detailed features of its anatomy.

Armed with a flint-tipped spear, a Eurasian Neanderthal peers out from its forest lair. Less hairy than their European cousins, Eurasian Neanderthals were nevertheless covered in a thick coat of protective fur which probably moulted in summer.

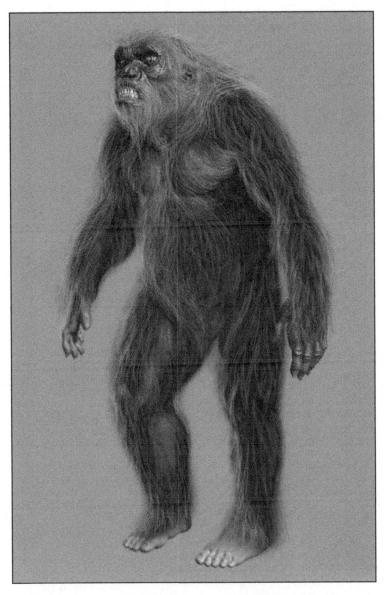

Twenty-eight thousand years after the last Neanderthal roamed the earth, forensic science is able to reconstruct a far more accurate representation of a Eurasian Neanderthal. Their thick coat of fur, hunched back, bow legs and distinctive gait added to their unique appearance.

A creature that looks like an athletic gorilla but uses complex weapons to hunt its prey is so foreign and counterintuitive it has hampered our understanding of Neanderthals for one hundred years. Anthropologist John Shea's description of Neanderthals as "wolves with knives" comes close to describing their paradoxical nature.

PART II

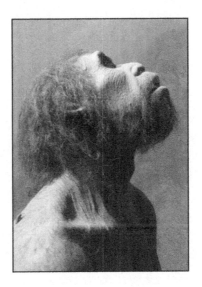

US

NP theory is a theory of coevolution—how the interaction between two sibling species changed each other forever. Having drawn on the latest scientific evidence to paint a more accurate picture of Eurasian Neanderthals, we can now examine how Eurasian Neanderthals altered the trajectory of human evolution.

9 THE HORROR! THE HORROR!

wolves with knives

Having discarded the anthropomorphic view that Neanderthals looked and behaved much like us, the challenge now is to assimilate something beyond our experience—a species with features that have never before been associated with humans or hominids. This will not be easy. It will require a quantum leap to envisage a creature that looks like an upright gorilla, with all its imposing brute strength, yet can fabricate complex tools. Yet, despite having a brain larger than humans, Eurasian Neanderthals did not develop art or culture. They knapped stones into razor sharp blades but never strung beads or shells onto a leather thong to make a necklace. And of all the pieces of bone that litter their campsites, not one shows evidence of being carved. These contradictions prompted anthropologist John Shea to describe them as "wolves with knives".[352]

What emerges is a paradoxical hominid as merciless as a hyena but caring enough to bury its dead.[353] A creature as ferocious as a tiger, able to bring down a woolly mammoth or rhino, but also capable of constructing 10 metre wide windbreaks.[354] Perhaps the ultimate paradox is a capacity to hunt and eat humans but also to have sex with them.

If this is difficult to digest, spare a thought for our Levantine ancestors. They must have felt as if they were watching leopards rubbing sticks together to make a fire, or seeing a bear melt birch resin to glue a flint

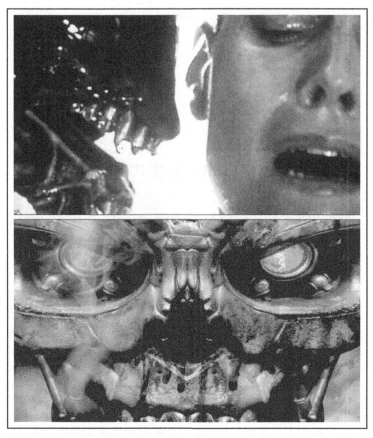

Predation rendered early humans so hyper-vigilant to Neanderthals that modern humans are still terrified by imaginary monsters that resemble them. Although the cinematic creatures above lack body fur and large eyes, their phenomenal strength, speed and predatory inclinations are enough to trigger innate fear responses.

point onto a spear. And how disconcerting would it have been for them to square off against a slightly shorter hominid knowing he was actually six times as strong.

The Skhul-Qafzeh people had survived Eurasian lions, cave bears, wolves, leopards and other terrestrial predators, but this new predator was a different kettle of fish. It marshalled a sizeable intelligence, physical superiority, weaponry, communication skills and strategic capabilities into a single formidable package—the heady mix of features that had elevated Neanderthals to the peak of the European-Eurasian food chain. To comprehend the Skhul-Qafzehs' bewilderment (as well as their terror and confusion) we might draw on nightmare scenarios of alien invasions from sci-fi films and novels.

Imagine, for example, a group of Skhul-Qafzeh humans gathering mushrooms in a forest and encountering the first hunting party of Neanderthals. What happened next—on that fateful day some 100,000 odd years ago—would not only disrupt the ecology of the Levantine humans, but would change the course of world history and write its first modern chapter. Here—in a perhaps bewildering first meeting, probably full of tension, curiosity and awe—is where it all started. From that moment, the destiny of humanity spiralled off on a new tangent. From that moment, their garden of paradise no longer felt safe. Men had to come to grips with a new sexual competitor determined to poach their females. Everyone became more aware of their body odour because they knew Neanderthals could track their scent. Life went on—but not as before. It was as if aliens had invaded the Earth.

multidimensional predation

One of the reasons I believe Neanderthal predation exerted such a dramatic affect on the Skhul-Qafzeh humans was because it did not just involve killing the occasional human. Its tentacles enveloped every aspect of human existence, including:

- sexual predation
- lethal raiding
- resource competition
- coalitionary killing
- intraguild predation
- territoriality
- sexual competition
- cannibalism
- nocturnality

I call this, *multidimensional predation* and I believe it is unique in animal evolutionary history. Each element constricted, threatened or impeded human ecology, some perhaps in minor (sustainable) ways. Collectively though, this 'total predation' was extremely maladaptive and therefore generated significant selection pressure.

While labels like multidimensional predation are helpful in understanding the anthropological complexities and evolutionary implications of NP theory, they tend to obscure the personal experience of predation. Safe in our homes, guarded by police and military forces, it's perhaps difficult to appreciate the long-term psychological consequences of multidimensional predation. However, a central plank of the NP hypothesis is that it was the emotional trauma that the survivors experienced that kick-started and maintained the evolutionary pressure to transform the Skhul-Qafzeh people into modern humans.

close encounters of the traumatic kind

The idea that personal trauma played a pivotal role in human evolution will not be acceptable to some evolutionary biologists. For them, emotions are too nebulous and ephemeral to quantify scientifically and any discussion of emotions is simply too speculative. However, there is now ample evidence that emotions directly influence both physical and behavioural evolution. Sex, for example, which is comprised almost entirely of powerful urges and desires—all undeniably affective states—is a major driving force in evolution. Likewise, the emotional terror that prey species experience in their struggle for survival informs every aspect of their biology.

Humans are a special case when it comes to emotions and emotional receptivity. We have the largest web of neuronal connections between the prefrontal area and the limbic system of the brain. This means we're not only the most intelligent animal species, but also the most emotional—with a range of feelings, moods and emotions that far exceeds that of any other species.

This appreciation of the functional role of emotions (or affect, as psychologists call it) justifies consideration of the traumatic psychological effect that Neanderthal predation may have had on the Skhul-Qafzeh humans.

How did a human woman feel about giving birth to a Neanderthal child, and what might be the evolutionary consequences of those feelings? What did humans think as they tried to get to sleep, knowing that those creatures might be out there, lurking just beyond the firelight? What was the attitude of the males towards females who consorted with the intruders? How did the human children feel, knowing they were especially vulnerable to the marauders? For them, the 'bogeyman' was real, and he was out to get them.

While speculative, unless the psychological impact of 50,000 years of predation is considered, I don't believe we can understand who we are today. We need to know what it felt like to be hunted—like an animal.

Although 'predation stress' has not been studied in modern humans, considerable research has been conducted on other animal species. This research demonstrates that it is the unpredictable nature of predation that makes it so stressful. Field studies in south-western Yukon by zoologist Rudy Boonstra have shown that chronic predation stress can cause molecular changes in the area of an animal's brain called the hippocampus.[355] Even if a rat only smells a cat, its brain releases a cocktail of potent stress response hormones that renders it anxious and hyper-vigilant.[356] In a study even more relevant to humans, chronic predation stress has been observed in free-ranging baboons in the Moremi Game Reserve, Botswana by Dorothy Cheney and Robert Seyfarth from the University of Pennsylvania. They found:

> Predation is a pervasive and inescapable part of baboon life. It is the single most important cause of adult mortality, and it affects individuals of all dominance ranks equally. Even the survivors suffer; in months when a group member is killed by a predator, glucocorticoid levels in males and females are significantly higher than at other times. Attacks that result in group separation—like the lion attack that divided the group for two days—produce significantly greater stress than less intense encounters. [357]

We can only guess how terrifying it is for school students or office workers to be stalked by a gunman for ten minutes—or maybe an hour. Now extend that to a lifetime of being hyper-vigilant, never being able to completely let your guard down. This reiterates the question—what are the evolutionary consequences of being attacked by a Neanderthal? And what long-term effect did predation stress have on our ancestors?

the first panic attack

The reassessment of Neanderthal behavioural ecology provided by NP theory puts speculation about the psychological impact of predation on a surer footing. As evolutionary detectives, we now have enough new forensic evidence to reconstruct an archetypal interaction scenario—a nocturnal raid by Neanderthals on a Skhul-Qafzeh encampment.

The culprits of this primordial 'home invasion' have, of course, been identified. There's even a new identikit picture of one of them—it shows a hairy, bug-eyed creature brandishing a spear, an ugly brute that would send shivers down any juror's spine. We also know their MO—to strike at night under cover of darkness, relying on their superior night vision and an exceptional sense of smell to catch their victims unawares.

We know their motives—to kill or chase off the males and rape and abduct the women and girls. Because they have a track record of cannibalism, it's likely they ate some of their victims immediately (either raw or cooked on improvised fires) then carried others off to eat later.

CSI analysis can also tell us what weapons they used—flint-tipped spears and stone axes. Finally, we have considerable forensic evidence about their victims—because they were our distant forebears.

All this information helps us reconstruct the events of a typical nocturnal raid. The raid would begin an hour or two before dawn. The Neanderthals would burst from the darkness with their spears, growling and grunting, and would quickly surround the humans to prevent their escape.

There's a familiar word that describes what happened next—panic. Nowadays, the word has lost much of its potency; we use it to describe mundane events like running late for work or a hard drive crashing. But in the Levant, I suggest the concept was only just gaining currency. For our ancestors, panic was a front-line defence against predation. It caused physical reactions, including heart palpitations, dizziness, shortness of breath, clamminess, diarrhoea and fainting. But, additionally, it produced an overwhelming urge to flee. Anyone who has experienced a panic attack will have some idea of what our terror-stricken ancestors went through on a regular basis.

But unlike today's panic attacks, which don't serve any adaptive purpose, panic in the Levant became an anti-predator strategy. There would have been few options available to the Skhul-Qafzeh people during a raid. They couldn't rely on the dark to hide them, because Neanderthals could see them even on a moonless night and, with their highly-developed olfactory senses, Neanderthals could sniff out anyone hiding in the undergrowth. The only humans likely to survive were those that ran. And kept running. Panic precipitated haphazard flight which made it harder for the Neanderthals to catch them. The genes for panic were then spread by the survivors.

This would explain why today, panic is still part of the human condition, and why, even after thousands of years, it is still the most intense and debilitating of all human emotional states. The emotions are so powerful they are considered symptomatic of psychopathology and are often treated with pharmacological interventions. Common symptoms include extreme anxiety, trembling, sweaty palms, a racing heart and an impulse to run away—anywhere. In milder forms, panic manifests as stressed anxiety, agoraphobia and paranoia.

Panic is just one example of a possible evolutionary response to Neanderthal lethal raiding. There may be many more. For the humans who managed to survive a raid, the next days and weeks would be no less harrowing. The group would be scattered. Individual survivors would be hungry, afraid, and possibly lost. This would trigger feelings of guilt, loneliness, grief and despondency—but also abandonment and despair. More evolutionary detritus?

On top of this was the need to find out what happened to their family and friends. Who was taken? Who survived? Were the children eaten? What if the creatures returned? They needed to know—they needed the latest news.

To shed more light on the psychological impact of lethal raiding, we can look to recent terrorist attacks like the Mumbai siege and the September 11 attacks on the US. In a study undertaken immediately following 9/11, researchers found "a significant increase in the number of depressive symptoms reported during the 4 weeks after the attacks".[358] Another study, conducted by the American Psychological Association five months after the terrorist attacks, showed a significant number of Americans were still suffering mental health effects. Among the findings:

- Nearly one in four Americans (24 percent) report feeling more depressed or anxious today than at other times in their life; and

- While most of these Americans attribute their feelings of depression or anxiety to personal trauma or financial woes, 16 percent say their depressed or anxious mood is a direct result of September 11. In real terms, there are about 8 million Americans who report they are feeling depressed or anxious because of the attacks on New York and Washington.[359]

I don't believe it is a coincidence that the feelings that might reasonably be attributed to Levantine humans as a result of predation stress include all the medically recognised symptoms of clinical depression:

Television and newspapers unwittingly tap into our vestigial need as a prey species to maintain predator vigilance. In the Levant, this kind of 'news' was highly adaptive.

- feeling sad, empty, hopeless, or numb;
- loss of interest in things you used to enjoy;
- irritability or anxiety;
- thoughts of death and suicide;
- sleep disturbance;
- feeling guilty or worthless; and
- difficulty making decisions.

life in the death zone

Applying this data to the Levant suggests that stress, depression and anxiety were organic responses to chronic predation stress and therefore common conditions for the Skhul-Qafzeh people. In short, life was scary, depressing and stressful.

Some of this stress came from being constantly on the alert for Neanderthals. In the weeks and months following a lethal raid, alertness would increase to a state I call 'hyper-vigilance' which became the mainstay of the humans' anti-predator response. One consequence of hyper-vigilance would make them more suspicious and fearful of all 'foreigners'—including other Skhul-Qafzeh neighbours. In this specific context, xenophobia was adaptive.

Archaeological data tells us Eurasian Neanderthals occupied the higher inland forested area of the Levant—so another response for the humans would be to keep to the savannah-like coastal plain along the eastern edge of the Mediterranean (evidence shows they did) as well as to stay well clear of woodland areas. Obviously they would no longer venture from their camp alone, and never after dark. Children would have been kept within sight and women constantly watched. Individual foraging gave way to group expeditions.

In this way, the traumatic personal experience of predation gradually inculcated the Skhul-Qafzeh psyche.

them and us

When the disparate Skhul-Qafzeh tribes of the Levant met on hunting and gathering expeditions, they learned to appreciate their commonality—and their shared plight—which provided a standard by which their common enemy could be identified. This gave rise to a new dualistic concept—*them and us*. Initially, this demarcation was culturally disseminated. But gradually, *them and us* became inculcated into the molecular fabric of the human genome.

Nebulous, intuitive and ill-formed as the concept of *them and us* was, it provided an adaptive demarcation—a means of identifying friend from foe. In a time before military uniforms differentiated combatants, *them and us* provided uniforms. It allowed humans not only to identify their predator (early enough to effect an escape) but to accumulate a suite of defensive adaptations that were triggered by Neanderthal characteristics.

For at least 50,000 years, the genetic awareness of our natural predator was the single most important adjunct to survival. This innate sense of a second identity—residing ominously alongside our own—is the key to understanding how we became human. It's as if the Skhul-Qafzeh people no longer existed as a single species. They could identify themselves only as one half of a malevolent duality. Life continued, but it was now all about them and us. Humans had been deposed, and now existed only as part of a predatory-prey relationship. To borrow an analogy from Abrahamic religions, man had fallen from grace and the Garden of Eden had become the killing fields. In this, I'm reminded of some lines from Joseph Conrad's novella, *Heart of Darkness*:

> He cried in a whisper at some image, at some vision—he cried out twice, a cry that was no more than a breath—"The horror! The horror!"

10 WHEN MUTANTS
ROAMED THE EARTH

the holy trinity

The theory that Eurasian Neanderthals subjected Skhul-Qafzeh humans to continual multidimensional predation generates three major predictions that can be used to test the hypothesis:

- Neanderthal sexual predation would gradually result in a proliferation of hybrids—mutants—displaying a mix of both Neanderthal and human traits;

- Neanderthal predation would gradually deplete the prey population—as occurs in animal populations in the wild. This would push the Levantine Skhul-Qafzeh population to the brink of extinction; and

- the few humans that survived would be those born with physical and/or behavioural traits that would allow them to withstand Neanderthal predation. These 'Neanderthal proof' survivors would become the founders of modern humanity.

According to NP theory, each of these predictions corresponds to a major phase in the transformation of archaic humans into fully modern

humans. These predictions are the holy trinity of NP theory and therefore need to be tested against reliable palaeontological, archaeological and
genetic datasets.

bring on the mutants

Because both species were descended from the same common ancestors,
sexual encounters between Eurasian Neanderthals and Skhul-Qafzeh females would likely result in fertile offspring. This predicts that the period
of predation resulted in numbers of hybridised half-Neanderthal/half
humans.

In theory, these hybrids would have features from both species, and
eventually this would affect the appearance of each population. Physically,
the Eurasian Neanderthals would begin to look less like classic European
Neanderthals, and the Skhul-Qafzeh humans would start to show some
Neanderthal features. Eventually, we would expect to see two highly variable
'mutant' populations (sharing common features) appearing in the Levant.

In practical terms, this means the Eurasian Neanderthal specimens
from the Levant (represented by skeletal material from Tabun, Amud,
Kebara and Shanidar sites) should display some human features, while
the early human skeletons from the Levant, represented by the Skhul and
Qafzeh fossils, should display a number of Neanderthal features.

So, is there any evidence of hybridisation in the Levant?

The first place we would normally look to answer this question is the
DNA evidence—and geneticists have tried hard to extract DNA from
at least two Eurasian Neanderthals (Amud from Israel and Dederiyeh
from Syria)[360] to test for hybridisation. Unfortunately, extracting ancient
DNA is a complex and difficult task, not only because the DNA in bones
deteriorates over time, but also because the process of amplifying what
little DNA exists is prone to contamination by modern DNA from the
researchers and archaeologists themselves. Despite the best efforts, the
world's foremost authority on Neanderthal DNA Svante Pääbo informed
me he had been unable to extract enough viable DNA from Levantine
specimens to conduct hybridisation tests (*personal correspondence, November,
2007*). The main reason for this is that the DNA in fossils is destroyed
over time by heat, and usually survives only in cold dry climates like per-
mafrost or high altitude caves. In warm humid environments like the
Levant, it quickly deteriorates, making it unlikely we will ever get useable
DNA from Levant fossils.[361]

In the absence of viable DNA from Eurasian Neanderthals, or from

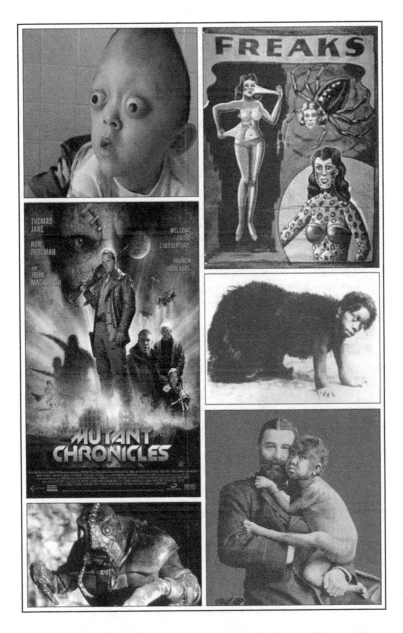

Today, the evolutionary dread of human-Neanderthal hybrids is still expressed in social attitudes and derogatory labels like 'mutants' and 'freaks'.

the Skhul or Qafzeh skeletons, testing the Levant hybridisation hypothesis has to rely on other methodologies, and the most obvious is archaeological evidence from occupied sites.

The researchers involved in examining the Levantine fossils have noted the skeletal similarities between Eurasian Neanderthals and early human assemblages from Levantine contexts and many of them have interpreted this as evidence of interbreeding between the species.[362] The mosaic nature of both the Skhul-Qafzeh humans and Eurasian Neanderthals led to the view (still maintained by a minority of researchers) that all these Levantine assemblages form part of a single highly variable population.[363,364]

Certainly, the Skhul early human fossils from Mt Carmel (among the earliest representatives of modern humans) share many skeletal features with Eurasian Neanderthals.[365] Although Skhul 4 and Skhul 9 are generally thought to be early human, cranial features like the forward projection of the skull and the thick brow ridges, are considered by anthropologist Robert Corruccini, from Southern Illinois University, to be more Neanderthal-like than modern human.[366]

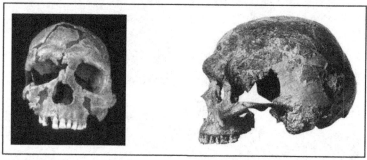

Although Qafzeh 6 (left) and Skhul 4 (right) are considered human, both display characteristics normally associated with Neanderthals.

Even though the Tabun C2 specimen from Mugharet-et-Tabun, Israel is considered a Neanderthal,[367] Rolf Quam and Fred Smith claim it is so similar to the Qafzeh and Skhul mandibles (jaw bones) as to suggest they are related. They conclude that the possibility of interbreeding between Levantine humans and Eurasian Neanderthals cannot be ruled out.[368]

Another team of anthropologists, led by Baruch Arensburg and Anna Belfer-Cohen, undertook an extensive re-evaluation and comparison of Neanderthal specimens from Israel (Tabun, Amud, Kebara), and Iraq (Shanidar) with the early modern humans from Skhul and Qafzeh. They too found a distinct resemblance between the groups:

...both groups display a similar pattern of marked morphological variability. In both groups, specimens display numerous plesiomorphic traits as well as many that are common to both archaic and modern *Homo sapiens*.[369] ['Plesiomorphic' describes a trait that species share because it is inherited from a common ancestor.]

In the ancient world, it was widely believed that dozens of mutant races existed, including dog-headed Cynocephaly (left) and big-eared Panotti.

Their conclusions reveal, "numerous incongruencies, such as assumed 'Neandertals' lacking specific Neandertal traits and AMHS [anatomically modern *Homo sapiens*] manifesting Neanderthaloid features."[370]

Originally, it was thought there was only one species of Neanderthals—those that inhabited Europe. But as excavations in the Levant increasingly dug up Neanderthals who looked noticeably different from their European cousins, a distinction had to be drawn to separate them. While the term *Neanderthal* is still widely used in the media, the term *classic Neanderthal* or *European Neanderthal* is now commonly used by anthropologists to describe the original population, while the atypical Levantine Neanderthals are known as *Eurasian Neanderthals*. The emergence of the Eurasian sub-species is consistent with the argument that a degree of hybridisation occurred in the Levant as a result of Neanderthals forcibly interbreeding with local humans.

In *The Neandertals*, Erik Trinkaus and Pat Shipman discuss admixture, quoting the findings of anthropologist F Clark Howell, whose comparison of Eurasian Neanderthal specimens suggests that, over time, they gradually became more human looking:

...instead of neandertalizing through time, the western Asian Neandertals undergo "sapiensation". The more modern looking Neanderthals from Tabun and Teshik-Tash turn, not into something like La Chapelle-aux-Saints, [classic European Neanderthals] but into the even more humanlike populations whose remains were found at Skhul.[371]

In 2008, anthropologists Philipp Gunz and Ekaterina Bulygina re-examined the infant Neanderthal skull from Teshik-Tash because "some have considered the morphology of the Teshik-Tash cranium to be more similar to modern humans such as those represented at Skhul and Qafzeh". At a meeting of the American Association of Physical Anthropologists, they reported that, "the Teshik-Tash frontal bone morphology is intermediate between classical Neanderthals and early modern humans."[372]

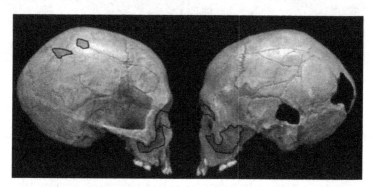

The cranium of a Neanderthal child from Teshik-Tash in Uzbekistan displays some distinctively human features, indicative of a degree of interbreeding between early humans and Eurasian Neanderthals in the Middle East.

Still, while these various lines of evidence support my theory of coercive interbreeding in the Levant, until DNA can be extracted from Levantine samples, it will not be possible to resolve the issue.

TO THE EDGE OF EXTINCTION

the predator-prey cycle

The second prediction of the multidimensional predation model comes from the existing knowledge of predator-prey interactions. If Levantine Neanderthals and humans were locked in an intractable predator-prey interaction, then this dynamic should conform to well-understood aspects of predation ecology—the *predator-prey cycle.*

The predator-prey cycle describes how predators continue to capture and consume prey, until the prey numbers are reduced to such an extent that they're no longer worth the time or effort to hunt. This leaves the predator with few options. They can turn to other prey, move to a new

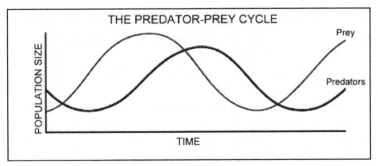

THE PREDATOR-PREY CYCLE

POPULATION SIZE

Prey

Predators

TIME

territory or starve, in which case their own numbers begin to fall.[373] All
these scenarios allow the prey population to recover its numbers.[374]

Importantly, while the prey population may be heavily reduced—
causing what's called a *population bottleneck*, or near-extinction event—it
doesn't normally disappear completely.

If multidimensional predation by Eurasian Neanderthals followed the
same predator-prey cycle (and there is no reason to suspect it wouldn't),
then there should have been a gradual reduction in the Skhul-Qafzeh
population in the Levant until there were too few humans left to make it
worthwhile for Neanderthals to hunt. It's what ecologists call becoming
'economically unsustainable'.

The prediction of a population bottleneck is tremendously important
in the evolutionary scheme of things. Near-extinction events are one of
the few means of generating the kind of powerful selection pressure
needed to create a new species. For example, on the Galapagos Islands,
two ornithologists researching finches actually witnessed a rare example of
the impact of a near-extinction event. During a protracted drought caused
by El Nino, 85 percent of the finches on one island died of starvation
because the small seeds on which they normally fed failed. The only birds
to survive were those with unusually large beaks, able to crack open the
bigger seeds that had survived the drought. When the drought ended, all
the new hatchlings featured this larger, more robust beak.[375]

Only a near-extinction event could have generated sufficiently potent
and prolonged selection pressure to kick-start and consolidate the
speciation event that created modern humans. In effect, a near-extinction
event was the door through which our ancestors had to pass. On one
side, they were primitive stone-age people. But when they emerged on the
other side, they were fully human, smart and articulate—much like us.

MODERN HUMANS AND FULLY MODERN HUMANS

For simplicity, I describe the Levantines who survived the
population bottleneck as 'modern humans', and reserve the term
'fully modern humans' for today's people. This acknowledges
that the post-bottleneck people (although ostensibly Upper
Palaeolithic) still had to undergo some last-minute tinkering
and fine-tuning before they became fully modern humans.

To determine when the near-extinction event occurred—when our Skhul-
Qafzeh ancestors were thrust through the magic portal—we need to con-

sult the archaeological record. It
tells us that up to around 55,000
years ago, the Levantine people
were still Middle Palaeolithic.
It also shows that Upper Palaeolithic culture appeared in the
Levant 46,000 to 47,000 years
ago, which indicates the bot-

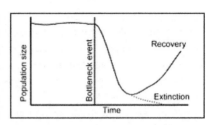

tleneck was at its most extreme around 49,000 years ago. That would
leave one or two thousand years to rebuild the population before it again
became visible in the archaeological record. By predicting an estimate of
approximately 50,000 years ago, NP theory has provided a figure to test.

Whether there were multiple population reductions, as seems likely,
or only one major bottleneck is impossible to say. But reliable genetic
evidence indicates that one severe population bottleneck began around
70,000 years ago and reached its nadir between 50,000 and 48,000 years
ago. In other words, although the two Levantine species may have
coexisted in the same region from 100,000 years ago (or even earlier),
low population densities, migratory patterns, maintenance of separate
territories and evasion meant the near-extinction event did not occur
immediately. The Skhul-Qafzeh humans managed to hang on, finding
ways to survive in small groups and out-of-the-way places. Eventually,
though, the Neanderthals grew too strong, too numerous, or simply too
predatory, and slowly but surely the numbers of early humans living in
the Levant began to decline.

Because the prediction of a recent human population bottleneck goes
to the nub of NP theory, it is important to prove this hypothesis before we
proceed. The first proof comes directly from the archaeological record in
the Mediterranean Levant, which shows that around 80,000 years ago the
population of archaic humans in the Levant is reduced to such an extent
that they effectively disappear from the fossil record.[376,377] Then, around
50,000 years ago, they reappear.[378]

The disappearance of human artefacts and bodies from Levantine
sites 80,000 years ago may simply mean that all the disparate tribes
of humans occupying the Middle East decided to migrate out of the
area simultaneously (for whatever reason.) But it is also consistent with
the argument that the population, having been drastically reduced by
Neanderthal predation, was so small it could no longer be detected in
the fossil record. In archaeology, this is called *insufficient sampling* and it
just means that the original population was so small, and fossils so few

and far between that there is little likelihood of finding remains. For example, it is salutary to note that the complete history of Neanderthal and human occupation of the Levant—numbering hundreds of Middle Palaeolithic sites,[379] and hundreds of thousands of individuals over nearly 300,000 years—is represented by diagnostic skeletal remains from only 11 stratigraphic levels.[380]

If the Levantine humans had been driven out of their caves by Neanderthals and forced to adopt a nomadic existence below the Neanderthals' radar, this would also contribute to the group's invisibility in the Levant archaeology. If their numbers were reduced to a few tribes, and they were constantly on the move to stay one step ahead of the enemy, they would not leave the same archaeological footprint as large populations permanently occupying sites for thousands of years.

Attempting to answer his own question, "What happened to the humans at Skhul and Qafzeh after 80 Kyr?" John Shea notes that, in their place, Neanderthal fossils appear in the same Mt Carmel caves once inhabited by early humans.[381] This cluster of limestone caves, rock shelters and overhangs on Israel's Mt Carmel, and the stone tools found there, testify to a continuous occupation by early humans for thousands of years until, abruptly, they are replaced by the distinctive tools and weapons of Eurasian Neanderthals. The Neanderthals had taken over the caves once inhabited by the Skhul-Qafzeh people.

While Shea concludes Neanderthals may have competitively displaced the Skhul-Qafzeh humans from the Levant, a range of other theories has also been put forward to explain the disappearance of the early humans after such a long occupation, as well as the spread of Eurasian Neanderthals across the Levant. Some researchers believe it was due to the proliferation of Neanderthal populations and settlements in the Levant.[382] Others claim that cold adaptation traits may have allowed Levantine Neanderthals to survive better when the climate got colder.[383] Another view is that Neanderthals' increased mobility patterns gave them the edge over humans, allowing them to get around more and locate more prey and better sites.[384] And some researchers believe that the two groups became assimilated into a single group through interbreeding.[385,386]

One scenario that has received scant attention is the possibility of violent replacement. One reason is that the Levantine archaeological record does not reveal clear and unambiguous fossil evidence of warfare (crushed skulls, cut marks on limb bones, etc) between the species.[387]

This is not surprising. The only place archaeologists have found skeletal remains is at campsites and caves when carcasses have been brought back to consume. Normally, once a predator has killed a prey and eaten its fill, the remains are quickly scavenged by wild animals or birds. Field observations of avian and terrestrial scavengers in Africa suggest that carcass remains (including teeth and bones) are completely eradicated within a day.

It has also been argued that violent melees between present-day hunter-gatherers and large carnivores are dangerous and often lethal, so Neanderthals and humans may have tried to avoid each other whenever possible. But this speculation is based on the assumption of mutual fear, as between two equal adversaries. This wouldn't apply to an apex predator like the Neanderthal. Predators don't avoid or fear their prey, they actively stalk them.

here be dragons

The one thing we know for certain is that between 70,000 and 50,000 years ago, at exactly the time it is suggested that Neanderthals controlled the Levant, there were no new African migrations into the region. No one came north to claim the territory once occupied by the Skhul-Qafzeh people. Here was an incredibly fertile stretch of land surrounded on all sides by arid deserts, and yet no group of hominids thought to colonise it. Instead, African migrations exclusively followed an eastern route, along the Indian Ocean coast through the Indian subcontinent and as far as China.[388,389]

This is exactly what would be expected if the Levant had become a no go zone—due to the belief that dreadful flesh-eating monsters lived there. This would suggest that, even in the low-brow world of Late Pleistocene hominids, the Levant had become known as a place from which very few returned, a land peopled by terrifying creatures. This is a forerunner of the warnings medieval cartographers placed on the margins of their maps to describe dangerous or unexplored territories. Often accompanied by images of sea serpents and other mythological monsters, would be written, "Here be dragons".

"...within a cigarette paper's thickness of becoming extinct"

Even though the near-extinction scenario complies with Darwinian theory and ecological modelling of predator-prey interactions, it is impossible to know exactly what transpired 50,000 years ago to those Levantine humans living precariously on the eastern shoes of the Mediterranean. Fortunately, some recent technological advances in molecular biology have allowed geneticists to date when major evolutionary milestones occurred. This technological marvel hinges on the fact that certain elements in the DNA molecule are known to mutate at a steady predictable rate so, by counting the number of these mutations, geneticists can estimate roughly when major new mutations occurred. For example, the number of these markers in say, a language gene, can be used to calculate approximately when we acquired the capacity for complex spoken language.

In one such study, Pascal Gagneux, from the University of California at San Diego, and a team of European geneticists examined and compared a unique sequence of genetic markers from nine African or African-derived primates—including all gorilla, chimpanzee, bonobo and orangutan species—plus human and Neanderthal DNA. Not unexpectedly, they found considerable genetic variability between the species, but what did come as a surprise was that, of all the species tested, humans had by far the least amount of genetic variation within one species.

Gagneux's group was nonplussed to find that chimpanzees have four times more genetic diversity than humans:[390]

> We actually found that one single group of 55 chimpanzees in West Africa has twice the genetic variability of all humans. In other words, chimps who live in the same little group on the Ivory Coast are genetically more different from each other than you are from any human anywhere on the planet.[391]

The implications of this are quite confounding. How can there be more genetic variety in 55 chimps in a remote African rainforest than in six billion humans—scattered across the globe?

It just doesn't make sense. Normally mutations accumulate in our genes at a slow but fairly predictable rate, and these genetic variations spread as populations move and interbreed. Besides, humans have been around for millions of years and should have accumulated an enormous genetic range by now. Logic suggests that if we split from our primate cousins six million years ago, we should have at least as much genetic variation as they have. But this is not the case. It is only the human branch of the genetic tree that has been drastically pruned.

These results directed the researchers to a single inescapable conclusion—at some point in our evolutionary history, a severe population bottleneck (or near-extinction event) had occurred.[392] At some point in our evolutionary history, the human race came within a whisper of becoming extinct.

According to Bernard Wood, Professor of Human Origins at George Washington University, this severe pruning of our family tree was totally unexpected. "The amount of genetic variation that has accumulated in humans is just nowhere near compatible with the age [of our species]. That means you've got to come up with a hypothesis for an event that wiped out the vast majority of that variation."[393]

The most plausible explanation is that at least once in our past some situation caused the human population to drop to what Wood describes as "within a cigarette paper's thickness of becoming extinct".

When unexpected or controversial findings like this crop up in science, there is usually a rush by other scientists to duplicate the experiment or study. If they cannot reach the same conclusions, the original findings are usually discarded or at least revised. But in the case of Gagneux's findings, they were quickly confirmed by several other studies.[394,395,396]

But just how low did our ancestral population go? How thin was the line between the six billion humans living today and our tiny band of founders? A meticulous study, headed by a geneticist at the Harvard Medical School David Reich, has come up with an answer. By analysing a non-random mutational process called *linkage disequilibrium*, Reich and his team calculate the population of humans dropped to as few as 50 individuals.[397]

What's more, they calculated the population stayed that low for a long as 20 generations.[398] According to their data, our ancestors were hanging precariously onto life by their fingernails—literally on the precipice of extinction—for 400 years.

This doesn't mean the 50 lonely people were the only archaic humans or hominids left on the planet at the time. There were doubtlessly countless others scattered throughout the vast expanse of Africa and Asia. But what it says is that it was only these 50 individuals that contributed genes to the human genome. I argue the great panoply of humankind is derived from 50 Skhul-Qafzeh individuals. These genetic castaways were to be the sole breeding stock for all of humanity. The others died out without contributing any significant DNA to our gene pool.

Now to the all-important question—when did the population bottleneck occur? Five million years ago? One? Or even 250,000 years ago? Any one of these dates would be enough to sink NP theory. Or did it happen, as the NP model predicts, very recently—a scant 48,000 years ago?

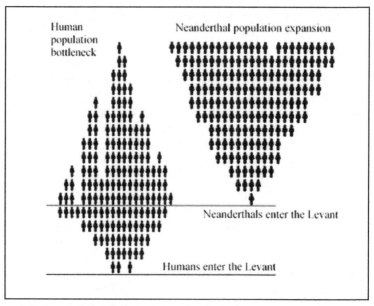

NP theory provides a new timeline for human evolution. It reveals that when archaic humans entered the Levant from Africa, their population gradually increased until Neanderthals moved in from Europe, beginning the period of Neanderthal predation. As the Neanderthal population grew, the archaic human population dwindled until it reached the population bottleneck. At this point there were as few as 50 humans left in the entire Levant.

In 1995, three geneticists—Simon Whitfield, John Sulston, and Peter Goodfellow—answered this question. Writing in *Nature*, the team reported their analysis of mutations in 100,000 nucleotides of the Y chromosome (the male sex chromosome) in males from five different ethnic groups. Their findings provided an estimate to the most recent common human ancestor of between 37,000 and 49,000 years ago.[399] This fits neatly with the scenario proposed by NP theory for when the bottleneck occurred.

In 2003, another team of geneticists and computational biologists, led by Gabor Marth from Boston College, painstakingly extracted data from 500,000 human mutations (*single-nucleotide polymorphisms*). Marth and his team calculated the population collapse happened around 1600 generations ago. The researchers estimated each generation at 25 years which means the population bottleneck occurred around 40,000 years ago.[400] But if the population was shrinking, then the normal reproductive cycle would be disrupted so the generation cycle would effectively increase. At 30 years per generation, which seems more likely, that yields an estimate of 48,000 years.

Another team, counting mutations in a different part of the DNA molecule (called *mitochondrial DNA mismatch distributions*) arrived at a figure of 40,000 years ago, or thereabouts.[401] And in 2001, David Reich's Harvard team estimated the bottleneck occurred sometime between 27,000 to 53,000 years ago.[402]

Allowing for stastistical margins of error, my estimate that a near-extinction event occurred around 48,000 years ago is in the same ball park, and consistent with both molecular data and the archaelogical record of the disappearance of the Skhul-Qafzeh humans from the Levant between 80,000 and 50,000 years ago.

there's only one gray's anatomy

As well as the archaeological and genetic evidence pointing to an unprecedented population reduction in recent human history, there is another line of evidence to consider. Modern humans all around the world are very similar, despite superficial external differences such as skin and hair colour.

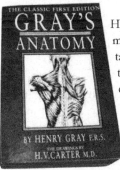

This close similarity also extends to behaviour. Human nature is invariant across cultures. There are minor cultural variations (or national character) but talk to people for a few minutes and you soon realise that from Timbuktu to Tallahassee, Taiwan to Tierra del Fuego, we're very alike. All humans belong to the same single species. It's what's called *homogeneity* in biology, and the only explanation for it is that all the members of the species are derived from the same small founding population, just as NP theory suggests.

The second prediction that Neanderthal predation drove our Levantine ancestors to the brink of extinction raises the question: who survived and why?

12   SURVIVOR LEVANT

outwit, outplay, outlast

All the archaeological evidence, the molecular genetic analysis, and the uniformity of modern humans supports the proposition that a near-extinction event took place in recent human history. But that doesn't explain what caused it. It exists in the anthropological literature as yet another enigma in human evolution.

However, in NP theory, a near-extinction event that almost exterminated the human race is precisely what is expected and predicted. It is the only ecological situation potent enough to precipitate the speciation event that created modern humans. It follows then that NP theory also predicts that, although it was severely reduced, the Skhul-Qafzeh population survived the bottleneck and recovered its numbers. This too is confirmed by the Levantine archaeology. Humans reappear in the Levant fossil record about 50,000 years ago.[403]

NP theory proposes that as the population was culled, the few remaining Skhul-Qafzeh survivors from across the Levant banded together into a single population (or tribe) for protection. Although originally from different tribes, these individuals overcame their xenophobia because unity provided an added degree of safety and security. This resilient group became the founding population of the human race.

This narrows the focus of our inquiry onto those hardy individuals who survived the near-extinction event, and raises a number of questions. But science is all about asking the *right* question and, in this case, that is: why did those few individuals survive when everyone else fell victim to the Neanderthals?

Charles Darwin offers a clue in *The Origin of Species*: "It is not the strongest of the species that survives," he writes, "nor the most intelligent. It is the one most adaptable to change."

The Levantines that survived did so because they changed—they adapted. But how? At the coalface of predation, what physical and behavioural traits were lost because they were maladaptive, and what new adaptive traits took their place? While the big picture answer is obvious— they survived because they acquired adaptations that assuaged the worst effects of predation—this explanation lacks detail. There is a need to understand precisely which existing traits increased their vulnerability (and were lost) and which new ones were acquired because they contributed to their survival and reproductive success.

anti-predator adaptations

Field studies confirm that natural selection retains adaptations that help prey species survive, avoid or accommodate predation.[404,405] So the third major predicted outcome of Neanderthal predation is that, as Neanderthal predation decimated the population of Levantine Skhul-Qafzeh humans, a range of 'anti-Neander-thal' defensive and avoidance adaptations were selected and fixed.

These new adaptive traits spread through the whole population—this didn't take long because the bottleneck population was initially so small. Theoretically, the more Skhul-Qafzeh humans that died as a result of multidimensional predation, the more selective pressure was generated for adaptations to reduce the death toll. It is ironic to think that the more adept Neanderthals became at catching and killing humans and poaching their females, the more the humans acquired adaptive countermeasures.

There were three separate but complementary evolutionary mechanisms that created the anti-predator adaptations and ensured their rapid fixation.

natural selection—
the levantine killing fields

The first and most obvious evolutionary mechanism is natural selection. In the Levant this worked in two ways. The first we can call *negative selection*—all the Levantine humans who could be caught by Neanderthals were caught and killed. The victims would include all the slow, reckless or not very bright individuals, and their deleterious genes would have been removed from the human gene pool.

But natural selection can also be positive. Positive selection would retain neurological and behavioural mutations that increased hyper-vigilance for Neanderthals and improved early recognition and escape strategies. Physiological adaptations that reduced capture rates, such as increased running speed, agility, hand-eye coordination, athleticism, language, intelligence and forward planning would also come under positive selection. What makes natural selection so powerful is that it is a two-edged sword.

sexual selection—looking for mister big

Contrary to the popular view that Neanderthals and early humans coexisted and voluntarily interbred, it makes more sense that if Neanderthals really were formidable, brutish and merciless predacious adversaries, the last thing a Skhul-Qafzeh human would want to do is fraternise with one. When it came to choosing a sexual partner, humans would chose only human mates, with a preference for those who were as dissimilar as possible to the dreaded Neanderthals.

In this way, sexual selection established a small exclusive breeding circle, where the members interbred only with those displaying a specific range of highly-prized physical and behavioural features. At the same time, they would also avoid anyone who looked or behaved like a Neanderthal (including hybrids in their own group) so these genes would be gradually removed from the gene pool.

This suggests that sexual selection and mate choice played an important role in the evolution of modern humans. In acknowledging this, we need to put aside our reticence to consider psychological factors in evolutionary dynamics, and recognise that mate selection is driven primarily by emotional and attitudinal factors. Skhul-Qafzeh humans would have feared and despised Neanderthals and these powerful emotions became set in stone over thousands of generations by the continual trauma of brutality, predation, sexual assault and being devoured. So, there is every reason to believe the emotional attitude of our ancestors towards Neanderthals, and the consequent selection of mates, was an important causal factor in the evolution of modern humans.

Among the higher mammals—and this is particularly true of primates—it is usually the female that is proactive in selecting a mate. While males will mate with any female in oestrus, females are more discriminating. This would suggest that Skhul-Qafzeh females used sexual selection as an evolutionary tool more than the males did. But, as we are about to see, the final mechanism of selecting anti-Neanderthal traits was wielded almost exclusively by males.

artificial selection—when the going gets tough, the tough start killing

When Darwin coined the term natural selection, he meant that nature was doing 'the selecting'—that the natural environment the organism lived in was a major determinant of which members lived and which died. In addition, Darwin described *artificial selection*: the way farmers and breeders intentionally select certain traits in domestic animals, which is a relatively benign form of artificial selection. However, the term also applies to the lethal form of selection—almost always applied by human males—as to who lives and who dies.

So the third way that anti-Neanderthal adaptations spread was by artificial selection—where coercion, ostracism, banishment and lethal violence by Skhul-Qafzehs gradually removed from the gene pool any individual who (for whatever reason) they considered too Neanderthaloid. NP theory holds that, throughout the Late Pleistocene, coalitionary groups of human males increasingly resorted to infanticide and homicide to eradicate Neanderthal-human hybrids, excessively hairy individuals, deviant neonates, or anyone who looked like a Neanderthal.

One of the most salient features of artificial selection is its speed. Unlike natural selection, which tends to create gradual change over thousands of generations, even benign forms of artificial selection can occur very quickly. A good example is the selective breeding experiments carried out in the 50s by the Russian geneticist Dmitri Belyaev to produce tame foxes. By selecting only the tamest foxes to breed, Belyaev and his team turned a colony of wild silver foxes into domestic pets within ten generations. The new animals were not only unafraid of humans, they often wagged their tails and licked their human caretakers in shows of

In eastern Spain, scrawled on a cave wall in red ochre, is one of the earliest known depictions of intergroup violence.

affection. Even their physiology changed—the tame foxes had floppy ears, curled tails and spotted coats.

However, this rapid transformation of Belyaev's foxes pales into insignificance compared to lethal and pernicious forms of human artificial selection—including genocide, ethnic cleansing, racial vilification, religious persecution and pogroms—that can exert a significant evolutionary impact almost overnight. The long history of such affronts and their ubiquitous application by disparate cultures separated by thousands of years supports the hypothesis that aggressive Skhul-Qafzeh males would have no compunction in eradicating anyone they felt was more *them* than *us*.

Historically, lethal violence and genocide have not been the business of women. Throughout human history, they have mostly been the preserve of males, and there is no reason to believe it was any different in the Late Pleistocene. Males claimed lethal violence as their own instrument of artificial selection. Groups of men decided what constituted a Neanderthaloid trait, and who felt like a Neanderthal. Men became the ultimate arbiters of who and what was acceptable. It was they who decided who lived and who died.

Given this, the use of artificial (or lethal) selection to remove anti-Neanderthaloid traits would be more prevalent on females, children and infants than on adult males. Sociological and anthropological evidence appears to support this more nuanced view.

Evolutionary biologist Ronald Fisher observes that when a trait conferring a survival advantage also becomes subject to sexual selection, it creates a positive feedback loop that leads to very rapid uptake of the trait. But we can now see that in the Levant it was not only natural selection and sexual selection that were working together to rid the population of hybridised individuals and Neanderthaloid characteristics. The process was also being logarithmically boosted by artificial selection—as coalitions of aggressive males banished or murdered their way towards the same common objective—towards a new kind of human that looked, sounded, smelt and behaved less like a Neanderthal. This blind, inexorable process would have made a substantial contribution to human evolution by identifying and quickly culling vestigial Neanderthal genes from the nascent human genome.

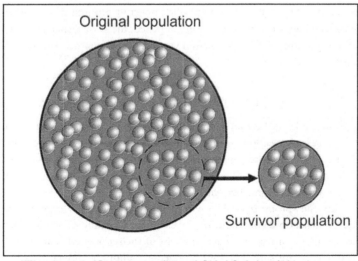

When the original Levantine population of Skhul-Qafzeh early humans was decimated by Neanderthal predation, the survivors became the nucleus of a new founding population of modern humans.

genetic drift—the founder effect

NP theory argues that the three Darwinian mechanisms of evolution (natural selection, sexual selection and artificial selection) focused on acquiring defensive adaptations to reduce the death toll, and to remove every vestige of hybridisation and Neanderthalism from the human lineage, but they were aided and abetted by the fourth Darwinian evolutionary mechanism—*genetic drift*.

Genetic drift is a dynamic that occurs when some members of a species are physically isolated from the parent population—either because they migrate away, or are separated by some geological feature—like a river or mountain range. When the isolated group begins interbreeding among itself, whatever distinctive physical and behavioural features were present in the breakaway individuals tend to spread throughout the group. This is particularly noticeable when the group is small. As the group expands, these sampling errors show up as a *founder effect*—for example, everyone ends up with red hair or blue eyes.

The tiny, bottleneck population of Skhul-Qafzeh humans in the Levant provided the ideal conditions for genetic drift to consolidate the changes brought about by the three other Darwinian evolutionary mechanisms. Had the Levantine population been in regular contact with the outside world at the time—if they had been exchanging genes with early humans from north Africa or central Asia—the impact of Neanderthal predation would not have been so acute. As it happened, the sexual isolation of the Levantine Skhul-Qafzeh population was a crucial fortuitous factor in the emergence of *sapiens*.

meta selection—the total package

So, now we have the four known evolutionary mechanisms (natural selection, sexual selection, artificial selection and genetic drift) all exerting blind evolutionary pressure in the same direction. And the closer to extinction the Levantine Skhul-Qafzeh population got, the more potent these four mechanisms became.

This four-pronged evolutionary assault represents an exceptionally rare biological phenomenon. In the extensive literature of evolutionary biology, there is no other documented case of such concerted, multi-faceted evolutionary pressure. The four-pronged evolutionary imperative—what I call *meta-selection*—is the only evolutionary mechanism sufficiently robust and focused, and possessing the requisite selection momentum, to create a new hominid species, radically different from every other, in such a short time.

Meta-selection is the key to modern human evolution.

The reason meta-selection was so effective was because it not only removed Neanderthaloid and primate traits, but selected a whole raft of distinctively new human traits. It also removed the victims of predation and consolidated new defensive traits in the remaining survivors.

This process of removal and replacement widened the species divide and effectively put human evolution into hyper drive. In the 3.4 billion years of the evolutionary history of life on earth, nothing like this had ever happened before.

The most effective way to thoroughly test these hypotheses is to examine the specific physical and behavioural traits that meta-selection removed, along with the new adaptations that replaced them. For the sake of this analysis, the anti-Neanderthal adaptations are separated into five categories:

- Adaptations to help identify and differentiate Neanderthals
- Adaptations to counteract sexual predation
- Adaptations to avoid being captured or killed
- Social adaptations
- Adaptations to protect against nocturnal predation

Remarkably, these adaptations include all the major features that distinguish humans from other primates. In short, they are what make us human.

13 TELLING FRIEND FROM FIEND

the ultimate make-over

When it comes to predation, prey species rarely get a second chance to rectify any lapse of vigilance. Because early detection and identification of predators have such a strong bearing on survival, selection pressure is generated for prey species to acquire neuronal networks and sensory organs to maintain vigilance for predators.

In addition, over time each prey species builds up an innate *description* of its predators to help identify them—even those they've never seen before. Although little understood by scientists, this instinctive knowledge of a predator's characteristics is thought to include visual, auditory and other sensory cues that trigger an adaptive response, usually an escape strategy. For example, in 1951 Dutch ethologist Nikolaas Tinbergen devised an ingenious experiment to show that new-born turkey chicks, fresh from their shells, will run for cover when they see a hawk, but will not respond to pigeons, gulls, ducks or herons.[406] So, too, birds like the great kiskadee that have never seen a coral snake before, can instantly recognise its distinctive stripes, comprehend that it is dangerous and make their escape.[407] Similar experiments with other animals confirm that animals that have never seen their natural predator can recognise and respond to its predatory markings.[408]

At Sydney's Taronga Zoo, I watched an Australian black-breasted buzzard pick up a stone in its beak and use it to crack open an emu egg. Young buzzards don't have to learn this clever trick because it's hard-wired into their genes. Likewise, I once saw a friend's toddler respond to a huntsman spider that crawled into his cot by instinctively slamming his fist down on it. His amazed parents assured me he'd never seen a spider before.

As a prey species, there can be little doubt that early hominids acquired a range of similar innate *predator identifiers* through natural selection. But in the case of Levantine humans and Neanderthals, this would have been more difficult because the two species originally looked somewhat similar. When they first saw each other, they would have been immediately struck by the differences, but they may also have recognised a kindred soul—of sorts. After all, they were both bipedal hominids, roughly the same size and shape and, if they both had primate faces and were covered with hair (even if of a different colour and thickness) then, for these simple-minded folk, identification may well have been problematical. It is safe to assume, therefore, that any feature that accentuated any physical or behavioural difference between the sibling species, and facilitated early and accurate identification, would become an identifier and therefore the subject of meta-selection.

For example, if Neanderthal fur was longer and denser, the eyes larger, and the pupils a different shape, then these features—in humans—would come under the closest scrutiny. This preoccupation with hair and eyes would result in selection pressure in humans to be different—to 'increase the visual gap' between the species.

Over time, the demands of predator identification would gradually accentuate the physical differences between the two species. Nobody would want a mate who looked like a Neanderthal, so the new 'human look' became increasingly subject to sexual selection. As the 'new look' became de rigueur, the old look became subject to artificial selection. Not having 'the look' was not only seriously 'uncool'—it was likely to get you killed.

The characteristics which came under the most intense meta-selectional pressure were physical features that could be seen from a distance, because early identification of a predator is at the core of survival. This would mean that, for humans, body hair (length, density and colour) gait, posture, body silhouette and facial features were the most obvious foci of predator identification and differentiation.

a hairy problem

Although it is interesting to speculate on what colour skin the Skhul-Qafzeh people had, it was not a factor at the time because it is almost certain that the Skhul-Qafzeh people were covered in dense body hair.

While readers may find the prospect of recent human ancestors sporting so much body hair unpalatable, this is precisely what NeoDarwinian theory predicts. Coming from Africa where they occupied an open savannah environment, it is highly likely that the Skhul-Qafzeh people acquired a coat of protective hair to insulate them from the hot African sun and its equally cold nights. The same reasoning suggests that—like lions, monkeys and other mammals occupying the same grassland environments—light-brown fur would probably have been most adaptive because it facilitated concealment from predators. So, what happened to the hair? Can NP theory shed any new light on this age-old question?

The loss of body hair in humans—but in no other primate—has generated a vigorous debate among anthropologists for decades. It's particularly puzzling in light of the fact that hairlessness is maladaptive in terms of climate extremes, heat stress, sunburn, skin cancers, hypothermia and low ambient temperature environments.[409,410]

HUMAN HAIRLESSNESS

Actually, modern humans are not hairless. But discarding our thick, long and highly pigmented hair, (called terminal hair) in favour of fine, short and unpigmented vellus hair has created the impression of hairlessness.[411] For the purposes of this book, terms like *hairlessness* and *denudation* are used even though they're not strictly correct.

In *Before the Dawn* Nicholas Wade outlines the paradox:

> Hairiness is the default state of all mammals, and the handful of species that have lost their hair have done so for a variety of compelling reasons, such as living in water, as

do hippopotamuses, whales and walruses, or residing in hot underground tunnels, as does the naked mole rat.[412]

Innumerable theorists have attempted to explain why only humans turned into a 'naked ape', including Charles Darwin who argues:

> No one supposes that the nakedness of the skin is any direct advantage to man; his body therefore cannot have been divested of hair through natural selection.[…]in all parts of the world women are less hairy than men. Therefore we may reasonably suspect that this character has been gained through sexual selection.[413]

A variation of Darwin's sexual selection theory has been proposed by American psychologist Judith Rich Harris. She believes that hairlessness and pale skin are the result of sexual selection for beauty, which operates through a form of infanticide she calls *parental selection*.[414] Harris argues that historically, parents frequently killed infants they didn't consider beautiful enough, and one of the criteria for beauty she nominates is hairlessness.

Another group of scholars contends that hairlessness emerged six to eight million years ago in hominids who lived an aquatic or semi-aquatic existence for between one and two million years.[415,416] This is the controversial aquatic ape theory which, despite arousing some initial interest, has not stood up well to critical evaluation and has been largely discredited.[417]

Yet another group of anthropologists claims hairlessness was selected because it helped in detecting and removing ectoparasites likely to harbour diseases.[418] But why other primates did not lose their hair for the same reason is not explained. Nor does the theory address the retention of warm, moist pubic hair, which is a veritable haven for body lice.

But probably the most popular theory remains thermoregulation. Its advocates argue that hairlessness helped to cool bipedal hominid hunters when they migrated from the African rainforests to the savannah and began hunting large animals.[419] Anthropology professor Albert Johnson Jr suggests:

> Specifically, any diurnal hunter on the African high veldt would have needed a mechanism to dissipate excess heat which would almost have certainly been generated due to moving about under the equatorial African sun. Therefore,

selection would have operated to reduce the amount of
body hair on these hominids largely because heat dissipation
would not have been possible if they had remained covered
with hair.[420]

This makes sense in theory, but not in practice. Medullated terminal hair
is actually an excellent insulator against both heat and cold, and creates a
consistent 'microclimate' that is adaptive in a wide variety of climatic conditions.[421] Losing this hair would in fact subject humans to both increased
heat and cold stress.

Writing in the *Journal of Human Evolution*, Lia Queiroz do Amaral
reported that, at high temperatures, thermal stress is up to three times
greater on a naked human than on a primate covered with terminal hair.[422]
This is why, according to another study, the fur of savannah primates
is actually denser than that of forest-dwelling primates.[423] Chimpanzees,
bonobos, baboons, and gorillas—all from the hottest equatorial regions
of Africa—have retained their thick body hair.

Also challenging the thermoregulation theory is the sunburn factor.
Hair protects animal skin from sunburn and melanomas. And, if
hairlessness doesn't make sense as an adaptation to heat, it makes even
less sense when temperatures on the African plains can drop to minus
zero just before dawn.

The thermoregulation theory claims that hairlessness evolved to cool
hunters as they chased prey on the African savannah. However, cross-
cultural studies of human hunter-gatherer societies show that hunting
large animals is exclusively the preserve of men.[424] If only men hunt, why
did women also lose their hair?

Lastly, neither the thermoregulation theory, nor any of the other
theories adequately address the gender difference in hairlessness (females
are less hairy than men) nor the continual preoccupation with hairlessness
in modern humans. These gaps, and the lack of a consensus about the
evolutionary origins of human denudation, justify re-examining the
problem using the NP model.

why we *really* lost our hair

NP theory proposes that hair loss was driven by the needs of a prey species to quickly and accurately identify its principal predator.

It was not simply a matter of distinguishing Neanderthals from Skhul-
Qafzehs. Identification per se has no survival value—unless it occurs

early enough to prevent capture. So if extra thick and long body fur was an eye-catching feature of Eurasian Neanderthals, it would allow the less hairy Skhul-Qafzeh people to identify Neanderthals from far away, giving them time to escape.

This would be enough to establish long body fur as a reliable visual demarcation between the species—especially from a distance—which in turn would create a negative association towards hairiness in humans. Fairly soon, this would translate into a sexual preference for less hairy partners, and hairy humans would increasingly be seen as 'Neanderthaloid'.

In other words, just as female peacocks choose males with the biggest fan-like display of colourful feathers, so too Skhul-Qafzeh humans grew to prefer mates who were less hairy.

This would place all the hairy humans—the outcasts and the wallflowers—not only on the proverbial shelf, but also in danger of being socially ostracised and even murdered: artificial selection. The net effect of this meta-selection ensured that the genes coding for body hair in humans were gradually removed from the gene pool.

It may seem strange that humans could develop such a powerful aversion to something as natural as body hair. But when this aversion is placed in its correct evolutionary perspective, it's hardly surprising it remains so strong today, 28,000 years after the last Neanderthal has disappeared. Negative attitudes to hirsutism and a preference for hairlessness (personally and in prospective mates) are universal across human cultures throughout recorded time.

Because artificial selection was practised almost exclusively by males, the selection pressure for female denudation would have been even more acute, resulting in women becoming even less hairy than men. This indicates that the pressure on women and girls to be hairless is anchored in the threat of lethal force wielded exclusively by men since the Late Pleistocene. While hairy aggressive men were quite prepared to kill hairy women, they were less enthusiastic about topping themselves.

This reasoning is supported by considerable sociological research which shows modern women and girls traditionally come under greater pressure to be less hairy than men.[425,426] For example, a study of 678 UK women in 2005 found that 99.71 percent of participants reported removing body hair.[427] Citing examples of depilation in ancient cultures (Egypt, Greece and Rome) and in a variety of modern societies (Uganda, South American and Turkey), cultural anthropologist Wendy Cooper contends that the need for women to remove body hair is deeply embedded in human nature.[428]

clothes maketh the man

The Neanderthal predation hair loss theory predicts several outcomes that can be empirically tested. Firstly, it argues that hair loss did not occur gradually over millions of years in Africa. It happened in the Levant and coincides with the first contact with Eurasian Neanderthals around 110,000 to 100,000 years ago.

Because body hair protected our ancestors against both heat and cold, allowing them to maintain thermoregulatory homeostasis in extreme climatic environments, its loss was potentially deleterious. Being hairless was particularly dangerous for newborn babies and infants because of the risk of hyperthermia and hypothermia. Newborns are especially susceptible to cold stress due to their thin skin, intensive vascularisation, and the high surface area of skin to body mass.[429,430] Even in adults, being stripped of body hair would raise the risk of brain anoxia and acidosis.

This tells us that hairlessness must have occurred concurrently with the evolution of clothing to maintain homeothermy, which in turn provides an excellent means of testing the theory.

Trying to determine exactly when humans started wearing clothes is difficult because skins and fabrics are not generally preserved in archaeological sites. Fortunately, in 2003 a German team of geneticists noticed that the human head louse (*Pediculus humanus capitis*) feeds and lives on the scalp, while the body louse (*Pediculus humanus corporis*) (*right*) feeds on body skin, but lives in our clothing. They reasoned these two species of ectoparasites were originally one species and diverged only when humans began wearing clothes. By dating mutations in their DNA, the scientists were able to date the emergence of body lice and, by inference, the human use of clothing.[431] They estimated humans started to wear clothing around 107,000 years ago.[432]

This agrees with my proposition that denudation and the development of clothing began with the onset of Neanderthal predation in the Levant about 110,000 to 100,000 years ago. However, this is not to suggest that the Middle Palaeolithic Skhul-Qafzeh people had the wherewithal to make needles and sew tailored garments. The first stitched clothes are thought to have been made by using pointed stone awls (which have been found at Levantine sites) to pierce holes in animal skins, which were then sewn together with fibre or leather throngs. Importantly, the gradual loss of body hair by the Skhul-Qafzeh people generated increasing selection pressure for the cognitive modules required to make tailored garments.

walking the walk

Modern humans have a distinctive, straight-back gait unlike any other primate, and this has sparked considerable discussion about its evolutionary origins. Although paleoskeletal evidence indicates archaic hominids were walking bipedally over 3 million years ago,[433] anatomically modern human anatomy is much more recent. At some stage in their evolutionary history, humans abandoned their ancestral primate swagger and adopted the flowing stride of today. But what caused the change? And when did it happen?

If the way we walk today is the result of modern human skeletal anatomy, the focus of the search can be narrowed to *after* humans became anatomically modern. The Kibish hominids from southern Ethiopia, reliably dated at 195,000 years old (±5000 years), are probably the earliest humans discovered with a relatively modern skeleton.[434] So theoretically, the mechanical-skeletal components of the modern stride were in place sometime in the last 200,000 years. This puts the emergence of the modern human gait within the range of Neanderthal predation, so it is appropriate to ask: could it be yet another legacy of Neanderthal predation?

An animal's gait is such a distinctive feature and so easily recognised, even over long distances, it provides prey with a quick and convenient method of identifying predators. If chimpanzees, gorillas and humans have each acquired their own species-specific gait, it seems logical that Neanderthals did too. In that case, their distinctive gait would provide early Levantine humans with a conspicuous means of recognising their dreaded foe even at a distance of several hundred metres.

This would generate selection pressure on humans, firstly to abandon

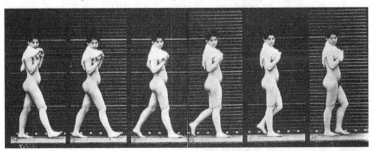

The modern human stride, as captured by Eadweard Muybridge, is so distinct it could not have been mistaken for that of a Neanderthal, or any other primate.

aspects of their own gait that were similar to that of Neanderthals, and secondly to develop a new distinctive gait. Very quickly, this could lead to the preferential selection of mates who displayed the new gait. A sexy walk soon became the latest must have feature on the Palaeolithic dating scene. Eventually meta-selection for the new stride wiped out the old ape-like gait altogether.

This hypothesis is based on the assumption that Neanderthals originally had a different gait from the Skhul-Qafzeh humans, and this assumption needs to be tested. While we can observe other primates and speculate from that how Neanderthals walked, a better way is to examine fossilised Neanderthal pelvic, hip and spinal bones to see if they offer any insight into the Neanderthal gait.

When Erik Trinkaus undertook his meticulous re-examination of nine

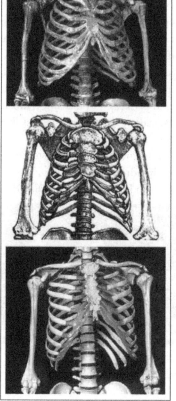

Neanderthal skeletons from Shanidar cave in the Zagros Mountains of Iraq, he found the unique configuration of their pelvis bones, gluteal muscles and lumbar robusticity was quite different from that of early humans and that this would have caused Neanderthals to have a distinctive gait. He also worked out that the curved long bones of their legs would have given them a decidedly bow-legged look.[435]

Ian Tattersall, another authority on Neanderthal physiology, observes that the barrel-shaped rib cage, flared pelvis and articulation of the last lumbar vertebra with the sacrum

Despite the popular belief that Neanderthals and humans were anatomically identical, the physical difference between the species is evident in the shape of their rib cages. The Neanderthal rib cage (top) is pear-shaped, like that of the gorilla (centre) while the human rib cage (below) is more tubular. This gave the Neanderthals a distinctive visual appearance that humans could use to quickly identify them, even over great distances.

deep in the pelvic bowl (which has the effect of shortening the waist) were all distinctive Neanderthal physical features that "would have assured that the two hominids would have presented very different appearances on the landscape".[436]

Tattersall goes on to make the point that the shortness of the Neanderthal waist would have restricted upper body rotation and stiffened the Neanderthal gait, rendering their movement very different from those of modern humans—more ape-like.

These lines of anatomical evidence square with the one universal modern human attitude to gait. Humans everywhere consider a slouched ape-like walk, typified by hunched shoulders, rigid torso, bow-legged, forward lean and loosely swinging arms as physically unattractive.

From the perspective of NP theory, it is not a coincidence that the characteristic modern human stride is universal. Unlike body hair, which varies slightly around the world and between the sexes, there is only one modern human walk. There are no cultural variations, no bow-legged, hunched-over exceptions. The evidence suggests this is the result of concerted and prolonged meta-selection pressure for a single uniform human gait.

sexy curves

Many physical anthropologists—and a good many doctors—have long wondered why the human spine has a pronounced S-shaped curve when every other primate has a much straighter spine. This distinctive characteristic (*lumbar lordosis*) is perplexing because it seems badly designed and injury prone. From an engineering perspective, the spine is a tension-compression structure and the more vertically the lumbar vertebrae are aligned, the more efficient they are at transferring stress, resulting in less injuries. In the human spine, lordosis is produced by a combination of the angle of the sacrum and the wedge shape of the lowest vertebra. Ninety-nine percent of lumbar prolapses occur in these lower vertebrae. Among urbanised, industrialised peoples, the chances of having lower back pain ranges between 50 to 80 percent.[437]

Natural selection would result in a curved spine only if it somehow increased reproductive success. There must have been some significant advantage, to compensate for the injuries and immobility of the new weaker spine. Could the S-shaped spine be

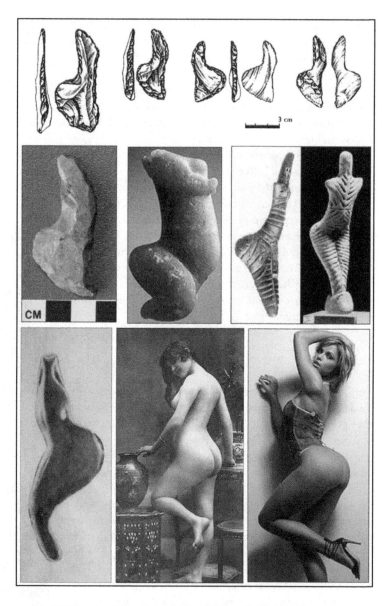

The 15,000 year old flint plaquettes from Wilczyce, Poland, the curvaceous calcite Venus de Sireil from Dordogne, France and the Victorian and modern erotica suggest the appeal of women with curved spines accentuated by rounded buttocks (typical of the medical condition, lordosis) is not just a modern phenomena.

the result of preferential selection during the Late Pleistocene because it helped differentiate the two warring species?

This would mean the human spine acquired a degree of lordosis because, in conjunction with rounded buttocks, it would present a very different appearance from side-on (than Neanderthals) and therefore would be an advantage in the critical issue of identification. Further, this would translate into a curved spine being considered desirable—read *sexy*—especially when accentuated by rounded buttocks.

This aspect of the theory finds support from sociologist Christopher

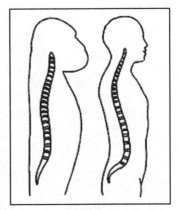

The spine of the other great apes is much straighter than humans and less prone to injury.
Illustration courtesy of the Australian Museum

Badcock, who—in the interests of science—pored through countless men's magazines to study what kinds of bodies and poses men preferred. On the basis of how many poses featured the accentuated curve of the spine, he suggests that modern human males find this look particularly appealing.[438]

The lordosis theory is only plausible if Neanderthals had the same straight spine as modern primates. Because the literature on this is scarce, I consulted Erik Trinkaus, an authority on Neanderthal physiology, who said the question of Neanderthal spinal curvature still hasn't been resolved (*personal correspondence*). This is partly because Neanderthal vertebrae, when excavated, are nearly always broken or distorted. Often this is exacerbated by the body having been bent to fit a burial pit but, in addition, the weight and movement of the ground is enough to scatter and squash the vertebra. Thus, it is practically impossible to determine the amount of lordosis in the Neanderthal spine.

the hourglass figure

Devendra Singh, Professor of Psychology at Texas University, has carried out some interesting research into universal male preferences for certain female body types or shapes. He found one striking preference that men

Almost 2000 years separates these artistic representations of idealised femininity and yet they all share one physical characteristic—a hip-to-waist ratio of .7:1 This degree of curvature became highly prized because it helped distinguish human females from straight-waisted Neanderthals.

from over 18 different cultures consistently share. They prefer women with a waist-to-hip ratio of between .67–.80.[439] Women whose waists are on an average seven-tenths as wide as their hips (that's a ratio of 1:0.7)—regardless of the woman's overall body size and weight—have been considered ideal by men across time and culture.[440]

The male body shape differs from the linear torso of Neanderthals—it's more trapezoid: narrow at the hips and broad at the shoulders.

A team of English psychologists led by Martin J Tovée, from the University of Newcastle, reaches similar conclusions.[441] Comparing 300 supermodels (including Claudia Schiffer, Naomi Campbell and the Wonderbra model Sophie Anderton), 300 'glamour models' from *Playboy* magazine, 300 average women, plus smaller samples of anorexics and bulimics, they find that, even though the supermodels are taller and thinner, they nevertheless still have .68 hip-to-waist ratios. Glamour models averaged .71.

Evolutionary psychologists have not been able to explain men's attraction for this particular body shape, so there is no harm in proposing that its evolutionary origins may lie in Neanderthal predation. Judging by preserved Neanderthal rib cages, their torsos (viewed from the front) were straight or even slightly rounded, suggesting that humans may have preferred the hourglass figure because it helped tell friend from foe. The important thing about figure shape is that, even from a distance, the distinct curvy silhouette is very easy to recognise as human. Because this body shape was like a stamp of approval—a guarantee that a female wasn't a hybrid, or worse still a Neanderthal—men would have found this curvy shape more desirable.

putting on a new face

Perhaps because the expressive powers of the face are thought to provide a window into the soul, among modern humans the face is the most important indicator of who we are. It is our most admired, studied, decorated, depicted, altered and mutilated feature. Research into the field of subliminal perception reveals that we are constantly on the alert for angry and threatening faces. We subliminally register threatening faces even in a crowd, well before we are consciously aware of them. As a species, we are habitual face readers, shaped by nature to be hyper-aware of subtle facial characteristics.

We see faces everywhere, as if our minds are determined to detect all the faces hidden around us—behind every tree, concealed in every bush. We are particularly aware of facial deformities and simian features.

Such an important function would ensure the human face became subject to meta-selection. This would redesign the conspicuous soft tissue features to create as much visual distance between humans and the Neanderthals' primate appearance, resulting in the selection of morphological novelties like protruding noses, unwrinkled skin, tumescent lips, facial flatness, clear eye whites, pale skin, reduced brow ridges, a pronounced chin, and facial symmetry. If faces occupy such a privileged position in human consciousness, if we have an abiding interest in what our lovers, children, friends and especially strangers look like, if we are subliminally attuned to threatening faces in our midst, it follows that this innate fascination also extended to Neanderthal faces. What their faces looked like was important to our ancestors and the reason, according to NP theory, is that at close quarters the face provided the most reliable means of differentiating Neanderthals and hybrids from humans.

Today, lethal (artificial) selection is applied less frequently against people with 'non-standard' facial features, although in some cultures infanticide still occurs with deformed and exceptionally 'ugly' infants. However, sexual selection against Neanderthal-primate facial features in favour of human facial features remains strongly normative in every human culture.

Let's take one example—facial symmetry. Today studies show that, even though people are usually not aware of it, they universally prefer partners with symmetrical faces.[442] This suggests this innate preference may have been acquired because Neanderthal faces were asymmetrical, just as modern chimpanzee faces are.[443] In fact, humans have an extraordinary ability to subliminally detect even the slightest facial asymmetry and to associate it with unattractiveness.

Similarly, because we know from examination of Neanderthal mandibles that they didn't have a chin, humans would acquire an innate dislike of weak chins and a sexual preference for a pronounced chin. This may explain why today the human chin is unique among mammals.[444]

This hypothesis offers a simple explanation for why the human face is one of the most important visual factors in selecting a sexual partner in modern humans.[445] And why it has so many features that are unique to humans. It also adds weight to evolutionary biologist Tomomichi Kobayashi's proposal that the preference for the "handsome type face in humans" was acquired relatively recently, as a result of sexual isolation

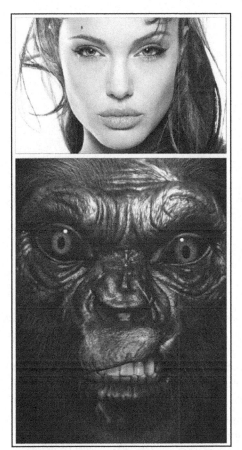

Philosophers and scientists have pondered the aesthetics of human beauty for thousands of years but are still no closer to explaining them, or why our faces look so different from those of every other primate. Finally, we have a simple answer—the human face evolved to be visually different from Neanderthals—allowing us to tell friend from fiend. Today, Neanderthal facial characteristics (as depicted in the forensic reconstruction, left) provide an innate standard by which humans judge ugliness and beauty. The less like this Neanderthal you look, the more 'beautiful' you are.

during or after the emergence of modern humans.[446] This is because all the indicators of human beauty and desirability which people universally use to choose a partner, bear no resemblance to primate features. They are unique to modern humans so, consistent with NP theory, must have emerged as part of the Upper Palaeolithic revolution.

14 NO SEX PLEASE, WE'RE HUMAN

the sexual revolution

Neanderthal sexual predation not only reduced the Skhul-Qafzeh population, but also contributed to the hybridisation of the Levant population so, unless humans could find a way of preventing—or at least minimising—the worst excesses of Neanderthal sexual predation, their future as a separate species looked bleak. This generated selection pressure for adaptations to counter, or at least reduce, the impact of Neanderthal sexual predation.

Ostensibly, the goal of Skhul-Qafzeh males was to out-compete Neanderthal males and retain access to fertile females. But, from a Darwinian perspective, the stakes were much higher. Sexual compatibility exposed humans to overwhelming aggressive competition from Neanderthals, a competition so powerful and destabilising it rendered the existing Skhul-Qafzeh sex system obsolete and maladaptive. If the Levantine humans could not reclaim sexual exclusivity, their viability as a species was in jeopardy.

Given the enormous selection pressure this situation generated, we can use Darwin's model to predict what happened next. In the struggle for survival, random mutations that increased the Levantine humans' chances of sexually out-competing Neanderthals were selected and fixed.

What I propose is that the process of natural selection gradually came up with an entirely new human sexuality.

This hypothesis claims that sexual adaptations against Neanderthal predation that accrued via natural selection formed the basis of a uniquely human mating system. The new system was unique in the animal kingdom and achieved the almost impossible—it excluded Neanderthals and brought Neanderthal sexual predation to a complete halt. By abandoning most of the primate-Neanderthal sexual protocols—the pheromonal scents, swollen genitalia, colouration, vaginal sniffing and violent status contests—the new human mating system became 'Neanderthal proof'.

To be adaptive and effective, the new sexual protocols had to achieve fixation (or close to it) in the Skhul-Qafzeh population. Normally, this would take thousands of generations. But, because the Levantine human population was so small (ironically due to the Neanderthals themselves), the new system spread rapidly to fixation via genetic drift.

The break from sexual tradition and the emergence of a new human mating system did something else equally important. It indelibly stamped the Skhul-Qafzeh humans as a sexually isolated new breeding population. As human sexuality developed along new isolationist lines, the demarcation between the species increased.

From then on, there would be no more sexual compatibility, no more interspecies sex, and no more hybrids.

In this radical new theory of human sexuality, the devil is in the detail. Analysis of the new mating system reveals how each of its constituent components served an adaptive function *vis-à-vis* reducing Neanderthal sexual predation. Let's begin with *patriarchy*.

the battle of the sexes

Winning, and then defending fertile females from other males is a core element of primate reproductive strategy. So keeping human females from falling into the arms of Neanderthal males would become the responsibility of every male Levantine adolescent and adult. Any systemic failure of this imperative could contribute to the extinction of the Levantine population. It is to be expected then that, during the attenuated 50,000-year period of Neanderthal predation, the Levantine males' fear of losing their mates to Neanderthals became innately associated with hyper-vigilance, anxiety, suspicion, guilt, control, resentment, depression, paranoia, grief and loss of self-esteem.

Levantine males would have been terrified of Neanderthals, and this would have discouraged direct retributive aggression against them. It would have been far easier (and safer) to sublimate those hostile feelings and redirect them towards their females. By virtue of their greater strength and aggression, men would unilaterally have asserted physical control over their females and their sexuality.

While primate males regularly use dominance to control access to fertile females, the Levantine humans took this to a whole new level. For the first time in human evolutionary history, males imposed mandatory (sexist) restrictions on female behaviour that included an insistence on monogamy, obedience, fidelity and sexual modesty, plus a ban on public flirtation and copulation, overt sexual displays and especially any form of fraternisation with Neanderthals—or any strangers.

The hypothesis also asserts that groups of dominant young males would have enforced these draconian protocols with threats, banishment, physical coercion and lethal violence. In this way, early human Levantine society was abruptly reconfigured from a promiscuous sexual society to a male-dominated, sexually restricted hierarchical society.

Is this when a proprietary sense of 'ownership' was first insinuated in gender relations? I believe so. After millions of years of casual female promiscuity, men began to claim females they had sex with as their own. Females were no longer free to copulate with multiple partners or to migrate to outside groups. Promiscuity was out. Women lost control of their bodies and their sexuality. The sexes were no longer equal. Sexism had arrived.

Another name for the control of females and their sexuality by males is patriarchy. Although many primate species (including chimps) display some patriarchal elements, others (like bonobos) display very few. But no other primate species imposes such draconian restrictions on its females as humans. And in no other primate species do males kill females to maintain sexual control, although male primates have been known to kill their infants if they have been sired by another male.

Because patriarchy is such a ubiquitous feature of human society (no genuine matriarchic society has ever been documented),[447] we tend to take it for granted and assume it is simply another facet of human nature. Or assume, as some do, that it is a cultural artefact that sprang from preclassical western civilisations. But NP theory makes the case that patriarchy emerged in its present form and became entrenched in the male psyche only because Neanderthals drove a wedge into human sexual relations. Patriarchy makes sense in evolutionary terms only as part of a

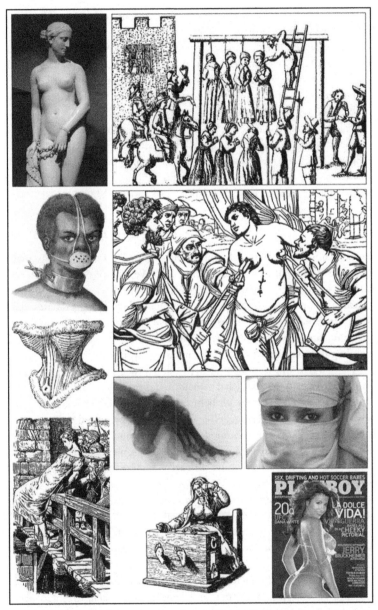

Men's fear of, and their need to control, women's sexuality has found expression in myriad ways, from sexual torture and acid attacks to objectification and the dictates of fashions such as waist deformation and foot binding.

suite of male mate-guarding adaptations that emerged to provide some relief against Neanderthal sexual predation.

One indication of the important adaptive function patriarchy provided during the Late Pleistocene is that today it remains the prevailing social structure of virtually every human society. Modern women are still subject to far greater sexual control than men.[448] Social anthropologists say this mechanism of control is expressed through marital customs, rape laws, sexual harassment, wife beating, abortion laws, femicide, birth control restrictions, eating disorders, sexual jealousy, and cosmetic surgery.[449] Enforced monogamy is as ubiquitous as female modesty. Adultery by women in many human societies is still punished by severe penalties, while adultery by men is often condoned or ignored.[450]

the green-eyed monster

Perhaps nowhere is patriarchy more keenly expressed than through male sexual jealousy. But let's make a distinction. We are not talking about the kind of jealousy a young male chimp displays when his amorous advances towards a female are gazumped by an alpha male. Among primates, that kind of sexual jealousy serves an adaptive function. It's part of mate-guarding protocols that ensure certainty in paternity and prevents expending time and effort on another male's offspring.[451]

By comparison, if human sexual jealousy was forged, as I contend, in the furnace of Neanderthal sexual predation this would explain why humans acquired a far more virulent and potentially lethal variant. Human sexual jealousy has been fuelled and maintained by hatred built up over thousands of years and encompasses, not just anger and frustration, but murderous rage, hyper-vigilance, severe beatings, mental cruelty, femicide and even suicide—behaviours virtually unknown in other primate species.

For example, no other primate demonstrates morbid jealousy, psychotic jealousy, conjugal paranoia or the so-called *Othello Syndrome*[452]—a lethal form of sexual jealousy, characterised by irrational thoughts and emotions, violence and an unfounded belief in a partner's sexual infidelity.[453]

Morbidly jealous individuals are much more prone to domestic violence, including homicide and suicide.[454] Because lethal jealousy is unknown in the primate order, and appears so maladaptive, it is likely that the Othello Syndrome evolved in humans as an adaptation against Neanderthal sexual predation.

honey, I killed the kids

Despite the Levantine males' best efforts to protect their females from Neanderthals, some women inevitably fell pregnant to Eurasian Neanderthals and, because they were sister species,[455,456] these conceptions occasionally produced fertile offspring. What happened to those hybrid offspring is one of the most important aspects of the Neanderthal predation paradigm.

If Levantine males saw these children as mutants—abominations—then it's likely that they were summarily killed. A similar fate may also have been dealt out to the mothers, notwithstanding that they had little choice in getting pregnant. In other words, throughout the Late Pleistocene, infanticide and femicide may have been widely implemented as crude adaptive strategies to thwart the Neanderthalisation of the Levantine population.

This explains why today's humans do not reveal residual evidence of interbreeding with Neanderthals when the Levantine fossil record indicates interbreeding occurred there.

It suggests too that infanticide and femicide were specific agents of artificial selection—in that they impacted on the evolution of the Levantine human population by selecting against women who were victims of rape, promiscuous women and hybridised babies. It was cruel and murderous—but it was effective. Infanticide is relatively common among animals, and particularly among social predators like lions.[457] It is an effective way of ensuring that the genes of dominant males are passed on. Among the Visoke mountain gorillas that Dian Fossey studied, for example, it emerged that at least 37 percent of the infants who did not live beyond three years, died as a result of infanticide.[458]

Sadly today, the violent innate proclivities that men inherited from their Levantine forbears still skew the statistics on spousal homicide and infanticide. Sociological research reveals that many more husbands murder their wives than the reverse.[459,460] Similarly, the deeply subsumed attitude of men towards offspring sired by someone else (a Neanderthal) is reflected in the so-called *Cinderella Effect*. Researchers have found that a child under three years of age is up to one hundred times more likely to be abused or killed by a step-parent than by a genetic parent.[461]

throwing them off our scent

If Neanderthals had an exceptionally acute sense of smell and pheromonal detection that allowed them to sniff out prey from miles away, what effect would this have had on the Skhul-Qafzeh people? Neanderthals were not only using their acute sense of smell to hunt humans as cannibalistic prey, but also as sexual prey, which placed females at an even greater risk. Not unreasonably, we may expect the Skhul-Qafzeh people became hyper-aware of their body odour. This, I believe, manifested as a preoccupation with personal hygiene and scent concealment. What's more, scent concealment was an even greater issue for ovulating females because sexual pheromones could be detected over great distances.

According to NP theory, throughout the Late Pleistocene, both men and women (but particularly ovulating females) began regularly bathing and washing, concentrating on the genitalia and underarms. Females very likely used flowers, aromatic herbs, oils and plant extracts to conceal their natural body odours before setting off on foraging expeditions.

Because the aim of this new focus on personal hygiene was not health or beauty or elimination of germs but to minimise and mask telltale body odours and pheromonal secretions that attracted predacious Neanderthals, having BO wasn't just a social faux pas. It could get you killed.

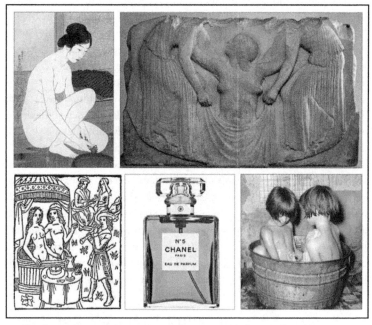

Regular washing and the use of perfumes to conceal body scents have been so widespread throughout history as to qualify as universal human proclivities. Now NP offers an explanation.

NP theory also proposes that, although the human preoccupation with washing and scent reduction (concentrating on the genitals) is expressed in culturally diverse ways, they are in fact innate (or instinctive) behavioural proclivities and therefore universal. Regular bathing is a universal feature of human society, and many religions prescribe it as a duty.

Unfortunately, the fossil record is of no use when it comes to testing these hypotheses—it can't reveal when humans first developed their preoccupation with personal hygiene and regular washing. All we know is that our closest primate relatives do not share this enthusiasm, so *sapiens* must have acquired this behaviour after the split as a result of adaptive necessity.

my cave or yours

No modern primate species demonstrates humanity's preoccupation with private sex. Nor have evolutionary biologists or cultural anthropologists been able to explain it. Here though, I argue, it makes perfect sense as an adaptive response to Neanderthal sexual predation.

Field studies of primates show that their mating behaviour is public, noisy and conspicuous, with lots of sexual scents and distinctive vocalisations. Another distinguishing feature of primate sex is that the participants are generally indifferent to the presence of other members of the group. We may infer from this that archaic human males, competing for sexually receptive females, would have been no different.

Under normal circumstances, this kind of loud, boisterous behaviour would not be maladaptive. But in the Levant, the distinctive visual, auditory, scent and pheromonal cues that normally accompanied mating risked attracting Neanderthals from near and far. As public human copulation became associated with increased risk and anxiety, Levantine humans gradually opted for more clandestine, 'low key' sex.

To understand how this impacted on the timid Skhul-Qafzeh folk, it's necessary to consider how they would have felt when sexually-charged Neanderthals descended on their camp. In many cases, the Neanderthals would have copulated with the females then and there, in full view of the cowering human males. It was not just the aggressive perfunctory execution of the sex act itself that would be so disturbing. Or even their disdain for the hapless humans. For Skhul-Qafzeh males in particular, Neanderthals' belligerent sexual displays, threatening behaviour and physical violence (aimed at cowering rivals and establishing their dominance) would be distressing and intimidating. It would also politicise sex in the minds of

Skhul-Qafzeh males by associating it with anguish, guilt and humiliation. Thus, public displays of crude, lustful sexuality became negatively associated with a most dreaded and feared natural enemy, soliciting feelings of disgust, anxiety and anger. Over time, any Skhul-Qafzeh couple practising public sex, or even displaying sexually in public, risked being identified with the enemy—not something that would be conducive to a long and healthy life. Sexual repression became the order of the day.

When the Skhul-Qafzeh humans did manage to find somewhere private to have sex, instead of the traditional retrocopulation (dog-style) position favoured by modern primates (and, presumably, Neanderthals too) they opted for frontal sex (the missionary position) to distinguish themselves from their natural enemy and avoid the negative connotations.

Today, this position remains the default sexual position, ostensibly assisted by medieval theologians who proselytised in favour of the 'male superior' position because it demonstrated the natural hierarchical supremacy of men over women. In the United States, as late as 1969, at least six states proscribed having sex in any position other than the missionary position as legal grounds for divorce.[462] Meanwhile, the vestigial 'bestial' associations of retrocopulation are evident in the scientific term for retrocopulation—*coitus more ferarum*—'sex after the custom of beasts'.

The scientific literature on the evolution of private sex in humans (and in no other primate) is scant and unable to offer a simple explanation for what is undoubtedly a very unusual behaviour. Only NP theory appears to provide a plausible explanation for the adaptive nature of private sex and the selective forces that drove it to fixation.

how modesty could save your life

Earlier, I suggested that when humans divested themselves of their thick body hair because it looked too Neanderthaloid, they began making and wearing clothes to protect themselves from heat, cold, rain and sunburn. Yet clothing serves a secondary purpose—modesty. As well as combating the elements, clothes conceal genitalia, which justifies reviewing a question that has long intrigued cultural anthropologists—what is behind humanity's universal preoccupation with using clothes to conceal genitalia?

NP theory proposes that clothes were vital for concealing the anatomical features that attracted Neanderthals. By covering the genitalia (particularly those of females in oestrus) clothes provided an adaptive functionality (they saved lives) and so attitudes towards them became an innate proclivity. This predicts clothes would be worn irrespective of thermoregulation issues, even in summer when they weren't needed for warmth, and even when swimming.

In any case, where a human behaviour is universal it indicates the behaviour was subject to strong selection pressure from multiple sources. As well as hiding the visual sexual cues that may have attracted Neanderthals, garments would also have helped distinguish humans from Neanderthals. Humans wore clothes, Neanderthals did not.

Here NP theory once again proposes a simple explanation for a thorny evolutionary problem and, again, that solution fits effortlessly into a broader holistic theory of human sexual evolution.

to wax or not to wax

I have proposed that the loss of body hair in humans, the preference for less hairy partners, and killing anyone considered too hairy were all driven by the same imperative—to distinguish humans from Neanderthals. But there are three notable exceptions to hair loss in humans—three areas that retained at least some hair—the head, the pubic area, and the armpits. Any theory that purports to explain denudation in humans must also accommodate these exceptions.

Explaining why we've kept the hair on our heads is not difficult. It is widely held that head hair was adaptive in upright bipedal species because it insulated the brain against hypothermia and hyperthermia.

But what about pubic hair? The NP model of Skhul-Qafzeh sexuality proposes that genital tumescence at oestrus was a principal indicator that a female was sexually receptive. It points to pubic hair being selected in Levantine human females because it concealed the protruding tumescent labial tissue that signified oestrus. By hiding oestrus advertisement—one of the most visually prominent triggers of Neanderthal sexual attraction— pubic hair would reduce the frequency of Neanderthal sexual predation.

There may be another reason why pubic hair was adaptive, in both sexes, which at the same time could resolve another long standing evolutionary puzzle—why humans of both sexes also have underarm hair. Pubic and underarm hair would serve an adaptive function by trapping and minimising the florescence of airborne scent molecules and tiny pheromonal particles, reducing the chances of them becoming airborne and therefore detectable by Neanderthals. This increased body odour close up, but minimised it over long distances.

that time of the month

Once a prey has been wounded and is bleeding, it leaves a scent trail that predators can track. Neanderthals would be no exception. They would be able to detect the pheromones in blood from miles away. But it is not just wounded animals that bleed. Bleeding occurs during the normal monthly menstrual cycle that is part of every woman's life. For modern women, having periods may be an inconvenience, associated with mood swings and painful cramps. But it is not normally life-threatening. In the Levant however, menstruation provided a strong scent cue that Neanderthals could track, making that 'time of the month' particularly scary for the Skhul-Qafzeh people.

It would follow that menstruation in a young Skhul-Qafzeh female was associated with increased personal stress, anxiety and depression. In the context of Neanderthal predation, these responses were adaptive because they gave rise to greater vigilance and caution, which eventually became genetically embedded in female developmental biology.

Because menstruation is an integral part of the human reproductive cycle, natural selection couldn't simply do away with it. But as Neanderthal success in tracking nomadic groups took its toll on the human population, natural selection finally came up with a unique left-field biological solution. Women in a group acquired the ability to pheromonally synchronise their menstrual cycles, so they all menstruated at approximately the same time. Synchronised menstruation reduced the group's scent profile—and the risk of attack—to a few days per month. Significantly, synchronised menstrual cycles (*oestrus synchrony*) does not occur in populations of wild African chimpanzees.[464] It is a uniquely human adaptation and, until now, no evolutionary explanation of this phenomenon has been offered.

Even today, menstruation huts are common in many cultures.

The menstrual scent did not just affect females. Because menstruating women exposed the whole tribe to increased risk of Neanderthal raiding, it seems reasonable that tribal males also implemented crude cultural protocols to reduce the menstrual target. One outcome would be to stigmatise and segregate menstruating women from the group until menstruation was over. Vestiges of Levantine male attitudes to menstruating women are evident throughout history and are still common in many parts of the world today, where women are isolated in special 'menstruation huts'.

keeping abreast

As we know, the tumescent breasts that girls develop at puberty are unique in the animal kingdom. Countless theories have been offered to explain this, but none of them have gained wide acceptance. NP theory adds another, based on the observation that the only time the breasts of nonhuman primates swell slightly is when they're breastfeeding—and infertile. Once they stop lactating, the breasts virtually disappear. Female primates do not mate while they're nursing an infant, so protuberant breasts are a visible sign that a female is not sexually receptive or fertile.

As Harvard researcher Nancy Etcoff explains, "Breasts are not sex symbols to other mammals, anything but, since they indicate a pregnant or lactating and infertile female. To chimps, gorillas and orang-utans, breasts are sexual turnoffs."[463]

This means that permanently enlarged breasts would have acted as a 'false advertisement' that convinced predatory Neanderthals that females were not on heat, not receptive to their displays and not fertile. It is not difficult to see that, by offering a degree of protection against sexual assault, protuberant breasts became popular with human males. If they thought females with breasts were less likely to attract Neanderthals, men would gradually come to prefer women with breasts. This would explain the historical pre-occupation with breasts that has been evident in art (*see overleaf*) since the Stone Age.

hiding the sexy bits

Apart from humans, it is easy to tell when a female primate is ovulating. Males are well aware of the tell-tale signs (swollen, pink rumps etc.) so concentrate their mating efforts during these periods. Simple and effective. So why, in humans, did the conspicuous signs of ovulation become hidden? This question has fuelled enormous scientific interest and

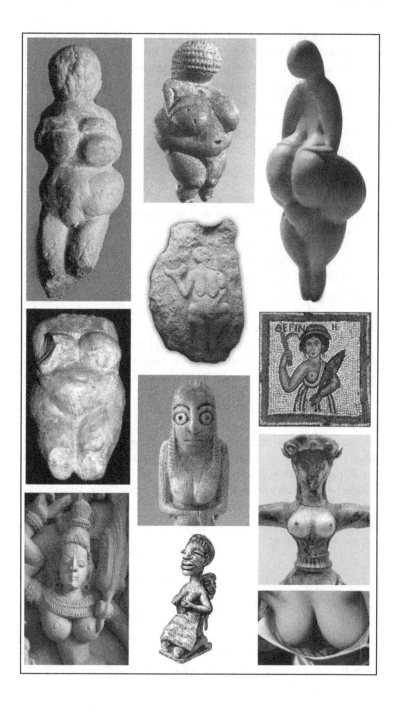

literally dozens of attempts to explain it, but so far there is no consensus. It is generally agreed that concealed ovulation in humans must represent a major adaptation, but what function it serves remains a mystery.

This justifies taking a fresh look at concealed ovulation in humans to see if it may be yet another adaptation aimed at reducing Neanderthal sexual predation.

The primate mating system that regulated hominid sexuality before the Neanderthals entered the Levant was centred around a male's ability to detect when females were ovulating. This ensured that his attentiveness, his macho chest beating, his participation in dangerous status contests and his energy expenditure were timed to give him the best chance of siring offspring. Natural selection helped by providing females with conspicuous signs that they were ovulating. It was these conspicuous signs that triggered the whole range of deleterious Neanderthal sexual responses. So, it follows that concealing the visible signs of human ovulation became a kind of holy grail of the new human mating system.

Theoretically, concealing ovulation inside the woman's body would have been enormously adaptive against Neanderthal sexual predation because it removed the conspicuous visual and scent cues that attracted their attention. Without the visual cues to trigger the hormones that stimulate sexual arousal, Neanderthal males would probably show no sexual interest.

But there was another important advantage that hidden ovulation conferred. Even if male Neanderthals abducted and raped a Skhul-Qafzeh female when there were no visible indications of ovulation, because she was only fertile for five or six days a month, it would be statistically unlikely to result in conception.

You get a sense of the biological complexity of hidden ovulation and this sexual make-over when you list the separate adaptations that contributed to it. They include hormonal reduction of vaginal scent production, control of the paraurethral glands to reduce female ejaculate, a decrease in genital secretions, reduction in clitoral tumescence, smaller labia minora to diminish protrusion beyond the vulva, reduced tumescence of the labia majora, lessening in the colouration of the labia, and the evolution of pubic hair to conceal tumescent labial tissue and minimise dispersal of airborne pheromones. In effect, all the old primate sexual traits that attracted Neanderthals had to be reconfigured to make them 'Neanderthal proof'.

These sexual changes represent the most dramatic modification of a mammalian species' mating system ever: a last ditch evolutionary experiment that pushed the limits of natural selection and—by tampering with sexual reproduction—risked the extinction of the entire Skhul-Qafzeh population. This is because, while concealed ovulation successfully reduced Neanderthal sexual arousal, it had the potential to reduce human male sexual arousal as well. Without the usual visual and pheromonal cues to arouse them, Levantine males would show the same indifference as Neanderthal males. And even if they practised occasional recreational sex, females are only fertile for five to seven days a month so this was unlikely to result in enough conceptions to maintain their population.

In summary, if the overt signs of ovulation were lost, then whatever replaced them had to maintain procreation rates. With no visible signals to tell males when the female was fertile, frequent regular sex was the only solution. But how was this achieved? Clearly it required an additional *patch* adaptation to maintain copulation rates throughout the monthly cycle. NP theory proposes that the patch that was selected was a radically new adjunct to human reproductive behaviour: something that separates us from all the other primates. It's called *romantic love*.

romantic love

There has been little effort on the part of evolutionary biologists to explain romantic love as a uniquely human phenomenon. This is partly because love has not been considered serious enough for scientific study.[465] Even though it is central to human existence, no one has yet answered psychologist Robin Allott's seminal question: "How was the capacity for love built into the human genome by the processes of selection?"[466]

Allott notes that although precursors of romantic love—empathy, friendship and sexuality—are demonstrable in many mammals, love itself, "appears to be an eminently human phenomenon".[467] Even though they are our closest relatives and display similar emotions, including courtship attraction, maternal love, empathy, group bonding, admiration, friendship and, in some cases, a preference for a particular female,[468] unrelated sexually mature chimps do not form lasting pair bonds.[469] Nor do they appear to fall in love—at least not like humans. Instead, mating behaviour in nonhuman primates is mostly about females responding to male dominance displays and hormonally activated sexual arousal. Sex itself is quick and perfunctory.

But it also raises a question that rarely gets asked—much less answered: when did human romantic love, recreational copulation and long-term pair bonding first emerge as part of our biology? They had to start somewhere. When did the transition begin and what caused it?

NP theory holds that love first emerged in the Levant during the Late Pleistocene as an alternative to the primate-Neanderthal mating system. It was the most important element of humans' new Neanderthal-proof sexuality.

Why was love so attractive? Why did it become the cornerstone of the new sexuality? Because romantic attraction ensures that when a sexually mature human couple fall in love, the associated sexual desire that accompanies the acute stage of romantic love (which typically lasts between 12–24 months)[470] predisposes them to engage in frequent recreational sex irrespective of whether the female is ovulating or not.

Like the best of Mother Nature's inventions, it was a simple, elegant and ingenious solution to an intractable problem.

What's more, as romantic sexual attraction replaced the hormonally-induced sexual drive, it ensured that Skhul-Qafzeh females only copulated with Skhul-Qafzeh males for whom they felt positive personal feelings—whom they 'loved'. This was obviously adaptive so the genes predisposing romantic love spread quickly among the human population.

daddy's home

Romantic love and long-term pair bonding also conferred another important adaptive advantage—improved child rearing. When a woman had a child as a result of her romantic attachment with a man, he inevitably took on the role of a father—for the first time. We are so accustomed to fatherhood today that it is easy to forget we are still the only species of great apes where males provide significant paternal care.[471]

In the Levantine context, fatherhood was both revolutionary and highly adaptive. It added a second devoted parent, a powerful new protector, a provisioner and a teacher of life skills—something the Neanderthals never had.

Love not only motivated men to selflessly provision their families with food and shelter, as well as generalised familial support, it also drove them to courageously defend their women and children against Neanderthal predators, often at the risk of their own lives. No other male primate does this. So, as well as being our most cherished emotion, romantic love is also among our most adaptive emotions.

mine's bigger than theirs

The new human sexuality was all about facilitating exclusivity. The pattern of evolutionary change was to create as much sexual distance as possible between Neanderthals and Skhul-Qafzehs. Natural selection blindly selected for alternatives that were as dissimilar as possible but that still maintained fertility rates. If Neanderthal sex was loveless and mechanistic—then humans opted for sex imbued with tender emotions. If Neanderthals didn't bother with foreplay, then human men paid attention to ensuring their partners were sexually receptive. And if Neanderthals had small, primate-sized penises, this would lead to selection for larger human appendages—which provides a simple explanation for why modern men have the largest penis of any primate.

Although today we joke about men's preoccupation with penis size (and scratch our heads at the multi-billion dollar industry it fuels) this

The preoccupation with the size of the male phallus, which transcends both culture and history, may have its origins in Neanderthal predation.

relates to the serious and subliminal male concern that penis size is a primary divide between *them and us*.

Any cursory study of human sexuality will confirm what we all intuitively know. Sexually, humans are unique in the primate order. I have attempted to explain how, why and when this happened. It is no coincidence, though, that if Neanderthals caused the sexual revolution that now separates us from every other primate species, they were also behind our deeply entrenched attitudes to the dark.

15 DON'T GO OUT IN THE WOODS TONIGHT

night terrors

Imagine for a moment you are one of the Skhul-Qafzeh people living in a cave on the slopes of Mt Carmel within sight of the Mediterranean Sea. Each day as you go out to hunt or gather food, at the back of your mind you're always aware of the hairy beasts that could attack at any moment. But it is when the sun goes down that you really know you're prey, because that's when they are most likely to be out and about.

Darkness is a time to gather the children, huddle together around the fire, listen for the slightest sound, and never—under any circumstances—venture out at night. And this quiet dread is not just for a week or two. It has been going on for as long as anyone can remember. It will be with you until the day you die, as it was with your parents, and theirs—going back to a time before memory. You are prey—food for another species—and these night terrors have become part of your very existence.

fear of the dark

If Neanderthal raiding occurred mostly at night, what would be the long-term impact of this on our ancestors? And on us? To answer these questions, fast forward 100,000 years and watch today's mother put her five-year-old child to bed. Yes, she'll leave the light on. No, the bogeyman isn't real. Yes, you're safe. Now go to sleep.

The contention that modern children have inherited fears from Neanderthal nocturnal predation and that these fears are triggered by darkness is corroborated by a wealth of research on night-time fears in children and adolescents.[472] Typically, studies of American children found the fear of monsters and ghosts was reported by 74 percent of children aged 4–6 years, 53 percent of 6–8 year olds, and 55 percent of 10–12 year olds.[473] And in a Dutch study of 176 children aged 4–12 years, 73.3 percent of them reported night-time fears.[474]

The specific nature of these fears appears consistent with the Neanderthal predation hypothesis. A recent Australian study involving 511 children and adolescents aged 8–16 years reports the ten most common night-time fears were:

> ...fears of intruders/home invasion, noises outside the house, bad dreams, noises inside the house, ghosts, skeletons, witches or spooks, weather noises, worry about daily events, darkness, being alone in the dark, spiders or insects, shadows in the room, and worry about the family's safety at night.[475]

This is consistent with several studies that found the most prevalent night-time fears were "bad dreams, nightmares, noises, shadows, monsters, intruders, burglars, kidnappers, and of being left alone at night".[476] Among older children (7 to 13-year-olds) fear of the dark and fear of a burglar breaking into the house were among the most cited fears.[477]

My modelling based on NP theory predicts that young Levantine pubertal females were the major focus of Neanderthal sexual raiding. This predicts that night-time fears among modern children will be more pronounced in girls than boys. This prediction is corroborated by research data. All the studies report that girls have more night-time fears and frightening dreams than boys (72.9 percent compared to 54.6 percent males).[478,479]

Obviously, it's impossible to say for certain that a child's night-time fears originate from traumatic events that occurred up to 100,000 years ago. But the association of night-time, imaginary creatures, invasions and abductions reported by children is consistent with an innate adaptive response to nocturnal predation in our evolutionary past.

Unfortunately, while there is copious literature on childhood fears, very little research has been conducted on nyctophobia (fear of the

Films like The Blair Witch Project *(left) and* I Am Legend *(right) in which vampire-like mutants swarm out under cover of darkness to hunt humans, tap into our innate fear of scary creatures lurking in the dark. But rarely do we stop to ask—what are the evolutionary origins of these fears?*

dark) in adults—and almost no cross-cultural data is available on this subject. Anecdotal first-contact reports claim Indigenous Australians never ventured from their camps after dark for fear of encountering evil spirits, and many hunter-gatherer societies report a fear of the dark, but apart from that there is almost nothing—certainly not enough to test the theory that modern humans are innately apprehensive of the dark and that low-level predation anxiety remains the primary cause of human insomnia. Clearly more cross-cultural research is needed.

getting a good night's sleep

For all prey species subject to nocturnal predation, getting enough sleep is a major issue that directly affects survival.

Each species acquires its own specific adaptations unique to its predators, habitat and sleep requirements. One solution is to limit the time spent asleep. While predators like lions sleep up to 17 hours a day, the hoofed animals they hunt have adapted to only a few hours sleep, and mostly on their feet. Giraffes for example, sleep less than two hours a day.

Another common solution is to find a safe place to sleep away from predators. Rabbits, moles, snakes and wombats retreat to deep burrows where they're usually safe, while bats that live in caves can sleep up to 19 hours a day.

Some species of birds, seals, manatees, whales and dolphins have acquired the ability to literally sleep with one eye open, (*unihemispheric slow-wave-sleep*) allowing them to be constantly alert for predators.[480]

This adaptation required the rewiring of their brains into two separate hemispheres, each able to operate while the other is offline. EEG readings from the brains of ducks show that half their brain sleeps while the other half remains in a mid state between alertness and light sleep. And when they sleep in a group, those on the outside, (where the risk of predation is higher) sleep with one eye open nearly 32 percent of the time, compared with only about 12 percent of the time for those on the inside.[481]

Chimps climb trees each night and build sleeping nests out of leaves—which is probably what African hominids did too. That is, until they discovered the art of fire-making about 750,000 years ago. Fire provided a new level of protection against nocturnal predators, its light keeping leopards, wolves and other nocturnal carnivores at bay and allowing our ancestors to sleep in relative peace for the first time.

During the Neanderthal predation, however, fire lost is protectiveness. The ingenious invention that protected hominids from the most savage carnivores would be useless against Neanderthals because they used fire themselves.

So how did our Levantine ancestors cope? I suggest that, as well as learning to fear the dark and not venturing out at night, our ancestors evolved at least two species-specific adaptations to the problem of sleep and security. The first required inventing a new kind of sleep.

Given that the brains of some prey species have evolved specialist neuronal networks to maintain vigilance for nocturnal predators while they sleep, it is interesting to find that human sleep is not constant throughout the night. It varies between periods of light and deep sleep. These variations are called sleep cycles, and they occur about every 90 minutes. Normally, we each experience between three to six cycles every night.

Each individual cycle is broken up into four stages. Stages one and two are considered light sleep and stages three and four signify deep sleep. During light sleep, a person is still responsive to sounds and movements and can be easily woken. This is because during light sleep, the sensory organs maintain communications with the amygdala—the part of the brain that monitors for threats, including Neanderthals. What's more, in the light stages of sleep, your muscles are not immobilised so if you have to move suddenly, you can. Light sleep is really a half-awake state.

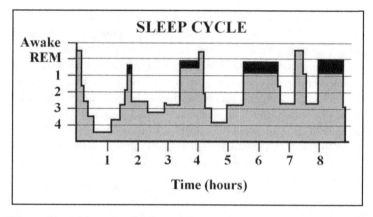

Why we have this cycle of light and deep sleep has never been explained. Despite mountains of research into sleep, researchers still have no idea why the cycle evolved or what function it serves. However, the unique oscillating sleep cycle, with its characteristic period of light sleep may be the human equivalent of a bird's hemispherical sleep.

At first, the light-deep sleep cycle may not seem like an adaptive solution to the problem of getting a good night's rest during the Late Pleistocene. But the ingenious simplicity of this solution becomes clear when you realise that the Skhul-Qafzeh humans were part of a primate lineage that traditionally lived and slept in groups, or troops.

Although Westerners abandoned communal sleep around the time of the Industrial Revolution, communal sleeping had been the norm for literally millions of years. So, with ten or more people sleeping together in the same cave, or around the same campfire, there would always be at least one person in a light stage of sleep. Someone in the group would always be half awake and able to respond to strange sounds or movements, and could quickly rouse the others if they sensed Neanderthals were sneaking up on them.

dogs really are man's best friend

As a nocturnal sentinel system, a 90-minute sleep cycle would be most effective on quiet, windless nights when the sound of approaching Neanderthals could easily be heard. But, unlike other animal predators, Neanderthals had roughly the same level of intelligence as humans and were probably cunning enough to counter this. Approaching on a windy night, or during a storm, when their sound and scent were diffused by the environment, they could possibly have got close enough before the alarm was sounded. Despite unique sleep cycles providing a degree of protection against nocturnal attacks, the hours between dusk and dawn almost certainly remained the most dangerous period in our ancestors' lives.

In the absence of burglar alarms, police, armies or sentries, what other remedies against nocturnal predation would have been available to our ancestors? I suggest the only thing that was within the realm of possibility in the Late Pleistocene, was a canine sentry. Our ancestors needed a guard dog.

With exceptional night vision and a nose that can detect scents one hundred times fainter than those humans can, dogs can detect intruders long before any human, making them ideal nocturnal camp guards. Even today, the sound of a dog barking in the dark can cause a primal frisson and alert you to a potential threat. The use of dogs as nocturnal guards throughout history, their universal appearance in world myths as guardians and gatekeepers, our instinctive affection for them, and the way they segue perfectly into a theoretical survival strategy suggests strongly that they played an important role in human evolution.

It's easy to see how this relationship started. Wolves would have been attracted to human camps to scavenge food. This probably suited the humans because it got rid of rotting meat and carcasses. Early human children may have taken in wolf cubs simply because they were cuddly and cute. The tamest of these would be kept as pets and bred. Once humans realised the tame wolves could smell Neanderthals and raise the alarm, the bond was formed.

To test this hypothesis, we need to remember that Neanderthal predation began between 100,000 and 110,000 years ago, which means that humans established canids as guard dogs roughly around this time. Is there any proof of this?

Egyptians hieroglyphics portrayed dogs, including different breeds that appear similar to today's greyhounds and mastiffs, but these hieroglyphics date only to about 6000 years ago. The earliest pictorial representation of dogs found anywhere come from a Spanish cave and is about 12,000 years old, which is also the date of the earliest human-dog burial in Israel.[482]

Until very recently, the fossil record shows that humans started to domesticate and interbreed dogs only about 15,000 years ago. Although these animals looked like wolves, they show slight physical differences.

The remains of one of these proto-dogs (dated at 14,000 years ago)[483] was found at Oberkassel in Germany, while another has been dated to between 10,000 to 15,000 years ago.[484]

Half the lower jawbone of a dog was also discovered in the Palgawra cave in north-eastern Iraq (part of the Levant) and radiocarbon dated at a minimum of 12,000 years old.[485] Although this fragment has often been held up as the first real proof of a domesticated dog, it's a bit risky making these kinds of assumptions on the basis of a three inch piece of bone and a few molars. Nevertheless, slight changes in the teeth and facial structures of wolf remains have been interpreted as evidence of a relationship between humans and canids, which in turn indicates domestication.[486]

This would indicate the wolves whose skulls were found in a 24,000 year old mammoth hunting camp in the Ukraine, with foreshortened muzzles, smaller teeth and dental crowding, had been domesticated. But that is considerably short of our 100,000–110,000 year target.

As recently as October 2008, a team of European archaeologists announced they had unearthed over a hundred fragments of ancient dog remains from sites in Russia, Belgium and the Ukraine. The researchers, led by palaeontologist Mietje Germonpré from the Royal Belgian Institute of Natural Sciences reported that one Belgian skull was 31,700 years old, and was "clearly different from the recent wolves, resembling most closely the prehistoric dogs".[487] Their analysis of the material led them to conclude these were the skulls of domesticated dogs.

While this latest finding pushes back the date of domestication to almost 32,000 years ago (when Neanderthals still lived in Europe) the dates nevertheless appear to challenge the proposition that dogs were used during the period of Neanderthal predation in the Levant . However, the proposal is not that Skhul-Qafzeh humans used modern dogs to guard their camps. It is that they used domesticated wolves as guard dogs.

A number of studies from different disciplines; (behaviour, morphology, vocalisations and genetics) all show that modern dogs are descended from the wolf, *canis lupus*. The 400 odd breeds of modern dogs are so

The 31,700 year old skull from Goyet Cave in Belgium, which researchers believe may be the earliest known dog.

closely related to their single common ancestor that, from the massive Saint Bernard and Irish wolf hounds to the diminutive Chihuahua, their mitochondrial DNA varies at most by 0.2 percent from the wolf.[488]

Unlike the dog, grey wolves have been around for at least 300,000 years[489]. They have exceptional hearing and sense of smell—and wolf fossils are found in ancient human sites.

The burgeoning science of molecular genetics, which allows species to be traced via their DNA has provided some startling new dates that have a bearing on this issue. In June 1997, a seminal paper 'Multiple and Ancient Origins of the Domestic Dog', by a leading expert on the origins of dogs Robert Wayne and others, was published in *Science*.[490] The geneticists analysed *mitochondrial DNA* taken from 162 wolves at 27 locations around the world.

MITOCHONDRIAL DNA

Mitochondrial DNA (mtDNA) are molecules that act as a kind of fuel cell for the main DNA by converting nutrients into energy that cells can use. In humans, mtDNA is inherited from the mother's side. Over the last decade or so, geneticists have been able to extract mtDNA from ancient fossils, including human bones.

Because wild dogs can interbreed, the geneticists also included DNA samples from coyotes and jackals. They then compared these sequences with mtDNA from 140 domestic dogs (representing 67 breeds and 5 cross-breeds from Europe, Asia and North America) to determine the degree of genetic variation. The idea was to calculate precisely when dogs first departed from their wolf ancestors. The findings confirmed an earlier hypothesis by the authors, that dogs were descended from wolves.

But the most startling find was yet to come. The DNA analysis traced various dog breeds into several 'clades'—segments that evolved from common ancestors. Clade 1, for example, "contained representatives of many common breeds as well as ancient breeds such as the dingo, New Guinea singing dog, African basenji, and greyhound". The scientists then analysed the divergence within each clade. The degree of divergence between wolves and coyotes reveal they separated about one million years ago. But most significantly, according to Wayne and his co-authors, the divergence between the dogs in clade 1 "implies that dogs could have originated as much as 135,000 years ago".

Humans and dogs undoubtedly have a special relationship, which NP theory argues was formed during the Neanderthal predation. Early humans domesticated wolves to provide a sentinel against raiding Neanderthals. Because all modern dogs are descended from these wolves, they have all inherited this guardian role.

Although the study warns that such estimates may be inflated slightly by the techniques used, Wayne notes, "the sequence divergence within clade 1 clearly implies an origin more ancient than the 14,000 years before the present suggested by the archaeological record". When all the factors were considered, Wayne concludes that the mtDNA evidence "suggested that dogs originated more than 100,000 years before the present".

In effect, the DNA evidence reveals that wolves were first 'modified' by contact with humans at least 100,000 years ago, which coincides with the hypothesis that Skhul-Qafzeh humans first raised wolf cubs 100,000–110,000 years ago and used them as guard dogs.

If domesticated wolves and proto-dogs provided humans with this vital protection during those fraught early years, then we probably partly owe our survival as a species to them. That may account for the special bond that exists between humans and dogs. And it would demand a new recognition of the extraordinary role they played in our survival. It explains why dogs really are man's best friend.

16

HOW NOT TO GET CAUGHT
BY A NEANDERTHAL

If you are a prey species your first goal is to not get caught. Your second goal is, if you do get caught, to escape with your life. These basic survival skills are accumulated over time by individuals that survive predation because they are born with a mutation for a trait allowing them to evade or escape a predator. These survivors then pass on the mutation to their offspring. Of course, predators are playing the same game, acquiring and passing on their own predatory mutations to maintain a competitive edge.

Applying this well-understood Darwinian dynamic to the Levant predicts that the Skhul-Qafzeh humans acquired their own suite of defensive adaptations which gradually became fixed in the dwindling population. To test this hypothesis, we must first identify these adaptations.

gaining the athletic edge

Despite being able to complete the 100 metre dash in under ten seconds, modern humans can't compete with four-legged animals when it comes to running speed and agility. When anthropologist Joseph Birdsell

compared the speed of humans to cheetahs, antelopes and various monkeys, he concluded that ancestral humans "could not escape from any
likely predator by running away".[491]

Similarly, based on his own study of human biomechanics, Owen
Lovejoy from Kent State University concluded that "bipedality is useless
for avoidance escape from predators".[492] In effect, the gap between archaic
humans and four-legged predators like lions and cheetahs was too great
for natural selection to overcome. However, if the predator is another
bipedal hominid, then the rules change. Then, even a slight increase in
sprint speed would be adaptive, and would bring natural selection into
the picture.

If humans were prey to Neanderthals, then the first kind of physical
adaptations you would expect to see are the same ones acquired by
herbivores to escape pursuit predators—qualities like sprint speed over
short distances, rapid reflex responses, agility, manoeuvrability, stamina
and general athleticism. If a human could duck, weave and run even a
little faster than a Neanderthal, these traits would be selected. Ecologically
speaking though, these athletic traits are expensive—they require a great
deal of energy expenditure and nutrient support, not to mention the
evolution of specialised physiological features like faster muscles, neural
networks, synapses and neurotransmitters. If humans had not been
subject to predation, these traits would not be cost effective to acquire
and we would look quite different.

NP theory not only argues that predation resulted in humans acquiring
the kind of exceptional athleticism seen at the Olympics, but it predicts
precisely when this prowess appeared—between 100,000 to 45,000 years
ago.

Fortunately, there is an easy way to test this hypothesis. Because the
theory predicts that these adaptations were acquired relatively late in human
history, the human genome might be expected to reveal evidence of these
recent adaptations in changes to the genes that regulate athleticism.

This appears to be the case. Recent genomic analysis of single-
nucleotide polymorphisms taken from African-American, European-
American, and Chinese samples in 2007 identified over 100 regions
of the human genome that had been subject to recent changes—what
geneticists call *recent selective sweeps*.[493] Among the genes that display the
strongest evidence of a recent selective sweep are those that encode
structural components of muscle tissue.[494]

If the Skhul-Qafzeh humans became quicker and more dexterous,
this must have occurred in conjunction with a reduction in skeletal

The brilliance that allowed Jamaica's Usain Bolt to run the 200 metres at the Beijing Olympics in 19.30 seconds is the result of continued selection pressure for increased athletic ability in the human lineage.

robusticity. Gazelle and rhino are both herbivores, but only the former needs to escape predators so it is the gazelle that is gracile, lean and light-boned, while the rhino is robust and stocky.

Accordingly, NP theory predicts a reduction in skeletal robusticity— from a big-boned, hefty early human skeleton to lighter, more gracile bones, indicating the emergence of a new smaller, more agile, faster human. Specifically, it predicts a shift towards gracilisation occurred in the Skhul-Qafzeh humans between 100,000 and 50,000 years ago. and this is convincingly corroborated by the archaeology. Skeletal analysis of the Qafzeh-Skhul fossils from the Levant by Erik Trinkaus and Steven Churchill demonstrate unmistakable evidence of a shift towards gracilisation.[495] The Levantine early humans were indeed significantly more gracile than other hominids of the period.[496,497]

xenophobia

If the need to distinguish *them* from *us* was a matter of life and death for our ancestors, then the earlier they identified a Neanderthal, the greater their chances of escaping alive.

In practical terms though, this would frequently have been difficult because the two species originally looked somewhat similar—at least through the eyes of the Middle Palaeolithic Skhul-Qafzeh humans. Even as the Skhul-Qafzeh humans underwent make-overs to accentuate visual differences, for thousands of years they were a highly variable transitional population. Throughout much of the Late Pleistocene, before the process of differentiation was complete, identification would rarely have been black and white so much as endless shades of grey. It was never as simple as evaluating a stranger as 'hairy or not hairy?'. It was 'how hairy?'. It was a similar story with eyes, noses and lips—how small must a person's eyes be to be considered human? Is that woman's mouth too thin? Precisely how protruding might a stranger's nose be before he was acceptable? Humans had to become adept at making quick and accurate determinations based on ephemeral criteria. If they got it wrong, the consequences could be fatal.

Because identification frequently had to be made on the spur of the moment—often in bad light or from a distance—it would sometimes be practically impossible to be sure whether a stranger was a Neanderthal or not. The only acceptable adaptive strategy was one based on caution—better to be safe than sorry. This translated into a heightened wariness of strangers. If a group of foraging women came across an unfamiliar male who looked even remotely like a Neanderthal, their subliminal alarm would sound and they'd run for it.

When this innate fear and suspicion of hominid strangers is semantically updated, it becomes clear we are talking about xenophobia—the fear of strangers. If xenophobia was an innate adaptive strategy to avoid Neanderthal capture, this would explain why it remains a vestigial feature of human nature.

coping with predation stress

Modelling based on NP theory indicates that Neanderthal predation was so inherently dangerous and stressful that the Skhul-Qafzeh humans lived their lives in a constant state of medium level anxiety. This raises a question that is almost impossible to answer scientifically, but which has a profound bearing on the debate on human origins—how did predation stress affect them psychologically? Other prey species, such as birds, rats and squirrels, have been imbued by evolution with a nervous restless energy and furtive behaviour. They are hyper-alert—constantly on the look-out and ready to beat a hasty retreat should a predator suddenly appear.

This must have been true for our ancestors too. Theoretically, the emotions they experienced would include anxiety, panic attacks, paranoia, anger, and the fear of anything or anyone unusual.

These intense emotions—especially when they involved a mortal fear for your life—would be extremely stressful. So it is useful to examine the medical and psychological implications of residual stress associated with Neanderthal predation.

Medical research into the impact of stress emotions on health and wellbeing reveals that stress can have a significant effect on the body, directly impacting health and longevity.[498,499,500,501] Over the period of

Neanderthal predation, this constant 'lifestyle stress' would be physically and emotionally debilitating, even life-threatening. In turn, this would have generated selection pressure for greater resilience which, in practical terms, required the central nervous system (CNS) to become more robust to cope with the stress of predation. Our ancestors needed a CNS make-over. And NP theory suggests this is exactly what natural selection provided.

the 'shock-proof' human

Several years ago, a zoo arranged to release some chimpanzees back to their original African habitat. The animals survived the plane trip but, despite the best care, being carried overnight into the jungle in small dark cages proved too much and one of the chimps died of shock. Those involved were surprised and saddened. They hadn't realised just how sensitive and vulnerable the chimps would be to the stress of their transportation and release.

This is a graphic illustration of the vulnerability of the primate central nervous system to trauma. Similar lethal reactions occur in animals captured for zoos or aquariums. There is a name for this kind of deadly stress: capture shock. For instance, capturing dolphins involves chasing the pod to the point of exhaustion and separating mothers from calves. This process is so stressful to the dolphins that, of those that survive capture, 53 percent die within 90 days.[502]

The fragility of the CNS in nonhuman animals is a puzzle. Humans are much tougher and more resilient, the striking exception in the animal kingdom. Mammals as big and as seemingly tough as elephants and rhinos often die of capture shock or waste away in captivity, but humans regularly survive horrific torture, prolonged imprisonment, solitary confinement, and the physical and psychological traumas of wars, pogroms, genocide, terrorism and accidents. Countless accounts of extraordinary survival serve as a testament to the durability of human physiology and, in particular, the resilience of our central nervous systems.

How and why did CNS robusticity evolve? What are its evolutionary antecedents? Current scientific theory cannot help here as the relevant literature is practically nonexistent. It's one of those subjects that biologists seem to have put in the too hard basket. This alone justifies taking a fresh look at the evolution of humanity's exceptional resilience and CNS robusticity from the perspective of NP theory.

Is it possible that the human CNS became 'trauma proofed' as a direct consequence of Neanderthal predation? A simple application of

Darwinian theory would suggest that predation and capture stress killed a significant proportion of the human population in the Levant. The only individuals to survive would be those born with a CNS robust enough to withstand the stress and strain of intergenerational Neanderthal predation. Gradually, a new adaptive trait—CNS robusticity—would spread to fixation in the Levant population. In other words, the constant physical and psychological stress that Neanderthal predation imposed meant that only the toughest survived. Or, to borrow from the old adage, 'What doesn't kill you makes you stronger'.

united we stand

Birds flock together, fish form vast schools and herbivores graze in herds. Flocking, schooling and herding are all common tactics adopted by prey species against predators. If Eurasian Neanderthals were such a formidable adversary and if, like other mammalian predators, they preferred to stalk solitary individuals, some form of 'safety in numbers' behaviour may be expected to become fixed in the Skhul-Qafzeh population. Not straying too far from the camp alone—and never at night—as well as hunting and foraging only in groups, are obvious social adaptations. Because women and girls were at greater risk, it probably became standard practice for females to be escorted wherever they went.

Throughout the history of *homo*, it is believed that hominids traditionally lived together in small family—and extended family—groups. But if combining into larger tribal groups (involving perhaps 50–100 people) provided a measure of defence against Neanderthal predation, then evolutionary pressure would build for social traits to facilitate this interdependence. These might include propensities for group living, collective identity, in-group distinguished from out-group, conformity to shared ideals, group loyalty, and hierarchical social structures. In other words, human society would move from an individualistic and family-based system to a tribal social system. Individualism would not only become maladaptive (individuals who preferred to 'go it alone' were less likely to survive) it would also be perceived as antisocial and antagonistic, so that *individuals* would be ostracised by the tribe (or worse). This would lead to the fixation of an innate tribal defence ethos.

In all probability, this wasn't an either-or situation. Individualism exists in all primate societies, along with a looser loyalty to the troop. While Late Pleistocene humans would have usually identified with their immediate families, when Neanderthals were active in the area and they felt threatened and anxious, they would close ranks around an experienced alpha male and function as a single unified group.

Even if the adaptations cited in this chapter helped the Levantine humans to escape capture and cope with the psychological stress of predation, ultimately they did not fix the problem. Neanderthals still ventured out of their forests to launch surprise incursions into human territory. They still made off with females whenever they could, and they still managed to catch and eat some slow-footed humans. So, while in many cases Skhul-Qafzeh humans reduced or minimised Neanderthal predation, they did not end it. Ultimately, all these defensive adaptations did was allow them to cope physically and psychologically with the negative effects of predation—for a whopping 50,000 years.

17

HOW NEANDERTHALS GOT INSIDE OUR GENES

S ome of the adaptations that the Skhul-Qafzeh humans acquired to deal with Neanderthal predation were purely physical, involving modifications to the human body and its reproductive system. Others were behavioural. Some behavioural responses were obviously learned and passed on culturally from one generation to the next. But others appear to be innate or instinctive, and include fears, sexual preferences, attitudes and other emotions that, I argue, are now part of human nature. It is imperative that we understand how these genetically programmed emotions, innate behaviours and instincts were biologically encrypted into the Skhul-Qafzeh genome, so that thousands of years later they are inherited by modern humans. And are still pulling our strings.

ethology, the study of animal behaviour

Ethology, a branch of zoology, is the study of genetically programmed behaviours known as instincts and innate behaviours in animals. In 1938, two of the founding fathers of ethology (and winners of the 1973 Nobel Prize) Konrad Lorenz and Nikolaas Tinbergen gave a name to the kind of innate responses that animals regularly display. They called them *fixed action patterns* of behaviour[503]—because when they are triggered by subliminally perceived stimuli, these behavioural responses tend to be rigid (or fixed).

In 1951, Tinbergen gave a name to the stimuli (or cues) that trigger

Yawning is an example of a sign stimuli because the sight of it in others often triggers a yawning response.

fixed action patterns. He called them *sign stimuli*, and they included any sensory stimuli or cue which evoked an innate behavioural response.[504] A sign stimulus is also sometimes called a *releaser* because it releases the innate behavioural response.

To date, sign stimuli and fixed action patterns of behaviour have been used almost exclusively in the study of nonhuman animal behaviour, but it is my intention here to apply ethological principles to recent human evolution. I take the view that there is essentially no difference in the way human and nonhuman animals acquire new innate behaviours and therefore ethological research on ducks, geese, and other animals can be applied to reveal the origins of human nature.

signs from the past

Borrowing the ethological terminology of Lorenz and Tinbergen and applying it to NP theory suggests that modern humans have inherited a number of Neanderthal-specific fixed action patterns from their Levantine ancestors. These fixed behavioural responses lie dormant until subliminally triggered (or released) by a sign stimulus, which can be a physical feature, a behaviour or something in the environment that acts as a cue.

Sign stimuli can trigger either a positive or negative fixed action. For example, among Palaeolithic males, flat female chests would tend to produce negative responses, while large rounded breasts would produce positive responses. In actuality, small variations in each trait acquired considerable significance as humans became adept at differentiating subtle differences between Neanderthal and nonNeanderthal forms. My speculative list of physical traits that may act as Neanderthal sign stimuli includes:

face   prominent brow ridges and connected eyebrows; midfacial projection; lack of symmetry; thin lips—no lips; flat nose with forward facing nostrils; large bulbous eyes with slit pupils and brown scleras; absence of defined chin; wrinkled, leather-like skin with little elasticity.

body	hunched shoulders; thick neck; bow-legged; flat buttocks; thick body hair; ape-like gait; humpback
babies	minimal antipodal body fat; wrinkled skin.
behaviour	brutish demeanour; lack of aesthetic appreciation; grunting—restricted vocal range; limited emotional repertoire; unanimated facial expressions; sexual promiscuity; incest; incomprehensible language, alien speech; stupidity; no sense of humour; no personal hygiene; smelly, dirty; public defecation; lack of sexual modesty; flagrant display of genitalia; sniffing and playing with excrement; public sex and masturbation; incapacity to form lasting pair bonds or fall in love; rape; no interest in clothes as fashion; no decorative art; no interest or talent for music; dance or singing; no body ornamentation, tattooing, scarification, jewellery, etc.; sniffing female genitalia; sexual predation; 'shadowing' (stalking) females for sexual opportunities
environmental	darkness; moonless nights; sudden noises (especially at night); caves and other subterranean abodes; dogs barking at night, forests at night.

It is a major tenet of NP theory that these clandestine Neanderthal sign stimuli became the most important single mechanisms of postNeanderthal human evolution. But this brings us to the imperative question—how did the Skhul-Qafzeh humans genetically acquire their Neanderthal sign stimuli in the first place? That is to say, Skhul-Qafzeh sign stimuli are innate and inheritable, which means they must have been biologically encrypted in their DNA. So how did this extraordinary molecular encryption of the Skhul-Qafzeh genome take place? This is such a seminal question—it extends out like a great veil to encompass the most basic questions of life on earth. How do animals (including humans) acquire new instincts and innate behaviours? How does information from the external environment get coded into DNA?

how new instincts are formed

The most obvious answer is that sign stimuli are derived from random mutations in the nucleotides of protein-coding genes, which become fixed because they confer a functional advantage. There are several major problems with this idea. Point mutations are random, essentially errors of DNA replication, and contain no coherent information in themselves. But sign stimuli are anything but random. They are external sensory cues, comprised of specific environmental information. Such non-random packages of coherent environmental information can have been acquired only from an individual's environment. They are therefore *external* to the genome. The information contained in sign stimuli are often so complex, detailed and specific to the organism's current environment that they could not have accrued by random means.

Secondly, point mutations only code for protein synthesis, which in turn builds physical traits—noses, cartilage, teeth, blood, capillaries and so on. No protein-coding gene for a complex behaviour or instinct has yet been discovered. Sign stimuli, on the other hand, are not physical. They are simply packages of 'non-physical' environmental information.

In biology, when information is acquired from the environment, the environment is said to *instruct the genome*, and this poses a problem for natural selection. This is because natural selection is not an *instructionist* process—it is a *selectionist* process—it just selects the most favourable random mutations that periodically occur. The distinction is important because the only way natural selection can function adaptively is if it prevents the environment instructing the genome with new physical traits. This is known as *the central dogma of biology*.

As formalised by Nobel Prize winner Francis Crick,[505] the central dogma means that genetic information does not flow from the environment to the genome. In practical terms it means that physical traits acquired during the life of the individual (such as bigger muscles, suntans, and broken legs) can not be passed on to the next generation via inheritance because the consequences would be catastrophic. It may seem adaptive for a blacksmith to inherit his father's big muscles, (which he acquired through exercise and hard work) but that would mean he could also inherit his father's angina and lumbago, acquired during the blacksmith's life. In other words, while it might be advantageous to inherit certain acquired physical characteristics, ultimately, the risk of fatally contaminating the genome with acquired detritus means that instructionist inheritance (*Lamarckian inheritance*) is untenable.

The Lamarckian concept of acquired characteristics incorrectly supposes that by constantly stretching to reach higher branches, giraffes develop longer necks and these can be passed on to progeny.

And yet to survive, animals need instincts that are specifically tailored to their current environments. Animals need to identify the latest predators and prey. They need to know how to find their favourite food, how to mate and generally survive the specific (and often variable) conditions of their current environment. Birds need to inherit complex maps to locate breeding grounds thousands of miles away. These instincts are particularly important in species that cannot learn such skills from their parents, like fish, reptiles, insects and many animals. So, while the central dogma prevents the environment instructing the genome with physical traits, when it comes to behaviours—and, in particular, instinctive behaviours—then it is advantageous for the environment to instruct the genome with new environment-specific information and behaviours.

No-one was more aware of this paradox than Charles Darwin. On his voyage in HMS Beagle, Darwin observed dozens of examples where the environment appeared to be instructing animals with new innate behaviours. He was particularly struck by how new environmental threats and dangers were quickly incorporated into new instincts. For instance, Darwin observed that large (edible) birds that had no contact with people did not fear humans, but species of large birds that had been recently hunted by humans quickly developed an innate fear of people which their offspring inherited.

As a result of his observations, Darwin came to believe that a second evolutionary process (besides natural selection) was responsible for animals acquiring *new* environment-specific instincts which were then inherited by their offspring.[506,507] Eventually, he developed an instructionist theory which he called pangenesis,[508] based on French naturalist Jean-Baptiste Lamarck's theory of acquired characteristics. Unfortunately pangenesis, like Lamarck's own theory, was soon shown to be incorrect.[509,510] In the absence of a new theory to explain how animals acquire environment-specific instincts, most evolutionary psychologists simply resort to Darwinian mutational theory.[511] But despite enormous advances throughout the last century in every field of biology, 21st century scientists still did not understand the innate ability of new-born turkey chicks to recognise predatory hawks, nor how this amazing feat was first encoded into its genome.

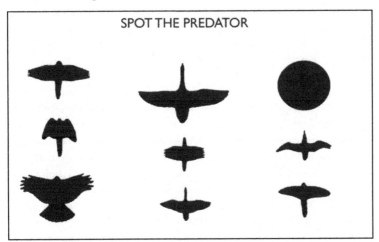

Using bird models flying along wires, ethologist Nikolass Tinbergen demonstrated that new born turkey chicks can recognise predatory birds from their shape. When they recognised a hawk, they instinctively ran for cover, but did not do so for other birds.

teem theory

In 2005, I proposed a new nonLamarckian explanation for how the environment instructs the genome of multicellular animals with new instincts and innate behaviours.

My paper, 'Noncoding DNA and the Teem Theory of Inheritance, Emotions and Innate Behaviour'[512] and subsequent papers[513,514] demonstrate that high intensity emotions (typically caused by predatory attacks, accidents and other traumatic misadventures) can be imprinted into an area of an animal's DNA called *nonprotein-coding DNA* (ncDNA). This is the area of DNA that was often dismissed as 'junk DNA'.

For example, if a turkey survives a hawk attack, its emotional response (terror, anguish etc.) can be encoded into its ncDNA and, under certain circumstances, these traumatic emotions can be inherited by its offspring.

When this molecular encoding occurs, it is inherited by progeny as a nebulous *emotional memory*. It is this emotional memory that future generations of turkey chicks use to identify dive-bombing hawks. Importantly though, the episodic memory of the experience is not inherited, nor are any physical consequences. If a boy is mauled by a dog, his lacerated wounds are not inherited, nor is the intellectual memory of the attack. Only the traumatic emotions are inherited. Because no physical effects are inherited, this evolutionary process (which I call *teemosis*) does not violate Crick's central dogma.[515]

Fracturing genetic homeostasis and encoding an emotional memory into ncDNA requires intense emotions—those usually associated with traumatic life and death experiences—the kind of powerful, out-of-the-ordinary affective experiences that would never be forgotten. For example, a young Skhul-Qafzeh girl abducted by a group of Neanderthals and subjected to a prolonged sexual assault may have been so psychologically traumatised by the attack that she encoded a 'rape teem' through which she could pass on the experience to her descendants—as an emotional memory of the assault (but not an actual memory).

Because only the emotional memory of a traumatic experience is encoded into the genome, I call these packages of inherited emotion *teems* (Trauma Encoded Emotional Memory). Teems provide a nonLamarckian means by which the genomes of multicellular animals can be encoded with adaptive information from their environment.

The development of Teem theory involved the identification and systematic analysis of many human teems to determine the traumatic environmental circumstances that may have been responsible for encoding them. For example, if most humans instinctively react to something small, dark and furry crawling on their skin, one can conclude that this is a 'spider teem', encoded by a forebear's harrowing encounter with an arachnid. Similarly, if you experience an anxiety attack while walking through a forest at night, it could suggest that a distant ancestor had been traumatised in a dark forest.

Species acquire many teems, but usually it is only the adaptive ones (those that contribute to survival) that are selected and passed on. For instance in 1960, Cornell University researcher Eleanor Gibson conducted a series of experiments that demonstrated that rats, kittens, lambs, puppies and human toddlers instinctively recognise a precipitous cliff and shy away from the edge.[516,517]

According to Teem theory, Gibson's experiments demonstrated a simple 'cliff teem', encoded perhaps by a prehistoric infant who survived a traumatic fall from a great height and encoded a teem as a result. Because the teem provided the toddler's ancestors with an innate aversive reaction to steep cliffs, it was highly adaptive and eventually became fixed.

An infant intuitively backs away from what it believes is a cliff.
From M. W. Matlin and H. J. Foley (1997) *Sensation and Perception* (4th Edition) Allyn and Bacon. P448

Similarly, if humans around the world are innately concerned with body odour, it suggests that when this teem was first encoded, it provided an adaptive advantage and so was retained and spread to fixation. This kind of analysis led directly to the formation of NP theory.

To understand why modern humans still carry so many vestigial teemic responses to Neanderthal predation, we need only note that teems are encoded only by extremely intense emotions. And predation—for those that survive it—is all about trauma and near-death experiences. We know from field studies, for example, that predation can be so traumatic that survivors often die later of shock from non-lethal injuries. Eugène Marais, who studied free-ranging baboons in northern Transvaal in the 1930s, observed that constant predation by lions and leopards meant that "the life of the baboon is in fact one continual nightmare of anxiety."[518]

While the physiological effects of predation stress on victims is well-known—including elevated levels of glucocorticoids,[519] cardiovascular disease and damaged immune responses[520]—similar responses have also been detected in individuals who witness a close relative or companion being killed.[521] Among modern humans, even bereavement caused by natural

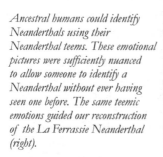

Ancestral humans could identify Neanderthals using their Neanderthal teems. These emotional pictures were sufficiently nuanced to allow someone to identify a Neanderthal without ever having seen one before. The same teemic emotions guided our reconstruction of the La Ferrassie Neanderthal (right).

causes is known to increase morbidity and mortality,[522] so we may expect the family and friends of Levantine humans taken by Neanderthals to be especially traumatised. This suggests it was not only the direct survivors of Neanderthal attacks that encoded Neanderthal teems but, by virtue of the generalised trauma of predation, their relatives and friends too.

Given this, and the fact that Neanderthal predation was consistently traumatic over so many millennia, it is hardly surprising that human nature is littered with Neanderthal teems. If, as my interpretation of the data suggests, every Neanderthal sign stimuli in the modern human genome was encrypted there (by the teemosis evolutionary process) as a consequence of an individual's traumatic personal experience with Neanderthal predation, then it strengthens the view that our ancestors led much more traumatic and fearful lives than the fossil record indicates. In addition, Teem theory pinpoints human sexuality as having been subject to a traumatic upheaval at some stage in human evolution.

For a more detailed explanation of the Teem theory of behavioural evolution, see my forthcoming book *The Second Evolution*, or my website (www.thesecondevolution.com). But for the purposes of NP theory, by outlining the biological mechanism by which traumatic emotional encounters with Neanderthals could be encrypted into the human genome and inherited, Teem theory fills a gap in the Neanderthal predation paradigm. Importantly, it reveals that Neanderthal sign stimuli are derived directly from Neanderthal teems, and those teems in turn are derived from the traumatic personal interaction between Neanderthals and early humans.

18 STRATEGIC EVOLUTION

the ultimate makeover

Despite defensive adaptations like xenophobia, changes in sexuality, raising wolves as guard dogs, becoming more athletic, developing a trauma-proof CNS, keeping to their own territory (and away from forests), plus a plethora of defensive teems, the fossil record reveals the Levantine population continued to decline. It seems that the Skhul-Qafzeh humans were slowly losing the battle for survival—and heading inexorably towards extinction. But at this pointy end of the predation cycle, things started to change, radically.

To understand what happened next, we need only examine the situation through the prism of Darwinian theory. This predicts the extraordinary and dramatic events that unfolded as the human population plunged towards extinction. For a start, it tells us that all the weak, slow-moving, dim-witted, gullible humans went the way of the dodo—their genes eradicated from the gene pool. Then, as all but the most diehard survivors perished, it generated intense selection pressure for a new kind of adaptation. Why? Because the old *defensive adaptations* were no longer adaptive. Neanderthal predation was continuing to decimate the Skhul-Qafzeh population and make their lives a misery. What was needed was a radical new adaptation, one that didn't just help humans evade or escape Neanderthals. To survive as a species and to be truly free of Neanderthals, humans needed to go on the offensive. This required a revolutionary new approach to the problem. And this is precisely what I theorise happened. The enormous selection pressure generated by Neanderthal predation gave birth to a completely new group of adaptations, which I call *strategic adaptations*.

Strategic adaptations are not defensive, they are offensive and, in the Levant, their blind objective was to empower the Skhul-Qafzeh humans to engage Neanderthals in combat and defeat them. Strategic adaptations were blindly aimed at the complete annihilation of the Eurasian Neanderthal.

The emergence of strategic adaptations makes sound evolutionary sense. Defensive adaptations were useful, up to a point. But ultimately, the only way the Levantines could achieve continuity and security and be predation-free was to permanently remove Neanderthals as ecological competitors. Skhul-Qafzeh humans had to depose Neanderthals from the top of the food chain and take over the mantle of apex predator.

The enormity of the task was mind-blowing. For a timid prey species to turn the tables on the top predator on the planet would require the reversal of an ancient and well-established predator-prey interaction and would almost certainly have been unprecedented in the animal kingdom. Humans had to evolve into a militaristic species, the likes of which had never been seen before. They would have to become more intelligent, ruthless, cunning, aggressive, cruel and determined than their lethal adversary—become a new super-warrior species with one specialist skill: to kill Neanderthals.

a superior killing machine

Skhul-Qafzeh humans born with offensive physical characteristics and aggressive teems—any kind of inheritable trait that allowed them to out-compete, kill, wound or chase off Neanderthals—lived to pass on their offensive genes along with their newly acquired Neanderthal battle teems. Strategic adaptations included any physical or behavioural adaptation that directly or indirectly contributed to Neanderthal extinction.

NP theory argues that, for the first time, a few humans didn't run and hide when they saw Neanderthals approaching. Instead, they courageously stood their ground and engaged Neanderthals in combat. Bolstered by their newly-acquired strategic adaptations, the humans began to win a few victories. Initially, they would have lost a lot of men, but this only concentrated the strategic adaptations into a smaller group.

Because the human survivor population was so small at the time and the strategic adaptations were so adaptive, the genes that encoded the most aggressive adaptations spread to fixation very quickly. Soon, a new transitional human emerged. Natural selection was gradually evolving the ultimate killing machine—the most virulent hominid species by far—modern humans.

Once acquired, what humans did with these strategic adaptations is not in doubt. Charles Darwin, in *The Descent of Man*, provides a salutary reminder of what lay ahead for the Neanderthals:

> We can see, that in the rudest state of society, the individuals who were the most sagacious, who invented and used the best weapons or traps, and who were best able to defend themselves, would rear the greatest number of offspring. The tribes, which included the largest number of men thus endowed, would increase in number and supplant other tribes.[523]

The strategic adaptations which I propose played a pivotal role in humans gaining the upper hand over their historical enemy are a disparate lot. They include high intelligence, cruelty, male bonding and aggression, language capacity, the facility to interpret intention from behaviour, organisation, courage, guile, conjectural reasoning, a genocidal mindset, improved semantic memory, consciousness, competitiveness and the ability to form strategic coalitions, or proto-armies.

These adaptations included a raft of new aggressive *them and us* teems that unified the Levantine humans into a cohesive combative force (the first proto-army) that encouraged them not only to stand their ground but to attack Neanderthals and exterminate them without guilt or remorse.

A major plank of the hypothesis is that strategic adaptations emerged only towards the end of the period of Neanderthal predation (during the population bottleneck) sometime between 70,000 to 50,000 years ago. To prove the strategic adaptations hypothesis, it must be demonstrated that they all emerged because they helped humans kill Neanderthals, and that they all appeared between 70,000 and 50,000 years ago.

Because there are so many strategic adaptations it is not possible to make a detailed examination of them all in this book. Instead, my analysis is limited to a sample of the most important strategic adaptations:

- Male aggression
- Courage

- Self-sacrifice
- Tough-mindedness
- Machiavellian intelligence
- Language
- Creativity
- Organisation—the origins of human society
- Gender differences
- Division of labour.

bloodlust teems

Courage, bravado and proactive aggression are normally anathema (or a last resort) to prey species. From a survivalist perspective, it makes more sense to be timorous and cautious. But, because killing Neanderthals would require hand-to-hand combat, getting into close contact required courage, audacity and even self-sacrifice. Gradually, timid defensive individuals lost out to a new breed of aggressive, courageous, tough-minded individuals.

It is not difficult to see how a 'bloodlust teem' could be encoded. If a group of Skhul-Qafzeh men came across a wounded or infirm Neanderthal, they might easily work themselves up into a highly agitated state and beat him to death before pounding his corpse to a pulp. This kind of frenzied excitement (observed so frequently among wild chimpanzees) could generate enough excitement in one individual to precipitate a directed (or teemic) mutation in an intron (the nonprotein-coding region of his DNA). If the affected intron happened to be on his Y (male sex) chromosome, the bloodlust emotions he experienced during the melee would be permanently encrypted into his ncDNA and subject to patrilineal descent. Once inherited by male descendents, the archived bloodlust emotions would remain unexpressed until triggered by the sight or sound of a Neanderthal. When expressed, the bloodlust emotions could precipitate the same kind of reckless and frenzied aggression.

Only in this specific and atypical ecological context were reckless daring, proactive aggression and self-sacrifice adaptive behaviours. When it came to fighting Neanderthals, risk-taking become both a laudable human attribute and a functional adaptation. In this context, foolhardy machismo and reckless bravado became laudable heroism. American anthropologist Joseph Campbell once said, "A hero is someone who

*The current anthropological model does not adequately explain the historic and cultural
pre-occupation with the hero's struggle against the forces of evil. However, in the context
of an adversarial struggle between two sibling species, it makes sound evolutionary sense.*

has given his or her life to something bigger than oneself."[524] And, while the great cause was genocide, for those Skhul-Qafzeh humans it would have been a noble cause. Heroic males would not only be praised and appreciated as altruistic and self-sacrificing by the folk they defended, but would also be highly sought after as sexual partners by admiring females. Even today, research shows that when choosing a mate, women place significantly greater importance on altruistic traits than anything else.[525] Thus, the nascent genes for courage, altruism, self-sacrifice—indeed for heroism itself—dispersed through the community, transforming the Levantines from a timorous prey species into a proto-militaristic tribe.

It follows that the Skhul-Qafzeh attitude to killing also had to change. Early humans obviously killed other animals, but only for food. Now for the first time, they had to kill something they didn't intend to eat, and another hominid to boot. And kill them without compunction, hesitation or guilt. This required a library of virulent new aggression teems.

These new teems were adaptable because, if early humans could not bring themselves to administer the coup de grâce to a wounded Neanderthal, then these soft-minded individuals risked retaliation, revenge and possibly their own lives. Selection favoured the cruel and the merciless. This was, after all, war before there was a notion of it—before civilisation, before even barbarism. There were no treaties, protocols, exchange of prisoners or rules of engagement. No field hospitals, no Red Cross and no POWs. In this context of quintessential savagery, mercy was not only maladaptive, it was not a practical option.

To dispatch Neanderthals efficiently and without pity, humans had to perceive them psychologically and emotionally in a new way. And this is where teems proved so functional. Teems can encode extreme antipathetic feelings into genetic sequences. Once encoded into ncDNA and inherited, Neanderthal hostility teems provided the emotions used to instinctively loath and dehumanise Neanderthals. They allowed the Levantines to perceive Neanderthals as sub-human, not even in the same category as animals. After all, the animals they regularly killed for food were not despised but were more likely revered for their speed, grace and life-force, and because they gave their lives so that humans could survive. This respect for prey (at times elevated to a spiritual relationship) is evident in every modern hunter-gatherer culture.

Neanderthals though, were a special case.

They were, in all probability, considered by humans as 'worse than animals', categorised metaphorically as pests, along with cockroaches, spiders and rats.

This would have served an important adaptive function. Seeing Neanderthals as subhuman allowed humans to slaughter them without guilt or remorse. Administering the coup de grâce to a wounded Neanderthal would be as easy as squashing a cockroach or crushing a rat with a rock.

The selection extended to favour men who were willing to give up their lives fighting Neanderthals. Under normal circumstances, male self-sacrifice would almost certainly be maladaptive, but in lethal combat with Neanderthals, this level of commitment and courage was obviously a strategic advantage that could turn the tide of a battle. Also, male bonding, pack mentality and obedience to the leadership would be eminently adaptive because discipline, organisation and hierarchy are essential elements of military success.

Within the context of the life and death struggle in the Levant between two adversarial sibling species, aggression, risk-taking, self-sacrifice, and the ability to exercise lethal violence without hesitancy (all derived from Neanderthal teems) were advantageous and essential to human survival.

Collectively, this disparate assortment of aggression traits in modern humans has been aptly described by psychologist Erich Fromm as 'malignant aggression',[526] which he says is biologically nonadaptive. Considering that during the last century alone, 203 million people were slaughtered by other human beings,[527] he's got a point.

But while malignant male aggression in today's fully modern humans is unquestionably deleterious, back in the torrid days of Neanderthal predation, malignant male aggression was the lynch pin of Skhul-Qafzeh survival and renewal.

The challenge to existing theories of human evolution is to explain how and why malignant aggression and its correlates—warfare, racism, and genocide—were initially selected, and what adaptive function they conferred. It is hard to imagine any situation, apart from Neanderthal predation, where such extreme levels of male aggression (levels that are still evident today) would be adaptive.

the words of war

According to language specialists Chris Knight, Michael Studdert-Kennedy and James Hurford, "language is one of science's great remaining mysteries. A central difficulty is that it appears so radically incommensurate with nonhuman systems of communication as to cast doubt on standard Darwinian accounts of its evolution by natural selection."[528]

And yet, most language researchers hold that human language must be a product of natural selection. As Jason Noble notes, "complex traits do not evolve without having some function."[529] American neuroscientist Steven Pinker, in his book *The Language Instinct*, suggests that language must be a basic instinct because elements of language are universal. Although numerous researchers agree with the basic tenet of Pinker's book, many disagree with the suggestion that it came about via natural selection. They argue that hominids had survived without complex language for nearly seven million years, and that every other primate species still manages to survive without it.

The central challenge to the selection theory then, is to identify the ecological factors which made it imperative for symbolic language capacity to develop exponentially in one—and only one—mammalian species. Despite considerable effort, no Darwinian theory of language has yet done this.

NP theory's explanation is that, prior to Neanderthal predation, the Skhul-Qafzeh people made do with a rudimentary proto-language. For the most part, facial expressions, vocalisations and body language were fine for communicating essential information about normal everyday things—like sex, dominance, food, affection and other basic needs. After the population bottleneck though, when Levantine males began forming the first proto-armies to engage Neanderthals, they needed more complex linguistic skills to become more effective warriors. In this battlefield context, spoken language would have found an immediate strategic application. Articulate speech would give them a powerful new weapon against the Neanderthals.

Speech allowed Levantine humans to communicate complex military tactics. It could be used to plan future events, like ambushes and rendezvous. In battle, groups could be mobilised and moved more rapidly and effectively. Complex military orders like "split into two groups, circle behind and attack from the rear". Or, "let's wait till dark then sneak up on them from the other side of the river" could be exchanged. Symbolic language could communicate intelligence about Neanderthal numbers, locations and intentions that basic gestures could not. Successful tactics could be taught, and even passed on to the next generation. Battle experiences could be woven into morale-boosting stories and embellished into inspirational myths. And, because a common language is a major means of creating group identity (and patriotism) in modern humans, we may suppose language also helped distinguish articulate humans from their linguistically inept natural enemies.

This hypothesis presupposes that human language was not acquired gradually over several million years, but more abruptly, between 100,000 and 50,000 years ago when the population bottleneck occurred. We can use this prediction to prove or disprove the theory. If language was acquired earlier, then it must have been a different set of evolutionary necessities that caused its emergence. If, on the other hand, it can be shown that the emergence of modern spoken language occurred precisely within the chronology of Neanderthal predation, then it substantially strengthens the hypothesis.

So, what does the scientific evidence tell us about the emergence of language? Well, British linguist Derek Bickerton believes that a basic proto-language emerged 1.5 million years ago based on simple primate vocalisations.[530] However, other linguists, including the noted American Merritt Ruhlen, draw a distinction between proto-languages and fully articulated modern human language.[531] He argues that the proto-language actually began to diversify into complex human language only between 40–50,000 years ago, about the same time that modern humans emerged.

Australian researchers from the University of New England William Noble and Iain Davidson, in their book *Human Evolution, Language and Mind*,[532] also provide a more recent estimate for the origins of human language—between 100,000 and 70,000 years ago.

This estimate is supported by Phillip Lieberman's group of linguistic researchers, who argue that fully human speech anatomy does not show up in the fossil record until the Upper Palaeolithic, about 50,000 years ago[533]. They say the mutations that enabled rapid speech were selected because they must have been adaptive in respect of certain unspecified events:

> These events which led to the emergence of fully modern speech, language and cognition appear to have occurred sometime in the period between 90,000 and 50,000 BP, the time frame between fossils like Skhul V and fully modern humans who were capable of talking as we do. [534]

These dates reflect a growing consensus among anthropologists and linguists that language did indeed develop rapidly and recently.[535,536,537] They argue that the *human revolution* would not have been possible without language, and therefore must have occurred simultaneously with it.

By identifying specific events capable of marshalling natural selection in the service of language capacity at exactly the time it is thought to have emerged, NP theory provides the foundation of a radical new theory of human language.

creativity and the arms race

In the kill or be killed world of the Levant, creativity, lateral thinking and inventiveness would have been adaptive, if only because creative individuals could invent new improved weapons 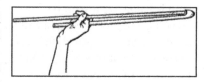 that would give humans a military advantage over Neanderthals. Innovations like atlatls (spear throwers) (*above*), slings, nets, traps, lightweight javelins, poison darts and ultimately the most complex but lethal Late Pleistocene weapon of all—the bow and arrow—required lateral thinking and imagination in their conception.

The great advantage that the bow and other projectile weapons offered was that they could be discharged from a safe distance, which neutralised the overwhelming strength advantage of Neanderthals. This elevates the invention of projectile point technology to one of the most important human strategic adaptations. A case could even be made that these weapons provided the only practical means by which a physically superior foe could be vanquished.

It follows that the creative proto-geniuses who invented the latest 'high tech' weapon would be respected, revered and much sought after as mates, which would propagate the genes for creativity. In other words, the proto-war with the Neanderthals generated tremendous selection pressure for the kind of lateral thinking and imagination that could produce strategic weapons.

The simplest way to test this hypothesis is to refer to the archaeological evidence to determine when projectile point technology first appeared.

The hypothesis would be falsified if the tangible products of human creativity appeared in the fossil record *before* 60,000–50,000 years ago. Although dating the earliest appearance of these weapons is difficult because nets, slings, wooden javelins and atlatls do not normally fossilise, stone projectile points do preserve and can provide dates for the origins of the atlatls, lightweight throwing spears, darts and even bows and arrows.

Still, it's sometimes difficult to establish whether a stone artefact is a projectile point, much less whether it was fired from a bow or javelin. Because of this, radiocarbon dates for the earliest appearance of the bow and other projectile technologies in the fossil record are not precise. But one thing archaeologists know for certain is that there is no real evidence of projectile-point technology before 50,000 years ago. [538]

Fortunately, research on the origins of projectile-point technology in Africa, the Levant and Europe sheds some new light on the topic. Using a method devised by University of Washington anthropologist Susan Hughes to identify projectile points,[539] researchers report that radiocarbon and thermoluminescence dates indicate the first transition between Middle Palaeolithic stone weapons (which tend to be fairly heavy and crudely made) to the earliest Upper Palaeolithic microblades (that resemble projectile points) appears 46,000 years ago.[540, 541]

This coincides with when NP theory claims early humans were developing their anti-Neanderthal arsenal. Where these earliest aerodynamically streamlined stone and bone projectile points were first discovered is also significant—at Ksar Akil, in Lebanon, in the very heart of the Levant. As well as resembling modern arrowheads, some of these points display damage similar to projectile-point breakage in modern hunter gatherers' spears and to damage recorded by spear throwing experiments.[542, 543]

As to whether projectile-point weapons emerged in other regions at the same time as they did in the Levant, John Shea observes, "Levantine initial upper paleolithic projectile points, such as Ksar Akil points and El-Wad points have no clear African 'ancestors'. The evidence currently available instead favours an indigenous origin for projectile point technology in the Levant ca. 40–50 Ka."[544]

The bow and arrow and lightweight javelin were obviously a quantum leap from the heavy thrusting spears used by Neanderthals.[545,546,547,548] The humans perfected a lighter, more aerodynamic spear and hafted it with smaller flints. This transformed the handheld thrusting spear into a javelin that could be accurately thrown over considerable distances. Tests on culled elephant hides in Africa showed that small flint tips when thrown or jabbed could penetrate deeply enough to inflict a mortal wound.

Bows had probably been around for some time, albeit in a different form. Small fire bows (*right*) are still used in some cultures to spin a stick fast enough to start a fire. But it was never just a matter of firing an arrow from a bow. Accuracy, balance, thrust and travel distance had to be achieved before it became an effective weapon. The invention that required the greatest act of creativity and lateral thinking was the application of feathers to stabilise the arrow in flight. This increased the distance an arrow travelled and greatly improved accuracy and penetrating power. The development of fletched, flint-tipped arrows and powerful bows enabled a major escalation in the campaign against Neanderthals.

It could be argued that the need for improved weapons like the bow was driven by the demands of hunting large and dangerous prey. Yet there is more than enough palaeontological evidence to show that Middle Palaeolithic hominids successfully hunted large, dangerous prey with only the most basic weapons.[549] This has been interpreted as evidence that Middle Palaeolithic humans did not need projectile weapons to capture large prime-age prey. [550] If hominids had survived for millions of years without bows and other high-tech weapons, why did they suddenly need sophisticated Upper Palaeolithic weapons?

Finally, the fossil record shows that the human transition to the Upper Palaeolithic was accompanied by a change of prey species hunted—not to bigger, more dangerous prey, but to smaller, less dangerous animals like birds, rabbits, rodents and tortoises.[551]

While the bow, the sling and the spear thrower may have turned the tide of the ancestral conflict, they represent only one piece of the strategic advantage that the revolution in lateral thinking provided. Human technological creativity also produced shoes and new kinds of tailored clothing. It conceived of sewing needles, fish hooks, woven nets, and animal traps. It devised ingenious military tactics, armour and shields to protect combatants. It devised new ways of making microliths—razor-sharp flint points that could penetrate flesh and damage vital organs. Technological innovation turned out to be an *umbrella adaptation* that affected almost every aspect of the protracted, intergenerational conflict with Neanderthals.

The *strategic creativity* hypothesis challenges the view of some scholars that it was aesthetic art (representational art, sculpture and so on) that drove the selection of genes for creativity. It is understandable why this theory has its adherents. Humans love and value art, so it follows that it must have had a significant evolutionary function. But while art was no doubt aesthetically pleasing, and may even have had religious and shamanistic value, it is difficult to see how paintings, sculpture and other art works made a major contribution to reproductive fitness in the Late Pleistocene.

Furthermore, the archaeological data shows that European cave art did not really get off the ground until 30,000 years ago[552]—nearly 20,000 years after human technological and scientific creativity first appeared.

This suggests it was not artistic expression per se that drove the selection of creativity networks, but something else.

The NP theory of strategic creativity demonstrates that by helping to defeat the Neanderthals, technological and scientific creativity contributed to fitness. This is consistent with Darwinian theory because creativity is known to be a function of consciousness—a major and uniquely human adaptation—which could only have emerged as the result of concerted and prolonged selection pressure.

This theory suggests aesthetic art emerged as a by-product of strategic creativity.

The biblical story of David (and his use of a 'high-tech' weapon—the sling) and Goliath highlights the strategic importance of intelligence, creativity and superior weaponry in the struggle against the 'forces of evil'.

machiavellian intelligence

High intelligence would help in the fight against Neanderthals, fuelling a cognitive arms race that would increase the collective IQ of the Levantine human population.

But to be really effective killers, humans needed something more. To get the upper hand over their adversary, they needed to be divisive, scheming, manipulative and crafty. In short, they needed a special kind of strategic intelligence. The Italian diplomat and political philosopher Niccolò Machiavelli (1469–1527) (*right*) gave his name to just such a kind of strategic thinking. Being Machiavellian is about the goal-orientated scheming involved in political intrigues and the deadly court manoeuvring for wealth and power. It condones lying, forming and breaking allegiances, duplicity, making false promises and other devious tactics to achieve objectives.

Psychologists now call this kind of thinking, *Machiavellian intelligence*,[553] and in the Late Pleistocene, I maintain, it was an important, newly emerging adaptation in the modern human community.

In the Levant, Machiavellian intelligence would result in new battlefield strategies. Guile, tactical deception, forward planning, interpreting intent from behaviour, coalition forming, deceit, dehumanisation, concealment of intent and betrayal—would translate into more victories and fewer casualties. Accordingly, the specialised neuronal networks regulating these high-level cognitive functions would be selected and become fixed via genetic drift.

gender and the division of labour

While most strategic traits (including high intelligence and logical think-ing) were acquired by both sexes, others tended to be gender-specific. For instance, because women would never be a physical match for the stronger Neanderthals in hand-to-hand combat, acquiring combat traits like physical aggression and competition would be ineffective. Besides, women had the primary responsibility for childrearing. For these reasons, women learnt to express their aggression and competition indirectly— through non-physical means. This use of indirect and passive aggressive behaviour remains a feature of modern female psychology to this day.[554]

Because it was mainly men who engaged in physical combat—which requires excellent visual-spatial skills—they acquired specialist motor skill networks that even today allow boys and men to throw things (like spears and rocks) much faster, further and more accurately than girls.[555] It also explains why men can run faster than women, jump higher, and longer and why they are 30 percent stronger than females.[556]

While premeditated killing without hesitancy, pity or regret became a highly prized male strategy, for human females these violent behaviours flew in the face of other deeply innate proclivities—as mothers, caregivers and nurturers. In these roles, empathy, compassion and generosity were highly adaptive (particularly in raising children), which meant that natural selection retained these attributes in females. With women less able to suppress pity and compassion, the proto-war became mainly the preserve of young males and even today, this gender demarcation remains largely intact.[557]

The struggle between Neanderthals and emerging modern humans would have demanded sacrifices from everyone. While they were generally absent from the frontline, women would have acquired many strategic traits that contributed indirectly to the war effort. This new division of labour provided logistical support. In practical terms, females became more adept at fletching arrows, hafting spears, chipping stones into arrowheads and weaving fibres into ropes and nets. Women would also take over responsibility for foraging for food, allowing men to devote more time and energy to hunting and fighting.

This hypothesis draws support from a review of the literature on gender differences that shows that girls and women have greater manual dexterity,[558] better motor coordination, and more precise finger dexterity than males.[559] These are all specialised skills that would have been useful in making tools and weapons during the Late Pleistocene.

Backing for this division of labour theory also comes from Palaeolithic archaeologist Olga Soffer, who has unearthed evidence of the extensive use of baskets, ropes, nets, woven garments, textiles and other perishable technologies during the Upper Palaeolithic—which she interprets as indicating a far greater role of women, children and the elderly in these industries in early human society.[560]

Today, the division of labour is such a ubiquitous feature of all human societies that it is mostly taken for granted. But innate divisions of labour do not exist to the same extent among any of the other great apes.[561] It had to start somewhere, and for some important adaptive reason.

the origins of human society

Every animal is born with a number hardwired into its genes. That number limits how many other members of its species it will live with. In the case of the orang-utan, that number is one. These solitary animals live their whole lives in the rainforests, and only get together to mate. For chimpanzees, the number ranges between 30–80, depending on available resources. Ants, on the other hand, live in colonies numbering in excess of half a million.

Generally species that have few if any predators (like the orang-utan) live in smaller groups (there is more food to go around) while prey species like wildebeests aggregate into herds of up to one million animals for mutual protection. Of course, there is a trade-off. The bigger the group, the more food it needs, so theoretically, small groups are more self sustaining.

Before the Neanderthals moved into the Levant, the Skhul-Qafzeh humans lived in small family-size and extended family-size groups. Once Neanderthal predation began though, it generated selection pressure on the Levantines to aggregate into increasingly larger groups. This required the genetically encoded social number to be recalibrated upwards to facilitate larger social aggregations.

The trouble is, large groups need some kind of order and social structure to make them work. Increasing the size of the tribe creates demands for expanded groups to interact cohesively—and behave as a single entity rather than a group of rowdy individuals. This encourages social and sexual interaction, reciprocal exchange, hierarchies, and the exchange of ideas.

In effect, this gradual resizing into larger defensive groups provided all sorts of positive spin-offs for the Levantine humans. And in doing so, I suggest, it elevated *society* to a strategic adaptation in the Levant. Why? Because society not only creates defence through unity, it creates offensive strength as well.

While the concept of larger militaristic groups would not have been too difficult to comprehend ('if 10 is good, 500 is better'), mastering the organisation required would have been another matter. The management of large-scale aggressive groups (or armies), both in terms of logistical and interpersonal dynamics, is a difficult and challenging business.

The strategic concept our ancestors eventually mastered was what we now call *society*. They needed to put aside their family and troop loyalties to form much larger coalitions. Alpha males who normally provided leadership to their families and troops had to aggregate under a single leader and accept subordinate roles.

The view that *society* may have been highly adaptive for the Skhul-Qafzeh people is hardly radical—it is axiomatic that, *united we stand, divided we fall*. But what this new social theory argues is that the Levantine humans developed society into an offensive weapon.

the warrior-tribe

During the population bottleneck, if a Skhul-Qafzeh youth in Syria was born with a creative streak that allowed him to invent a net for trapping Neanderthals, that would be good. If he killed a few Neanderthals that way, it helped. And if in southern Jordan, another Skhul-Qafzeh man was born so athletic and strong, he could wrestle a Neanderthal to the ground and strangle him, that was another plus. But these isolated victories would not defeat the Neanderthals, nor would they create a new human species. For that to happen, all the strategic adaptations acquired by the adolescent Syrian and the Jordanian—and indeed by all the fortunate individuals from across the entire Levant who acquired some form of strategic adaptation—had to combine. They had to be genetically concentrated into a single population so that the strategic adaptations spread through genetic drift. Otherwise, when the Syrian and the Jordanian died, their skills would die with them. And nothing would change.

The solution, and the Skhul-Qafzeh salvation, could have been achieved relatively simply. Scattered families and groups of 'Neanderthal hunters' gradually congregated to form a single interbreeding Skhul-Qafzeh population or tribe. The group's identity and raison d'être was forged around their common ability to kill Neanderthals, and their shared hatred of a despised enemy.

As this tribe of stone-age *X-Men* interbred, their strategic adaptations were concentrated—eventually forming a single warrior tribe—of proficient Neanderthal killers.

In this model it was not simply an aggregation of strategic adaptations that turned the tide. It was their militaristic application at the tribal level that was so effective. The tribe exponentially increased the effectiveness of the strategic adaptations, resulting in a militaristic synergy that allowed the Skhul-Qafzeh people to do what no other prey species had done before—reverse the predation dynamic. They turned the hunter into the hunted.

Each new generation of Levantine humans would have attained increased intelligence, cunning, physical dexterity and ability to fashion ever more effective weapons. Each generation was more flexible, more

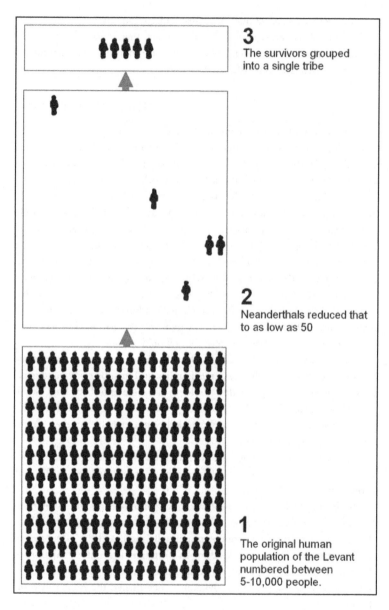

3
The survivors grouped
into a single tribe

2
Neanderthals reduced that
to as low as 50

1
The original human
population of the Levant
numbered between
5-10,000 people.

What made the population bottleneck such a potent mechanism of human evolution
was that the few remaining survivors concentrated their survivalist adaptations into a
single interbreeding group or tribe.

able to throw a javelin. And with each generation, teenage boys became smarter and braver. Eventually, a young Levantine David courageously faced up to a Neanderthal Goliath and, armed with his newly invented sling, he slaughtered the creature and earned the approbation of his tribe. These gallant young men with their magnificent victories must have seemed like the first 'superheroes', so extraordinary were their abilities to defeat their historic adversaries. There could be no question about it: the Skhul-Qafzeh people were changing.

While my portrayal of a young Levantine David slaying a brutish Neanderthal with a high-tech weapon is a speculation, it was recently supported by a scientific study published in July 2009, just as this book was going to print. The *Journal of Human Evolution* reports a study by Steven Churchill from Duke University that reveals a Eurasian Neanderthal (Shanidar 3) had been killed by a projectile point weapon, which at the time was used only by modern humans.

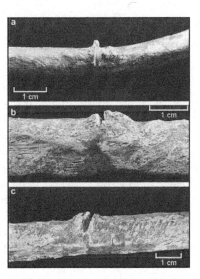

Researchers from Duke University have been able to demonstrate that the wound to the Shanidar 3 Neanderthal's ribs was made by a lightweight projectile point thrown by a modern human. This is the strongest evidence yet that post-bottleneck Levantine humans attacked and killed Eurasian Neanderthals.

This presents not only the first concrete evidence of humans killing Neanderthals in the Levant, but also provides a date. Churchill's team radiocarbon dated material found just below the Neanderthal's body to approximately 46,900 years, which is precisely when I suggest modern humans were morphing into a virulent new species and eradicating Neanderthals from the Levant.

19 NATURAL BORN KILLERS

"i am become death, the destroyer of worlds"

When all the strategic adaptations described in the last chapter are added to the defensive adaptations humans acquired earlier, the result is something that looks very much like a fully modern human. This is not a coincidence. As disagreeable as it may be, this combination of aggressive, murderous, devious, cruel, sexually repressive, devilishly clever and patriarchal characteristics is a substantial part of what define us as a species. These characteristics distinguish modern humans from their stone-age ancestors and from every other primate. Thousands of timid archaic humans went into the population bottleneck, and only a handful of ferocious, militaristic modern humans came out.

Transforming into the most virulent species on earth is what it took for humans to throw off 50,000 years of persecution. Only a superior predator could have reversed the predator-prey dynamic. And only by transforming into something more lethal and dangerous than Neanderthals themselves, could those early humans stake their claim to the top rung of the food chain.

From an evolutionary point of view, the struggle to reverse the predator-prey dynamic (despite being fuelled by genocidal rage) wasn't personal. It was simply a rudimentary and spontaneous expression of 'survival of the fittest'.

The Levantine reversal set the tumultuous course of human evolution for the next 50,000 years, honing the strategic adaptations that transformed the Skhul-Qafzeh humans from timid to triumphant, from fearful to fearless. It was here that the die was cast, from which all future humans would be forged. The Levantine humans had become something without precedent in the animal kingdom. For the Eurasian Neanderthals, this new breed of humans must have seemed like Frankenstein monsters, so different were they from their timorous predecessors. To comprehend the sinister nature of the human transformation, I am reminded of something the father of the atomic bomb J Robert Oppenheimer said when he witnessed the first nuclear denotation. He quoted a line from the Hindu scripture the *Bhagavad-Gita*. "Now I am become Death, the destroyer of worlds".

phoenix rising

With its red and gold tail plumage, the phoenix is a beautiful bird from Phoenician mythology that was said to live for 500 years. When it is about to die, it builds a nest of cinnamon twigs, nestles in, and sets fire to itself. When the firebird is completely consumed, a new phoenix rises magically from the ashes.

This mythic tale of resurrection and regeneration provides a fitting analogy for what happened to the Skhul-Qafzeh humans. The catharsis of Neanderthal predation decimated their numbers, devastated their lives, and drove them to the precipice of extinction. But just as they were about to disappear forever, enough strategic adaptations took hold to fan the embers and allow a few resolute souls to emerge—belligerent, deadly and looking for revenge.

This scenario of resurrection and retribution encapsulates two major tenets of the strategic adaptation hypothesis and, coincidently, provides two predictions that can be used to test the theory. The first is that strategic adaptations fixed during the population bottleneck transformed Skhul-Qafzeh humans into recognisably modern humans with a new Upper Palaeolithic culture. Secondly, this allowed the post-bottleneck humans to reverse the ancestral predator-prey relationship and go on a genocidal rampage of retribution against their ancestral foe.

If the first prediction is correct, the fossil record of the Levant should show that Upper Palaeolithic culture suddenly appeared there between 50,000 to 46,000 years ago. And it does. The Upper Palaeolithic transition first shows up in the fossil record about 47,000 years ago,[562,563,564,565] which is when NP theory proposes that modern humans were emerging from the population bottleneck. Secondly, a plethora of solid archaeological evidence confirms the Levant is the site of the earliest systemic transition from Middle Palaeolithic to Initial Upper Palaeolithic anywhere in the world.[566,567,568]

Most of the recognised indicators of modern behaviour are there— including prismatic blade technology, the transport of raw materials over long distances, complex multi-component tools (including, for the first time, bone and ivory tools), personal ornaments, specialised subsistence strategies, language capacity, symbolic notation systems, and so on.

The hypothesis argues that the gradual accumulation of new strategic adaptations created a *tipping point* that resulted in a new species.

One of the methods that biologists use to determine if two populations are the same species is to check whether they interbreed. Even if they look very similar, if they don't interbreed it's a sure sign they're different species. For example, Cope's Gray Treefrog (*Hyla chrysoscelis*) and the Gray Treefrog (*Hyla versicolor*) are visually indistinguishable. The only distinctive thing that separates them is their singing voices, but this is enough to prevent them interbreeding and so they're classified as separate species.[569]

So because the Levantine humans that emerged from the bottleneck were no longer subject to sexual predation and interbreeding with Eurasian Neanderthals, they were now a sexually isolated breeding population. If Neanderthal males came around looking for females, they would now be given short shift. The days of predation were over.

More to the point, though, the post-bottleneck Levantines were physically and behaviourally so different from their pre-bottleneck ancestors as to be virtually unrecognisable. This indicates that a speciation event took place. They were no longer Skhul-Qafzeh. Indeed they would probably look down on Skhul-Qafzeh folk as dumb, timid brutes with whom the prospect of interbreeding would be repulsive. In every respect, the post-bottleneck people were now effectively a new species. But what species?

the black sheep of the family

Although they possessed many characteristics of fully modern humans of today, when it came to outward appearances the post-bottleneck modern humans were most likely quite different from both their pre-bottleneck ancestors and fully modern humans. For a start, they had slightly larger brains (1600cc compared to 1400cc for today's humans)[570] and as a

This figure from the Natural History Museum in New York is described as a reconstruction of Homo ergaster, *a hominid species that lived in Africa between 1.9 and 1.4 million years ago. However, NP theory asserts that this is what humans looked like 50,000 years ago.*

predator species, acquired a more robust skeletal-muscular physiology,[571] so they looked bigger and beefier than fully modern humans. And, according to anthropologist Vincenzo Formicola's analysis of the data, the males were considerably taller (at 176.2 cm) than their predecessors.[572] In other words, this was a *transitional morphology*—not quite Skhul-Qafzeh, but not quite fully modern human.

Were a crowd of these post-bottleneck humans to appear on the high street today, we might be surprised by how visually different they were from us. Overall these post-bottleneck humans would convey a disconcerting impression. We would probably consider them brutish, ill-formed, hairy and uncouth. And, because their faces appear *unbalanced* (asymmetrical), we would probably judge them unattractive (even ugly) by modern standards. They are after all, still stone-age cavemen and women.

But it would be their behaviour more than anything else that would make them conspicuous. Over thousands of years of continual inter-species warfare, natural selection had retained the toughest, most aggressive, resilient, merciless individuals. Clearly the selection for aggression and risk-taking was directed primarily at adolescent and young adult males who were the ones doing most of the fighting. One simple mechanism of selection focused on males with abnormally high levels of hormones such as testosterone, which has been shown to increase verbal and physical aggression in young males.[573]

By a simple application of Darwinian theory, an hypothesis emerges which proposes that the continual selection for aggression in young males (because it was so adaptive) would gradually produce a cohort that was so innately aggressive and predisposed to violence that a new word was needed to describe them. Modern terms like *hooligans, ruffians* and even *barbarians* won't do. Modern descriptions of male group violence are inadequate for these post-bottleneck people, who existed before rules, civilisation, or even humanity as we know it. Their exceptional level of aggression was selected for because it was adaptive. It wouldn't be today. Only in the context of a war of unimaginable barbarity against a ferocious enemy would this level of aggression be necessary or warranted.

To distinguish this unprecedented level of male aggression, I use the term *hyper-aggressive*. It describes a repertoire of extreme behavioural responses that emerged in response to the aberrant environmental circumstances prevailing at the time. Male hyper-aggression includes a suite of teemic traits that, in addition to negligible impulse control and aggression, also includes paranoia, callousness, ruthlessness, sadism and absence of empathy, remorse and love.

In 1941, Hervey Cleckley, a psychiatrist with the Medical College of Georgia, described a similar list of personality traits and behaviours in modern humans and called it 'psychopathology'.[574] There can be little doubt that your average post-bottleneck male would be classified as a psychopath according to diagnostic criteria developed by Robert Hare from the University of British Columbia, the current world authority on the subject.

However, it's important to put the psychopathology of these early modern humans into context. They lived in a time before morals and ethics existed, so of course it follows that they were *immoral* and *unethical.* Romantic love was still in its infancy. Empathy for anyone beyond the family or the tribal group was practically anathema. And having a conscience, feeling guilty or empathising with one's victim was not only useless, it was almost certainly maladaptive.

This NP theory view of a malignantly aggressive 'psychopathic' transitional species is at odds with most palaeontologists who argue these people were fully modern—indistinguishable from you and me. Anthropology does not currently recognise the need for an interim species between Upper Palaeolithic stone-age people and ourselves. But NP theory argues that, although the new hyper-aggressive humans had come a long way, their journey was far from over. Natural selection still had a great deal of fine tuning to do (including exorcising the genes for hyper-aggression) before one of these post-bottleneck humans could attend the theatre without causing a riot.

To distinguish the transitional clade of hyper-aggressive early modern humans that sprang from the Levantine bottleneck—cantankerous and spoiling for a fight—I have revived the term *Cro-Magnon.*

it's payback time

In drama, good characters drive the plot. So, with the dramatic entrance of a compelling new protagonist onto centre stage, our Shakespearian drama of human origins is set for an exciting plot twist, one which will drive the drama to its cathartic climax.

From what we now know about Cro-Magnons, we can predict what happened next. Unconstrained by laws, religion, morals, treaties or codes of civility, hyper-aggressive Cro-Magnons would have embarked on a protracted campaign of retributive violence against the Eurasian Neanderthals.

CRO-MAGNONS

Cro-Magnon was the name given to the earliest modern humans to enter Europe by the French palaeontologist Louis Lartet. Lartet discovered the first five skeletons in the Cro-Magnon rock shelter at Les Eyzies, in south-western France in 1868. Cro-Magnons are the quintessential 'cavemen' of popular literature. Although today the term has mostly been supplanted by anatomically modern or early modern humans, I find the term useful to describe a transitional population between Initial Upper Palaeolithic (or modern) humans and *fully* modern humans.

The object of this 'proto-war' was not dietary predation or territorial encroachment, but something quite unique among the anthropoids—killing members of a sibling species out of extreme antipathy. This in turn is based on an innate sense that it was *them or us*—an instinctive awareness that the two species were mutually exclusive—that there is room for only one of them. Armed with their innovative projectile weapons, newly acquired military tactics, courage, cunning and aggression, Cro-Magnons took every opportunity to exterminate every Neanderthal they came across.

This, I believe, was the first time humans killed other than for the purposes of food, the first time they hunted for *sport*.

From the perspective of a virile young Cro-Magnon male, it is hard to imagine there would be any consideration of the social, political and evolutionary consequences of their murderous campaign. It was intuitive and instinctive—because it was already innate.

Just as lion cubs and other juvenile predators use play to practise the hunting and killing techniques they will use as adults, Cro-Magnon boys would have incorporated their new aggressive proclivities into their development. From an early age, they would have played with toy spears and clubs—the new tools of the trade—and practised hunting and killing Neanderthals. By the time they reached their teenage years, Cro-Magnon boys would be physically, hormonally and socially prepared to take on their fathers' lethal quest.

Today, boys around the world do not pretend to hunt antelope or mammoths to practise future skills. They play variations of 'Cowboys and Indians'—seminal *them and us* battles between humans. These games are the vestigial remnants of ancestral imperatives—innate proclivities that had served to hone the violent duties of adulthood.

There is reason to believe that hyper-aggression included a sexual component. I proposed earlier that one method of achieving hyper-aggression in young Cro-Magnons males was by selecting for extremely elevated levels of serum testosterone. Testosterone also happens to be the primary male sex hormone, elevated levels of which predisposes increased sexual arousal and activity. This means that, not only were Cro-Magnon men hyper-aggressive compared to modern humans, they were almost certainly hyper-sexual as well.

If Cro-Magnon social groups resembled modern hunter-gatherer groups, they would ostensibly congregate in tribes close to fresh water and good hunting grounds. From there, the young men would launch hunting and gathering expeditions, sometimes lasting weeks, or even months. These bands of heavily-armed hyper-aggressive, hyper-sexual young men—genetically charged with a bevy of powerful hormones—posed a threat not only to Neanderthals but to other human populations.

As a hunting and fighting group, the Cro-Magnon men depended on each other for their survival. They hunted, fought, suffered and died together. And doubtlessly they celebrated their victories together. These emotionally shared experiences would create an indelible bond between the men, far more intense than today's male bonding of football teams and fishing buddies. For Cro-Magnons, male bonding was not just social, it was a life and death issue. As such, it was a functional adaptation that directly contributed to their survival and reproductive success.

Also deeply ingrained in the Cro-Magnon psyche was the concept of *them and us*. For them, it represented more than a species divide. It was a life and death distinction, adaptive because it was plain and simple enough for them to understand at a visceral, intuitive level. It had almost nothing to do with rational thought and objective reasoning and everything to do with gut instinct—innate prejudices, sex and violence and deeply entrenched *them and us* mindsets.

There was no precise intellectual concept of *them*. The description applied to almost anyone and anything outside the group. Any mix of sex and violence could be meted out without the slightest remorse to anyone branded 'them'. The Cro-Magnons were probably the most psychopathic humans who ever lived—but they were creatures of their time. With a job to do. And if they had not done their job, none of us would be here.

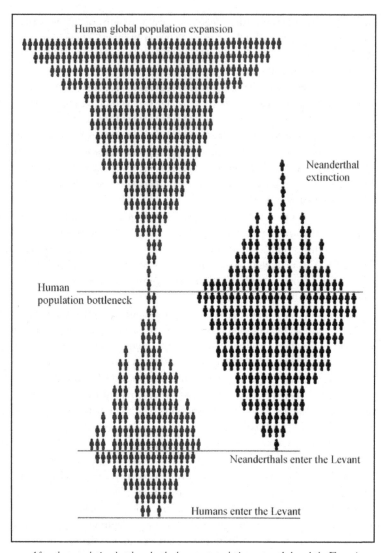

After the population bottleneck, the human population expanded and the Eurasian Neanderthal population plummeted towards extinction.

the first genocide

From a broader sociological perspective, it is immediately apparent what these nomadic bands of hyper-aggressive, hyper-sexed Cro-Magnons were doing. They were practising genocide. It was undirected, haphazard and certainly inefficient by today's standards, but it was highly motivated. And over a few thousand years, the Cro-Magnons drove the Eurasian Neanderthals to extinction.

The genocide hypothesis fits with sociological studies of lethal aggression by male coalitions (modern armies) and with a long history of human warfare, xenophobia and genocide.[575,576,577,578]

In *The Descent of Man*, Charles Darwin has this to say on the propensity of humans to kill off those they considered inferior:

> All that we know about savages, or may infer from their traditions and from old monuments, the history of which is quite forgotten by the present inhabitants, shew that from the remotest times successful tribes have supplanted other tribes.[579]

More importantly, the theory that humans annihilated the Eurasian Neanderthals is consistent with the fossil record of the Levant that shows the Neanderthals disappeared just after the first appearance of the first Upper Palaeolithic humans in the Levant.[580,581,582,583]

John Shea says:

> Throughout Western Eurasia, the end of the Middle Palaeolithic period marks the last appearance of Neanderthals in the fossil record. Between 30–47 Kya, Upper Palaeolithic humans expanded their geographic range to include all the territory formerly occupied by the Neanderthals and other anatomically archaic humans. The Middle Palaeolithic period in the Levant was the last period in which modern humans had serious evolutionary rivals for global supremacy.[584]

NP theory goes even further, predicting that a genocidal war took place, that it was successful, and that it was relatively quick. Why? Because the Cro-Magnons were not only militarily much more advanced than the Eurasian Neanderthals, they were socially bonded into a single massive military group that can only be described as an army—or at the very least a *proto-army*. This was the strategic application of the new socialisation process—a process that effectively united the disparate tribes of Syria, Israel, Palestine, Jordan and other areas of the Levant into a single combative force that swept all before it.

As the raggle-taggle proto-army grew, a tipping point was reached, and the tide began to turn. The Cro-Magnon campaign accelerated its onslaught into a blitzkrieg. Over time, this search and destroy operation became genetically encoded in testosterone-charged adolescent and young adult males and continued unabated—generation after generation—until not a single Neanderthal was left alive from northern Turkey to Egypt.

This view is supported by the archaeology. John Shea concludes in *Modern Human Origins and Neanderthal Extinctions in the Levant*, "that around 45,000–35,000 BP, Neanderthal fossils cease to occur in the Levant at exactly the point when Upper Palaeolithic industries first appear in Israeli and Lebanese cave sites."[585]

At the Amud Neanderthal cave, northwest of the Sea of Galilee in Israel, for instance, materials dated from the lowest levels of the cave reveals that Neanderthals first occupied the site 110,000 years ago ($\pm$ 8,000 years). The youngest date measured at the site comes from a single tooth from Level B1/6 which tells us the occupation ended 43,000 years ago ($\pm$ 5000 years).[586]

Until recently, it was generally assumed that the disappearance of Eurasian Neanderthals from the Levant was caused by a deterioration in the climate. But in April 2008, at a meeting of the American Association of Physical Anthropologists, Miriam Belmaker from Harvard University deftly demonstrated that the climate in the Levant at the time of their extinction was stable, ruling out climate change as a factor in their disappearance.[587]

power plays and mind games

If NP theory is correct and Cro-Magnons were a hyper-aggressive new transitional species, purpose-built by natural selection to kill Neanderthals, then it follows that even after the disappearance of the last Neanderthal, Levantine males would simply disperse further afield in search of more victims. They had spent several thousand years relentlessly hunting their ancestral foe—this is what young Cro-Magnon males did—and they were not going to stop now.

But NP theory and an understanding of human nature also predicts something else happened: the proto-army of the Levant began to fall apart, and ultimately turned against itself.

The alpha males who, by force of strength and aggression, had maintained cohesion within the group became besieged by eager and ambitious young males determined to assume their mantle. Here, I suggest, is the origin of that unique and ubiquitous pattern of human group dynamics, distinguished by male intergroup competition, power plays, political divisions, leadership challenges, Machiavellian intrigues, betrayals, 'civil war' and chaos. The techniques that had been so effective in conquering Neanderthals had found a fertile new outlet within Cro-Magnon society

As the proto-army grew too large to be effectively managed, fed, organised and controlled, secondary leaders (beta males) saw an opportunity. Taking advantage of the increasing frustration, they agitated, conspired and aspired to be alpha males with access to all the fertile females. Leadership challenges became a constant fixture of the times. Retributions for unsuccessful coup attempts were swift and violent, and deposed leaders would be banished or killed. Dissent spread, disorder became the status quo and eventually some beta males broke away or were expelled, taking their warriors and their families with them. These smaller armies then spread out from the Levant to conquer and colonise their own territories.

While this scenario is, at best, informed conjecture, it is supported by the genetic and archaeological evidence, which reveals the Levant human population did split into at least three large groups that eventually dispersed out of the Levant at precisely that time.

One group migrated east, around the coast of India into eastern Asia, and eventually across the Bering Plain (Beringia) to people the Americas.[588,589]

A second group dispersed from the Levant to Europe, while a third migrated back to Africa.[590,591,592] These migrations all date to between 45,000 to 40,000 years ago.

Suggesting that the third group of Levantine humans migrated south into Africa—their ancestral homeland—is at odds with the long-held assumption that the world-wide dispersal of modern humans began in Africa. Corroborative evidence for the *back migration theory* only emerged in December 2006, via a landmark study of mitochondrial DNA from ancient human fossils by an international team of 15 geneticists lead by Antonio Torroni from the University of Pavia in Italy.[593] The study, published in *Science*, reports that between 40,000 to 45,000 years ago, a group of modern humans living in the Levant split into genetically separate groups. Torroni traces one group as it moved north into Europe, and another that moved back to Africa.

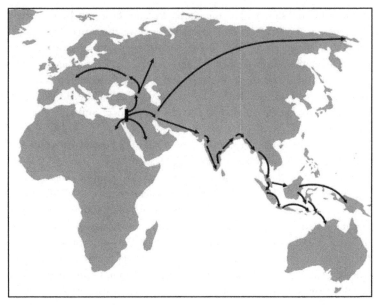

*The global expansion of modern humans began in the Levant and dispersed to
Europe, Africa, Asia, Australia and the Americas, via a coastal, island-hopping
route.*

By measuring the amount of genetic diversity in the mtDNA and on
the Y (male) chromosome, Torroni's group concludes, "the first Upper
Palaeolithic cultures in North Africa (Dabban) and Europe (Aurignacian)
had a common source in the Levant",[594] spreading by migration from a
core area in the Levant.

The Upper Palaeolithic Levantine people that Torroni refers to (that
first appeared 46,000 to 45,000 years ago) dispersed to south-eastern
Europe via Turkey around 43,000 years ago.[595,596,597,598]

The date of the dispersal from the Levant (45,000 to 40,000 years
ago) agrees with the near-extinction hypothesis of NP theory and the
emergence of a new human species as a consequence of Neanderthal
predation.

The pace of this dispersal fits with my more nuanced view that Cro-
Magnons, unlike their Middle Palaeolithic predecessors, were not averse
to risk-taking, exploration or territorial expansion. It also supports NP
theory's proposal that the incursion into Europe was not a nonchalant
nomadic migration in search of hunting and gathering opportunities, but
a militaristic blitzkrieg by hyper-aggressive males inherently confident

of their colonising and military capabilities. This indication of a new 'conquistadorial' component of human nature creates the impression that Cro-Magnons believed their technological and psychological superiority made them invincible—that nothing and no one could stand in their way. This was the first example of military expansionism, and it set the stage for the first real world war.

20 THE INVASION
OF EUROPE

In Europe, the Cro-Magnons encountered the European species of *Homo neanderthalensis* for the first time.[599] The narrative history of the two species proposed by NP theory predicts an inevitable outcome of this interaction: that from around 44,000 years ago, when they first entered Europe from the east, hyper-aggressive Cro-Magnon males threw themselves into a protracted campaign against a well-entrenched (and much larger) population of European Neanderthals. This first successful incursion into traditional Neanderthal territory had all the hallmarks of an invasion. Its intention was nothing less than the complete eradication of Neanderthals from their ancestral homeland.

The archaeology shows that the euphemistically named 'replacement' began in the east and progressed in a westerly direction across continental Europe.[600,601] The first Neanderthals to be replaced by Cro-Magnons were living in Eastern Europe, followed by those in France, Greece, Italy and finally Spain.[602]

What the fossil record and carbon dating agree on is that in every individual case of replacement, the Neanderthals disappear from the fossil record only after modern humans have moved into their territory. Even though Neanderthals had survived in Europe for over 300,000 years—often in the most extreme climatic conditions—it was only once Cro-Magnons occupied their territory that they disappeared. In other words, Cro-Magnons swept across Europe in an east-west direction and

THE CRO-MAGNON INVASION OF EUROPE

Arcy-sur-Cure

Cro-Magnon
Châtelperron

Ebro

Spain, the last stronghold

Gorham Cave

Africa

Neanderthals became extinct in the same east-west direction at exactly the same time.

Although isolated regional populations of European Neanderthals survived in mountainous regions of Croatia and the Caucasus until about 29,000 years ago,[603,604] the last remaining Neanderthals appear to have been pushed down the Iberian peninsula to Gibraltar on the southern tip of Spain.

This is not to say that the European Neanderthals were a pushover. They were a well-entrenched, formidable adversary, with exceptional hunting and tracking skills, knowledge of the terrain, superior physical strength and indomitable courage. And they were now fighting for their lives. The fact that the replacement began around 44,000 years ago and took 20,000 years to complete suggests the European Neanderthals put up one hell of a fight.

Another factor that almost certainly contributed to the protracted nature of the conflict was the size of the Neanderthals' territory. When Cro-Magnons from the Levant invaded Europe, they could have had no idea that the enemy occupied an area of 10 million square kilometres. And in the Late Pleistocene, a few hundred thousand Neanderthals could easily disappear for long stretches, particularly in the forests and mountains, avoiding contact with the intruders.

But I suggest there is one more important reason why it took 20,000 years to eradicate the last Neanderthal from Europe, and that reason should come as no surprise. The Neanderthals had begun to mutate.

oh no! the neanderthals are mutating

Earlier, I proposed that as the human population in the Levant collapsed under the impact of Neanderthal predation, it concentrated defensive and strategic adaptations in the few surviving humans. Could the same thing have happened in Europe with the Neanderthals?

As the European Neanderthal population crashed under the onslaught of the Cro-Magnon's military superiority, did the last remaining Neanderthals flee westward and form into small survivor groups? And did those survivors manage to hold on because they were smarter, tougher and more aggressive? I believe the dynamic is similar enough to suggest that the remaining Neanderthals did indeed gradually coalesce into small 'super-tribes'—just as the Skhul-Qafzehs did in the Levant. Individual adaptations like improved intelligence, language, aggression, creativity, and so on would then spread throughout the tribe. This would be perhaps the major reason why it took Cro-Magnons 20,000 years to conquer Europe.

This theory generates several specific predictions which can be tested against reliable archaeological data:

- Firstly, if European Neanderthals acquired their own collection of strategic adaptations, then there should be physical evidence in the archaeology. Some time between 35,000 and 28,000 years ago, when the European Neanderthal population was plummeting towards extinction, we should expect to see Upper Palaeolithic artefacts suddenly appearing in their sites.

- Secondly, constant close-quarter, hand-to-hand fighting generated selection pressure in early modern humans for greater athleticism, speed and agility in the Levant, so we might expect this to happen with Neanderthals in Europe. Because increased speed, manoeuvrability and athleticism require a more gracile skeleton, the model predicts that European Neanderthals who survived longest against the Cro-Magnon onslaught developed smaller, more gracile bodies that allowed them to move, dodge, weave and run faster than their predecessors.

Given that Neanderthals' Middle Palaeolithic culture (called *Mousterian culture* after the stone tools and weapons they fashioned) and their robust physiology had remained virtually unchanged for at least 300,000 years, a sudden last-minute transition to Upper Palaeolithic culture and a new gracile form are not what most palaeontologists would predict. The expectation would be of either continual stasis (nothing changes) or very gradual change over thousands of generations. Because the two predictions are so at odds with expectations, they provide an excellent test of my proposal that some European Neanderthals underwent a late transition to the Upper Palaeolithic.

Not only is there solid evidence that some European Neanderthals made a dramatic last minute transition to Upper Palaeolithic (often referred to as the 'late flowering') but scientists are at a loss to explain what caused it. All they know for certain is that between 35,000 and 30,000 years ago (just when the Neanderthals were becoming extinct in most of Europe) the archaeological record in western and central Europe shows unmistakable evidence of an abrupt and uncharacteristic transition to Initial Upper Palaeolithic culture at a few Neanderthal sites.[605,606,607]

These artefacts include Upper Palaeolithic stone tools and weapons, shell necklaces (*above*) and bracelets, plus carved ivory and bone artefacts. Nothing similar had ever been discovered at any Neanderthal site, so it caused considerable excitement and discussion in the scientific community when these artefacts were first uncovered.

The late flowering of Neanderthal culture has been labelled *the Châtelperron*, after the French cave where it was first discovered. Importantly, dates obtained from the Neanderthal Upper Palaeolithic artefacts (such as the spear point, *right*) at Châtelperron cave (la Grotte aux Fées), and from Arcy-sur-Cure (also in France) have been dated at 36,000 to 34,000 years old[608,609] and 34,000 years old,[610] respectively. This coincides with the westward progression of Cro-Magnons into central and western Europe between 40,000 and 35,000 years ago.

But there is more. Based on biomechanical analysis of the bones from the Saint-Césaire 1 Neanderthal specimen from another Châtelperronian site, Erik Trinkaus showed that a shift in locomotive patterns occurred in late European Neanderthals and was:

...associated with increased mobility and seen more frequently among early modern humans than among the Neandertals. The impression is of a late Neandertal, in the context of significant cultural change, reflecting in its otherwise fully Neandertal biology the emergence of an early modern human behavioural pattern."[611]

The Châtelperronian Neanderthals were becoming more gracile in their physiology, more competitive, and more dangerous. In a sense, they were becoming more like humans. After shunning the Upper Palaeolithic club for 300,000 years, the Châtelperronian Neanderthals had suddenly gate-crashed the party. Their unexpected transition to Initial Upper Palaeo-lithic behaviour supports NP theory's premise of a protracted struggle between two highly evolved, super aggressive, closely matched warrior species.

Because the Châtelperron was so unexpected—and its artefacts so different from anything the Neanderthals had produced in 300,000 years—it was initially thought to be the result of sloppy archaeological practices. But as the evidence for the late flowering increased, researchers started to develop a raft of theories to explain this aberration. They speculated that Neanderthals learned these skills by watching and imitating humans;[612,613] that the artefacts were made by later humans and transferred to Châtelperron levels by disturbances in the ground;[614,615] and that the Châtelperron was the result of cultural exchange with Cro-Magnons—what is called *acculturation*.[616]

Yet another theory argues the Châtelperron was caused by a genetic mutation that altered iodine-function in Neanderthals.[617] And another still that Neanderthals acquired this capacity coincidentally and independently of humans.[618]

Other researchers maintain the Châtelperronians were anatomically 'transitional' between modern humans and Neanderthals,[619] and that the Châtelperron was the result of interbreeding between Neanderthals and Cro-Magnons.[620]

None of these theories explains all the evidence, so none has gained wide acceptance, and the mystery of the Châtelperron remains. Because interbreeding has also been proposed to explain the trend among late Neanderthals towards a gracile (more human) skeleton, the possibility that Cro-Magnons produced offspring with Neanderthals is probably the most popular theory.

exterminate all the brutes!

So did Cro-Magnons interbreed with European Neanderthals? Do modern humans still carry some Neanderthals genes? And does this explain your Uncle Bert's ferocious temper or why that crass 'Neanderthal' at work behaves the way he does? It is certainly a valid question given that most anthropologists, including Erik Trinkaus, believe that interbreeding between sibling species like early humans and Neanderthals was biologically possible.[621]

Professor of Physical Anthropology at New York University Clifford Jolly's work with African baboons also supports the view that Neanderthals and humans could interbreed. Jolly argues that hamadryas and anubis baboons—sibling species—have been genetically separated for longer than humans and Neanderthals—and nevertheless they can still interbreed and produce fertile offspring.

Jolly reasons that Neanderthals and humans were biologically both still part of a common human ancestry and concludes that, "unless an undocumented, radical genetic event occurred in the 600 ka since they shared mtDNA ancestry with the Neanderthals, premodern humans were certainly able to interbreed with them and produce viable, fertile, offspring, as hamadryas and anubis baboons do."[622]

On the basis of his own analysis of the biological origins of human anatomy, Günter Bräuer, Professor of Biological Anthropology at the University of Hamburg, came to a similar conclusion: "there is no evidence from extant primates, current DNA results, or the fossils that would exclude Neandertals from having interbred with modern *Homo sapiens*."[623]

But did they?

When I first developed the NP model, the question of interbreeding was still unresolved. While some scholars argued the two species had been sexually isolated for too long for interbreeding to occur, others said that Cro-Magnons and European Neanderthals could not have coexisted in Europe for all those years without interbreeding.[624,625] After all, they reasoned, they were sibling species.

More and more papers appeared anthropomorphising Neanderthals to such an extent that it became widely held that the two species socially interacted, interbred as equals and probably even traded with each other.

NP theory asserts that, while the evidence points to involuntary interbreeding occurring in the Levant in the early stages of Neanderthal predation, Europe was a different story altogether. It seems inconceivable that humans would voluntarily form cordial sexual relationships with creatures they not only loathed, but considered sub-human. In other words, just because they could, it didn't mean they wanted to.

If NP theory is correct, the more intelligent Cro-Magnons had now added a new sense of superiority to their list of *them and us* differences. Enhanced cognitive capacity provides one of the most acute divides between pre-bottleneck and post-bottleneck humans. There is a rarely-used word that aptly describes this latest Neanderthal-derived addition to human nature. It's *ethnocentrism*—from the Greek, *anthropos*, 'human being'; and *kentron*, 'centre'. It describes the belief that humans tower over every other animal species in all major criteria.

Cro-Magnons had always looked on Neanderthals as ugly and deformed. Now, as the military balance swung in their favour, they would also have increasingly looked down on them as dumb, crass halfwits. Stupidity had become another Neanderthal divide. The idea of finding these creatures sexually attractive would have been repulsive, just as it would be today. Neanderthals, the Cro-Magnons' former nemesis, had become the object of ridicule—the butt of human jokes.

The reversal would also have changed Neanderthal attitudes towards humans. They would now avoid Cro-Magnon females, seeing Cro-Magnons as murderous invaders who killed without pity or mercy. Fearing their lethal arrows, darts and javelins, Neanderthals would have retreated further and further into the forests, mountains and higher latitudes.

So did Cro-Magnons interbreed with European Neanderthals? It is my contention that entrenched attitudes from both sides would almost certainly have stymied any form of benign social interaction—much less widespread interbreeding.

Having taken this position, the growing weight of opinion in favour of interbreeding was a major challenge to NP theory. Social interaction and interbreeding are anathema to the separatist dualism of *them and us* that underlines NP theory. If either the genetic or the archaeological evidence showed significant interbreeding in Europe, then there would be something wrong with NP theory. At one stage, the weight of opinion in favour of interbreeding and admixture was strong enough to suggest my theory was fatally flawed.

However, during the last five years, the study of paleoanthropology and human origins has been given a shot in the arm by the emerging field of comparative molecular biology. This involves extracting and amplifying snippets of ancient DNA from fossilised bones and comparing them with genetic material from other specimens, including modern human DNA.

In the last few years, a trickle of these genetic studies began appearing

Teem theory argues that an innate emotional description of our natural predator is hard wired into our ncDNA. This is sometimes portrayed in political propoganda (above and overleaf).

in anthropological and archaeological journals with titles like "No evidence of Neandertal mtDNA contribution to early modern humans".[626] In that study, comparative mtDNA data extracted from four Neanderthal fossils from Germany, Russia, and Croatia show that interbreeding between European Neanderthals and modern humans was *not* a feature of the European interaction.

Soon there was a flood of similar research—all reaching the same conclusion—human and European Neanderthal DNA was too different for them to be the same species. They were separate species and, if interbreeding occurred in Europe, it was at such an insignificant rate, it failed to show up in the data.[627, 628, 629]

In 2006, Svante Pääbo from the Max Planck Institute for Evolutionary Anthropology in Leipzig managed to sequence almost a million base pairs of nuclear DNA from a male European Neanderthal from Croatia. When he compared the sequence to that of a modern human, the result was unequivocal. They were palpably different in many important respects. Based on the degree of divergence, Pääbo estimated the two lineages had diverged approximately 300,000 years ago and since then, little or no interbreeding had occurred.

By late 2008, mtDNA had been extracted from 13 European Neanderthal fossils and nuclear DNA had been extracted from another handful and none of them revealed evidence of

interbreeding,[630] although there's always the possibility that the amount of Neanderthal DNA was so small it was swamped by the human genes.[631]

But what about the archaeological evidence from Europe—what do the bones themselves say? Probably the only plausible archaeological claim of European hybridisation is the 'Lapedo child' from the Lagar Velho rock shelter in Portugal, which was proposed in 1999 to be a Neanderthal-human hybrid.[632] This made news all around the world at the time but it was not long before it was challenged.[633] Researchers who re-examined the fossils claimed the child was just a heavy-boned human. The authors of the original paper issued a rebuttal[634] and, to date, the Lapedo child has not been resolved. However, one questionable case of possible hybridisation in Europe, which abounds with both Neanderthal and Cro-Magnon sites, is certainly not what would be reasonably expected given that the two species occupied the same area for 20,000 years.

In 2006, Jean-Luc Voisin, from the Muséum National d'Histoire Naturelle in Paris, conducted an exhaustive study of the anatomy of Eurasian Neanderthals (from the Levant) and compared it to a sample of European Neanderthals. He found that while the Eurasian Neanderthals were more 'modern', which he interpreted as evidence of interbreeding, European cousins showed no evidence of hybridisation.[635]

For anthropologists, the evidence that humans and Eurasian Neanderthals interbred in the Levant, but not in Europe does not make sense. But for NP theory, it is precisely what is expected and predicted.

sexual violence

Now for an important qualifier. Although Cro-Magnons did not have children with European Neanderthals, this does not mean they did not occasionally have sex with them. On the basis of the model of Cro-Magnon behavioural ecology developed from NP theory, there can be little doubt that some highly sexed Cro-Magnon males would have occasionally raped and sexually abused Neanderthal females and children.

This is admittedly a speculation, but it is supported by a voluminous literature on rape as a weapon of war,[636] and its use as a tactic of terror in war by the direct descendants of the Cro-Magnons—modern humans. The tradition of rape by Cro-Magnon males in that first proto-war hints at the evolutionary origins of the rape of war victims by modern human males.

But here we come to an important distinction. While the earliest historical, Biblical and mythical accounts confirm that soldiers habitually raped the women and girls (and sometimes boys) of vanquished peoples, they also show the victors did not always kill their victims. There are hundreds of accounts of women and girls being put to the sword once the soldiers had been gratified, but there are ample reports of females being kept alive, invariably to be used as sex slaves and concubines. This naturally resulted in a number of 'slave children' who were sometimes absorbed into their father's society.

When we apply this to the rape of Neanderthal females by Cro-Magnon men, it predicts that there should have been a proliferation of Cro-Magnon-Neanderthal hybrids. But, as we've just seen, there were none. The only scenario that adequately explains this, and that squares with the view of Cro-Magnons as a particularly violent clade, is that Cro-Magnon men *always* killed their Neanderthal rape victims. And if by any chance, a female survived and gave birth as a result of the rape, it too would be killed.

the last neanderthal bites the dust

Despite the sporadic late flowering of Neanderthal culture, the last Châtelperron assemblages (at Arcy-sur-Cure and Quinçay, in France) vanish about 34,000 years ago. Among the last surviving populations of European Neanderthals are those from Gibraltar,[637] dated to 28,000 years ago, but with some bone samples reliably dated as recently as 24,000 years ago.[638] With them disappeared forever one of the toughest and most durable hominid species of all time.

The reason why the European Neanderthal population became extinct when the Levantine human population recovered after its own near-extinction event was, I think, because the persecution of European Neanderthals by Cro-Magnons was not based on dietary predation. When predation is simply about killing for food, prey species usually recover in number when they are no longer worth the time and effort to hunt.

But if the objective of Cro-Magnon aggression was not dietary, then the cyclical pattern that normally allows the prey species to recover its numbers would not occur. Because NP theory nominates genocide as the objective of the European territorial incursion, it predicts that successive generations of humans kept relentlessly hunting Neanderthals throughout their entire European habitat until they were eliminated.

While the genocide model may seem somewhat melodramatic to those who take an anthropocentric view of humanity, it is a lynchpin of NP theory. Ironically, it is also one of the few elements of NP theory that accords with conventional anthropological thinking. The idea that Cro-

Magnons killed off the European Neanderthals is a view held by a sizable proportion of academics.[639,640,641,642,643]

In anthropological terms, it is known somewhat euphemistically as the *competitive replacement model*, and it was first proposed by French palaeontologist Marcellin Boule (the first person to publish an analysis of a Neanderthal) in 1912.[644]

Claudio Cioffi-Revilla, a computational social scientist from George Mason University in Virginia, calls the replacement a "large-scale violent eviction accompanied by purposive massacre"[645] and defines it as history's first genocide.

Another supporter of competitive replacement is Jared Diamond, who points out in his book *The Third Chimpanzee* that the genocidal replacement of Neanderthals by modern humans is similar to modern human patterns of behaviour that occur whenever people with advanced technology invade the territory of less advanced people.[646]

The competitive replacement model is not, however, universally accepted and one of the reasons for this is that it does not explain *why* Cro-Magnons eradicated the Neanderthals. NP theory's contribution to the competitive replacement model is to provide the all-important *motive*—the hatred of a former prey species of its erstwhile predator.

where are the bodies?

Another criticism of the competitive replacement model is a familiar one— that there are no mass graves or other unequivocal evidence of a genocide in either the Levant or Europe.[647] We learn from watching shows like *CSI* that violent crimes usually leave some forensic evidence, so we half expect to unearth mass graves or other unequivocal forensic evidence. Realistically though, it cannot be expected that archaeologists will dig up a pile of 40,000-year-old Neanderthal bones from some long-forgotten massacre site, complete with Cro-Magnon arrowheads embedded in their ribs.

Usually, the only time we find fossilised hominid bones is when they've been purposely buried or thrown into a bog. Unlike modern massacres like Srebrenica, where an estimated 8000 men and boys were shot and buried during the Bosnian War, Cro-Magnons would not be concerned about burying their victims. It is more likely that Neanderthals would be left to rot at the kill site, or butchered and consumed for their meat.

Although an unpalatable idea, a wealth of anthropological evidence reveals that from the beginning of recorded history, humans have occasionally eaten their victims—sometimes as a mark of disrespect, at other times to acquire valued attributes (like courage, strength) from their vanquished foes.

Proof for this theory arrived only in May 2009 when a paper in the *Journal of Anthropological Sciences* (**87**, pp 153-185) presented startling new evidence from an Upper Palaeolithic cave in France. When scientists from the Centre National de la Récherche Scientifique in Paris re-examined a number of human bones found in the cave, they discovered that one jawbone actually belonged to a Neanderthal. This was the first time the remains of a European Neanderthal had been found in a Cro-Magnon site. But what was even more remarkable was that the jawbone of the Neanderthal had been sliced with flint knives. None of the human bones showed cut marks. According to lead author Fernando Rozzi, the Neanderthal had been butchered by the humans, its tongue cut out and its flesh eaten, and its teeth possibly used to make a necklace. After the feast, the humans had tossed the bones onto a rubbish heap of butchered bones of deer and other animals. Rozzi concluded, "Neanderthals met a violent end at our hands and in some cases we ate them."

The Les Rois Neanderthal jawbone from south-western France reveals unequivocal evidence of butchering by Upper Palaeolithic humans. After processing, the remains were dumped in a pile of butchery waste inside the cave. This discovery adds to the growing body of evidence that Cro-Magnons wiped out Neanderthals in both the Levant and in Europe.

The violent replacement hypothesis is also supported by a wealth of circumstantial evidence. For instance, almost every excavated European Neanderthal skeleton reveals evidence of trauma injuries.[648,649,650] Significantly, almost all the injuries are head and upper body injuries that had healed, or else mid-shaft 'parry' fractures—the kind you get when you hold your arm up to deflect a blow. In the past, these head and upper body injuries have generally been thought to have been caused while Neanderthals were hunting large game.[651] And doubtlessly some were. But field studies of modern hunter-gatherers show that they're extremely cautious in stalking and capturing prey (as well as in their choice of prey) which means that hunting injuries are rare. This cautious approach makes sense. Even superficial lesions can result in septicaemia and fractures that prevent a person from walking, much less hunting and gathering.

Also, if these injuries were received from kicking, biting and thrashing prey, you would expect them to be evenly distributed over a Neanderthal's body. But the fact that they mostly concentrated around the head and torso suggests they were purposefully inflicted during combat. But with whom? Cro-Magnons or other Neanderthals?

Damage to the bones of European Neanderthal under-represents the number of trauma injuries they suffered during their short lives. This is because most lethal injuries are to soft-tissue organs like the heart, lungs, liver and kidneys, which do not affect the bones. For example, a US study found only 16.6 percent of assault injuries damaged bone.[652] This kind of data prompted bioarchaeologist Phillip Walker to posit that "the frequency of injuries detected in ancient skeletal remains is just the 'tip of the iceberg' in terms of the actual incidence of injuries." [653]

The osteological evidence of pervasive violence against European Neanderthals is also consistent with the fact that they lived, on average, to only 30 years of age, while early Eurasian Neanderthals from Shanidar Cave in Iraq lived to over 40 years. This indicates that something (or someone) in the European environment was killing Neanderthals prematurely. Evolutionary biologist Niles Eldredge notes that although there is no hard evidence for genocide, "we all know what has gone on throughout recorded times whenever one group of *Homo sapiens* invades the territory of another."[654]

what about climate change?

Various other replacement scenarios have been put forward and need to be considered as part of the discussion. While climate change has already been ruled out as being responsible for the extinction of the Eurasian Neanderthals, it has nevertheless been proposed as a factor in the extinction of European Neanderthals.[655] This theory has been put forward by British archaeologist Clive Finlayson, who believes deteriorating climatic conditions wiped out the European Neanderthals.

This argument is hard to accept given that Neanderthals were a cold-adapted species. Theoretically, they would be much more adapted to deteriorating climatic conditions than the warm-adapted Cro-Magnons.

This view is supported by University of Oxford archaeologist Sarah Milliken's comprehensive 2007 study of Neanderthals in Italy. Milliken reported that although the climate in Italy during their occupation included periods of fluctuating climates, even extreme ice-ages, the Neanderthals nevertheless adapted to the variable conditions by moving to more convivial regions:

> During the last interglacial and glacial cycle the Italian peninsula was characterized by a mosaic landscape in a constant state of flux, and Neanderthal occupation of different regions ebbed and flowed in both an altitudinal and a latitudinal sense in response to these climatic oscillations.[656]

Part of the reason for their success, Milliken suggests, is that, "Neanderthal foraging practices, technology and land use were clearly quite flexible, varying from place to place as a function of local environmental factors."[657]

The Italian Neanderthals were in fact so cold-adapted and so resilient that they could occupy sites 700 metres above sea level in the Swiss Alps and Apennines Mountains. None of their Lower Palaeolithic ancestors had ever occupied these high altitude sites.[658]

At about the same time as Milliken's paper appeared, a research team of palaeoecologists at the University of Leeds led by Chronis Tzedakis put another nail in the climate change theory. Writing in *Nature* in 2007, the researchers demonstrated convincingly that the most extreme climate change in Europe did not occur until 3000 years after the last Neanderthal became extinct.[659]

These findings are supported by climate research at the Planck Institute for Evolutionary Anthropology. In a recent press release, a palaeoanthropologist with the Institute Katerina Harvati says, "Our findings suggest that there was no single climatic event that caused the extinction of the Neanderthals."[660]

Finally, in late 2008, an international group of anthropologists reported the results of their detailed re-examination of the ecological and environmental factors thought to be implicated in the extinction of the Neanderthals. Their conclusions: "The southerly contraction of Neanderthal range in south-western Europe during Greenland Interstadial 8 was not due to climate change or a change in adaptation, but rather concurrent AMH [anatomically modern human] geographic expansion appears to have produced competition that led to Neanderthal extinction."[661]

all quiet on the western front

NP theory's prediction of the genocide of the European Neanderthals also fits circumstantially with the recorded history of humanity from the Neolithic onwards. That history is dominated by frequent human warfare, invasion, genocide and the violent replacement of indigenous populations by militarily superior forces. The tendency to divide humans into *in-groups* and *out-groups*, tribes or proto-nation states (all expressions of *them and us*) and to violently replace *the others* is well-established by the Neolithic Period (13,000 years ago). This too fits with the NP model. Also ubiquitous by Neolithic times are enormous coalitions of humans doing battle (the first real armies) with the social structures necessary to create, organise and control them.

Such large-scale militaristic aggregations are unknown among modern primates, prompting speculation that this innate propensity was selected into the human genome because it contributed to survival. While NP theory envisages perhaps the only scenario where the formation of large armies would be adaptive, it does not constitute proof, except of a circumstantial nature.

Ultimately, the only certainty is that by 24,000 years ago, the Neanderthals had disappeared forever.

There is a cave on a stony beach overlooking the Mediterranean Sea at Gibraltar, which ostensibly was inhabited by some of the last surviving

Gorham's Cave (centre), Gibraltar. Although the water now laps at its entrance, when Neanderthals lived there the sea level was much lower. According to Clive Finlayson, this is where some of the last European Neanderthals held out, hunting seal, dolphin and fish. Photo: C. Finlayson

Neanderthals. Carbon dates from Gorham's Cave tell us they held out here till 28,000 years ago (and maybe as late as 24,000 ago) long after their European cousins had perished. It appears these Neanderthals had been pushed west by the advancing Cro-Magnon proto-army until they hit the Atlantic Ocean. They then turned south, crossed the Pyrenees and headed down the Iberian peninsula. Finally, they reached the southern coast of Spain where the Mediterranean Sea stopped them dead.

Somewhat ironically, from the mouth of the Gorham's Cave they could look across the Strait of Gibraltar and, on a clear day, catch a glimpse of North Africa—their ancestral home. Unable to build boats to cross the 14 kilometre stretch of ocean, the Neanderthals were trapped there—in a continent now ruled by Cro-Magnons—to await the inevitable.

These particular Neanderthals appear to have been part of that late surviving group that acquired some Initial Upper Palaeolithic behaviours. For instance, recent excavations at Gorham and Vanguard caves reveal the Neanderthals harvested molluscs, seal, dolphin and fish,[662] which one of the study's authors, Clive Finlayson says reveals them to be intelligent and adaptable hunters, rather than knuckle-dragging brutes.

For the Cro-Magnons involved in that final engagement in southern Spain, it was perhaps just another battle—one more fight in a lifetime filled with warfare. Once that hardy band of Neanderthals were gone, the Cro-Magnons could have no idea of the extraordinary situation they now found themselves in. The world had changed. After more than 75,000 years, the great struggle was over. For the first time—humans were alone. They were now the undisputed 'masters of the universe'.

PART III

US ALONE

With the death of the last Neanderthal, it might reasonably be expected that the traumatic influence which Neanderthals exerted over human evolution for so many thousands of years had finally come to an end. Never again should humans fear the dark, the murky shadows of the forest, or a wide-eyed stranger. Unfortunately, it did not happen like that. The pervasive influence that Neanderthals had exerted over humanity was far from over. Even though we were now alone, the worst was yet to come.

21 TOWARDS A NEW SPECIES

alone at last

As the victors of Gorham's Cave were consolidating their position as the new masters of Europe, their Cro-Magnon cousins who left the Levant at the same time (between 50,000 to 45,000 years ago) to seek their fortunes in Africa and Asia were no less successful. Over the next 20,000 years, Cro-Magnons achieved a massive population expansion and colonised six continents.[663] This impressive achievement is hardly surprising given that not only were they highly intelligent, but they had the conquistadorial spirit and the sophisticated weapons to back it up. And they were still hyper-aggressive.

Inevitably, the three original migrations from the Levant (to Europe, Asia and Africa) gradually split into hundreds, then thousands of nomadic hunter-gatherer tribes that became the founding populations of the first ethnic groups and proto-nation states.

This is the short familiar story. What's left to be answered is how the Cro-Magnons made the final transition from gruff, maniacally aggressive cavemen and women to fully modern humans?

Cro-Magnons were ostensibly Upper Palaeolithic, but that does not mean they were as smart or as creative as today's humans. This is an important point and worth elaboration. The Cro-Magnons did not invent writing, the stone arch or even agriculture. The first representational cave art does not appear for another 10,000 years. Agriculture and the first pottery only appeared 30,000 years after the Cro-Magnons burst onto the world stage. The wheel was not invented until the fifth millennium BC (by the Mesopotamians), and even then it was only a potter's wheel. And although their lives depended on improved weaponry, Cro-Magnons never invented metallurgy and the smelting of copper and tin to produce bronze weapons. That did not happen until the late fourth millennium BC—40,000 years later—about the time the Mesopotamians created the first cuneiform writing system.

A hallmark of modern humanity is that motley collection of social, economic and political systems and settlement patterns we call *civilisation*, which dates to only around the sixth millennium BC, to the Sumerian culture of southern Mesopotamia.

Colin Renfrew, director of the McDonald Institute for Archaeological Research, calls this the *sapiens paradox*:

> It seems a paradox that while the most significant steps in human evolution in the physical sense occurred more than 40,000 years ago, with the emergence of our species, *Homo sapiens sapiens*, the salient aspects of human behaviour which distinguish our species so markedly from that of the other mammals emerged in many cases very much later. 'By their works ye shall know them' seems a good motto for the archaeologist, and the most prominent of those works post-date the Upper Palaeolithic period.[664]

Renfrew's paradox concept is a useful one, and any unified theory of human evolution needs to at least attempt to resolve it. From the perspective of NP theory, it is not a paradox at all. It is precisely what is to be expected if Cro-Magnons were only ever a transitional species.

The image of a Cro-Magnon correctly conjures up a half-formed being, something between a modern human and a Frankensteinian brute. Paradoxically, although Cro-Magnons were conceived as an antidote to the violence and destruction of the Neanderthals, they were themselves far more violent and destructive.

One of the reasons why the Cro-Magnons who left the Levant to conquer the world were such a highly variable group is because they left at different times. Some families and groups left very early—straight after the population bottleneck—with only enough Upper Palaeolithic traits to survive outside their familiar territory. Others stayed in the Levant and accumulated and consolidated more modern traits, so that when they left, they were better equipped to deal with the challenge of capricious foreign environments. Although there were three main migrations out of the Levant (to Africa, Asia and Europe), in reality, these consisted of countless 'trickle migrations' over thousands of years by disparate clans, families and tribes that had splintered away from the original post-bottleneck population.

This raises a new question of fundamental importance to the discussion on human origins. How did these globally dispersed transitional people, with their minor physical and behavioural variations, coalesce into a single unified species—*Homo sapiens sapiens*? In other words, if swarms of variable Cro-Magnon families and clans left the Levant between 50,000 and 40,000 years ago—all heading in different directions, with some ending up on different continents—how did fully modern humans all around the world end up looking and behaving fairly much the same?

This is one of those devilish questions that can throw a spanner into the works of any budding theory of human evolution, a question so intractable, it has hardly ever been raised, much less resolved.

This is not to say that, as Cro-Magnons colonised marginal environments, a few regional differences did not creep in. Of course they did. These included variations in skin colour, height, and hair texture, but these really are only superficial differences and can be simply explained as the result of natural selection selecting favourable traits to cope with specific regional environments like polar or equatorial areas.

For example, if the Cro-Magnons who returned to Africa were, as proposed by NP theory, mostly divested of body hair, this would be maladaptive in the equatorial environment because of the risk of sunburn, skin cancers, heat stroke and so on.

This would normally have generated selection pressure for a return to the thick body fur that protected their African ancestors. However, by then, Neanderthal identification protocols were well entrenched and these now effectively prevented the selection of body hair. The only viable alternative, I suggest, was to select for an increase in the skin pigment melanin, which protects the skin against ultraviolet (UV) radiation.[665]

Likewise, humans who colonised extremely cold climates became slightly smaller and stockier because this helped conserve body heat, just as people inhabiting high altitude acquired lungs with an increased sensitivity to low oxygen levels and hearts that could process glucose more effectively.

But these are minor differences. To illustrate just how similar modern humans from around the world really are, consider firstly that 99.9 percent of everyone's DNA is exactly the same, irrespective of which ethnic group they belong to. And of the remaining 0.1 percent, there is actually more individual variation between members of the same ethnic group than between individuals from completely different ethnic groups separated by continents.[666],[667]

So, despite inconsequential physical variations, modern humans are virtually identical and are all members of the same single species. This is particularly evident when it comes to behaviour. After all, there is only one 'human nature'. Given that species diversity is the rule in the animal kingdom (there are 10,000 species of birds for example) the fact that there is only one species of *sapiens* and we're all so uniform continues to perplex and fascinate life scientists.

So now we have two quandaries. What caused the transitional Cro-Magnons to make the final leap from prehistoric cavemen to smart, fully modern humans? And secondly, given that this transition happened long after the Cro-Magnons split into thousands of geographically isolated groups—separated by four continents and 30,000 years—how did they all end up as one unified species rather than dozens or even hundreds of different subspecies?

Because the current biological models can't even begin to explain the singular uniformity of modern humans, much less how Cro-Magnons came to invent the wheel, writing and other modern marvels, we need to look to Teem theory for answers.

out of sight, out of mind

Suppose for a moment that the last European Neanderthals did live at Gorham's Cave on the southern coast of Spain, as suggested by Clive Finlayson. The Cro-Magnon victors who swept down on them one fateful day could have no idea they had just killed the last Neanderthals.

When it was all over, and only the sound of the surf on the beach filled the air, those burly Cro-Magnon men would have looked around, scratched their furrowed brows, and asked themselves, "Where are the others?".

They probably assumed there were more of these creatures lurking further along the coast. Or in the Andalusian mountains that swept up from the Mediterranean sea. The hunt would continue. And when the victors of Gorham's cave grew old and died, their sons would have continued the hunt. And theirs in turn: for generation after generation.

During all that time, they could not afford to let their defences down. For all they knew, those hairy beasts were still lurking in their dark forest glades, in dank caves, or some hellish 'underworld' beyond human comprehension, making plans—preparing to attack—sneaking out on moonless nights to abduct young women and girls.

But gradually, over time, the real (episodic) memories of European Neanderthals dimmed and faded. Within even a few hundred years of the Neanderthal extinction, the Cro-Magnons would no longer be consciously aware of Neanderthals, or even that they ever existed.

It seems almost incomprehensible that, after being part of the prehistoric landscape for so long, all conscious memory of Neanderthals could be lost. Yet writing had not been invented then, and without a notational system to preserve their recollections of the predation, or their dramatic phoenix-like resurrection from the ashes, the collective memory of the great inter-species struggle would inevitably atrophy.

The upside was that, as the direct memory was lost, the conscious awareness of being hunted and harassed by Neanderthals and the anticipation of hunting them gradually faded too. Cro-Magnons no longer woke with the conscious expectation that they could encounter one of these fearsome creatures.

Is that the end of it then? Not quite.

gone but not forgotten

With the end of the Neanderthals, the innate teemic responses that the Levantine humans had acquired over thousands of years (initially to help identify and escape from Neanderthals, and later to hunt and kill them) were theoretically no longer needed.

This is quite common in evolutionary biology. When a trait no longer performs its original evolutionary function, it is said to be vestigial. The appendix and the coccyx are examples of organs that once performed an evolutionary function.

NP theory proposes, however, that the teems acquired during the Neanderthal predation and the innate behavioural responses they precipitated had been too adaptive for too long to completely disappear. These inherited emotional memories had, after all, protected humans for at least 60,000 years so were genetically encoded in the human genome. Rather than disappear altogether, the preoccupation with Neanderthals simply sank below the surface, into the realm of the subconscious, the imagination and dreams.

From that subterranean vault, the emotions encrypted into Cro-Magnon ncDNA maintained vigilance for Neanderthal triggers—any environmental cue or sign that indicated the presence of Neanderthals. The sight of a hairy newborn baby still sent a frisson up a mother's spine, a wide-eyed foreigner could still spark long-forgotten trepidations and even a raised voice could trigger a primal apprehension.

This is because, in all animal species, vigilance for predators and predator identification is controlled by a primitive area of the reptilian brain called the amygdaloid complex, part of the limbic system, which operates independently of higher brain functions. According to Teem theory, the amygdala is the nerve centre responsible for monitoring teemic triggers. In the case of humans, anything that looked, smelled, sounded, tasted or felt remotely Neanderthaloid would trigger a teem. When triggered, the teem would release emotions such as anxiety, dread, hostility, suspicion and aggression, which in turn would precipitate appropriate behaviours.

These instinctive responses evolved before the mammalian cortex, so still operated independently of consciousness and other cerebral functions. This means that Cro-Magnons were not aware they were monitoring for extinct Neanderthals, nor that such a creature ever existed.

Forty thousand years later, when the poet Percy Bysshe Shelley wrote "In each human heart terror survives", he was expressing what we intuitively know—that every human carries within them a dormant terror, waiting to be awakened.

the secret signs of sexual attraction

Because they helped identify Neanderthals (and Neanderthal characteristics), Neanderthal teems influenced mate selection, which played a major role in the emergence of a single unified species.

When Cro-Magnons selected a mate, their decision was being subliminally influenced by Neanderthal teems and sign stimuli acquired by their Levantine ancestors. All the men would know was that they preferred curvaceous, attractive young women with symmetrical faces, rounded bottoms and full breasts. Flat-chested, straight-waisted and unattractive females with hairy bodies (all subliminally perceived as Neanderthal) were left on the shelf.

Women were guided by their Neanderthal teems just as assiduously as men. Girls eyeing up a potential Cro-Magnon boyfriend would give the thumbs down to anyone who subliminally triggered a Neanderthal teem. That would include boys who were too hairy, did not have a proper chin, had no back to their heads, had hunched shoulders, wrinkled and leathery skin, low foreheads, bull necks, thick brow ridges, an ape-like gait or large, bulbous eyes. In other words, the more you looked like a Neanderthal (*right*) the less chance you had of finding a mate. Today, without knowing the secret history of predation, the word, 'Neanderthal' is used unwittingly as a derogatory term to describe just this suite of undesirable ape-like features and behaviours.

Because Neanderthals were on average slightly shorter than humans (males were 1.7m [5'6"] and females 1.6m [5' 3"] tall), women expressed a teemic preference for taller men. Even today, research shows the shorter the man, the less chance he has of fathering children.[668]

One of the more important evolutionary functions of Neanderthal teems was to provide quick first impressions of strangers. Because teems are automatically and subliminally activated by sign stimuli, they can trigger a subliminal emotional response to a stranger long before any conscious evaluation is formed in the brain. When a Cro-Magnon woman came across a strange young man, sensory stimuli from all her five senses would feed into her limbic system and, if a teem was triggered, it would release emotions that would subliminally inform her attitude towards him—her first impression. In many cases, that was as rudimentary as courtship was. It was either love at first sight, or repulsion. All the flirtatious chit-chat that followed was peripheral. The unconscious decision had already been made.

As the post-bottleneck population spread out across the world, they took their library of inheritable Neanderthal teems with them. These teems subliminally provided aesthetic emotional preferences and attitudes which guided the choice of sexual partners and friends. All over the world, humans began selecting the same kinds of people as mates and this gradually helped unify Cro-Magnon physiology and behaviour.

By providing the criteria to guide the sexual selection of mates, teems exerted an enormous influence over Cro-Magnon evolution. But teems did something even more significant. For the next 20,000 years, Cro-Magnon death squads used Neanderthal teems and sign stimuli to decide who lived, and who died.

EVOLUTION BY
DEATH SQUAD

once were warriors

During the period of Neanderthal predation, Neanderthal teems were amazingly adaptive. Someone who had never seen a Neanderthal could identify one just by the emotions released by their teems. And when Cro-Magnons gained the upper hand, the teems could release homicidal impulses that helped eradicate Neanderthals. But there was one thing teems and sign stimuli could not achieve. They couldn't be 100 percent accurate every time.

This is to be expected as neither teems nor their sign stimuli are regulated by cerebral modules in the brain. Nor, at the time, were cognitive-logic networks sufficiently developed to vet the sign stimuli for accuracy or to mitigate their expression. It must be remembered that the amygdaloid complex that controlled the library of human teems is part of the reptilian brain and functions only as a kind of crude but effective hair-trigger. It generates emotions, hunches, urges and intuitions, but not concrete thoughts, ideas or cognitive precepts.

This inevitably led to errors—not a problem during the years of Neanderthal predation because natural selection blindly opted for a policy of 'better safe than sorry'. But in the post-Neanderthal world, when Cro-

Magnon groups encountered each other and had to decide on the spot whether strangers were friends or foes, they were relying on an archaic emotional method of identification.

The pressure this placed on accurate interpretation of Neanderthal sign stimuli was clearly enormous. But what made it even more difficult was that Cro-Magnon physiology varied a great deal. Being nomadic people, the chances were that a group from, say, Greece could bump into a North African group and the small physical and behavioural differences they had accumulated by genetic drift during their separation would often be enough to trigger ancient fixed action responses.

Additionally, the sign stimuli that activate teems are subject to individual interpretation, including personality and gender factors. What one Cro-Magnon man considered deviant and symptomatic of *them*, another might consider within the range of normality. And when a Cro-Magnon woman might trust her intuition that the mob of scruffy humans she came across were harmless, her male partner might equally respond with paranoid aggression. In the end, they were all trying to make the same difficult call: is that stranger one of *us* or one of *them*?

The life-and-death decision as to whether strangers were *them* or *us* would have usually been made by groups of hyper-aggressive males. Cro-Magnons were so innately xenophobic, and their decisions so blurred by a torrent of testosterone, they could hardly be called impartial. When it came to assessing strangers, they were more lynch mob than judicial review committee.

Finally, vestigial Neanderthal teems need to be considered in their environmental context. The environment the Cro-Magnons inhabited as they spread out to colonise the world was inherently dangerous and stressful—and not only because of the hostile terrain and dangerous animals they encountered. The Cro-Magnons felt they were at war, even if they didn't know with whom. They lived in a perpetual state of subliminal vigilance and anxiety. Because they couldn't know that a large part of their mental functioning was preoccupied with monitoring for *others,* they were left with a generalised sense of unease—what can best be described as low-level paranoia. At the back of their minds were two beliefs—both encoded by teems—one said 'someone or something's out to get me', and the other said 'there's something or someone out there I've got to kill'.

Because teems do not produce detailed descriptions, the exact source of the threat was always open to interpretation. Even innocent events, like the appearance of a harmless stranger, could trigger a Neanderthal fixed action pattern—be it fear and trepidation or bluster and aggression.

In other words, Cro-Magnons had two major innate responses related to Neanderthals—'fight' and 'flight'—and paradoxically they were contradictory and mutually exclusive.

Schools teach our children that humans have a *fight or flight* instinct that originates from encounters with large dangerous animals. That may be true but we know from field studies on other animals that early humans would never choose to fight a dangerous animal if they had a choice. When confronted by a dangerous animal, the most adaptive response was flight.

This raises the prospect that the fight or flight reflex emerged as a result of two contradictory innate behavioural proclivities—to fear and flee Neanderthals, and to confront and engage them. This presupposes that, during the period of Neanderthal predation, humans encoded a number of prey teems that predisposed avoidance and escape. Following the population bottleneck, however, they encoded new teems that predisposed aggression and confrontation. Which kind of teem was released depended on the circumstances. If you were in a group of 100 heavily armed Cro-Magnon males, and you came across a small party of foreign interlopers in your territory, there is little doubt the collective consciousness would favour a fight.

the bloodbath

Applying these hypotheses to interaction scenarios between Cro-Magnon groups produces a number of likely outcomes. Young males would tend to interpret superficial cultural, linguistic and physical differences in other groups as signs of deviancy. Because deviancy is a primary Neanderthal sign stimulus, it would trigger one of two basic deviancy teems. One releases disgust, loathing and lethal aggression, while the other releases trepidation. In actuality, whenever two equally paranoid groups of armed Cro-Magnon males met, hyper-aggression and the absence of cultural restraints almost guaranteed there would be some form of violent interchange.

Another predicted scenario concerns the attitude of Cro-Magnons tribes towards outside groups. The tribes that annihilated the Eurasian and European Neanderthals did so because they were militarily superior, which would have been interpreted as evidence of their superiority as a species. This was part of the broader dehumanisation process that created a distinct hierarchical divide between the species. As this divide became innate, it manifested as an inherent belief in the Cro-Magnons' own mental, emotional, physical, intellectual and military superiority. This anthropocentric mindset would fuel a gung-ho attitude—male bravado—which would have been highly adaptive in the war with the Neanderthals, giving Cro-Magnons the confidence, courage and audacity to take on a formidable enemy. However, when male bravado and the dehumanisation process were directed at other Cro-Magnon groups, they would be anything but adaptive.

With the males of both Cro-Magnon groups—genetically hardwired to perceive their enemy as inferior, with each group innately confident of victory, and in the absence of cognitive faculties able to control these dehumanising mindsets—violence was inevitable.

This vestigial sense of superiority predisposed Cro-Magnons to underestimate the military strength and resolve of rival groups. This meant they occasionally went into battle against overwhelming odds in the belief that they were inherently superior and therefore destined to win.

DEHUMANISATION AND UNDERESTIMATION LIVE ON

Even today, the propensity to see one's enemies as inherently inferior (dehumanisation), means that warring sides continue to underestimate their opponent's military capacity and resolve. Historians and cultural anthropologists have cited underestimating the enemy as a major factor in innumerable military debacles, including the Americans in Vietnam,[669] and Iraq[670] and Israel's 2006 war against Hezbollah.[671]

Anthropocentrism contributed to intergroup violence in other ways too. It was originally adaptive (and selected for) because it helped distinguish humans from *the others*—it effectively dehumanised Neanderthals. It also emboldened Cro-Magnons with an innate belief in their ultimate victory. But now, long after the demise of the Neanderthals, anthropocentrism was being redirected at human surrogates. The propensity towards dehumanisation continued, but acquired a new focus. It exaggerated minor cultural differences between tribes into an irreconcilable abyss, where each tribe saw the other (subliminally at least) not as a different tribe, but as a different species.

In 1966, psychologist Erik Erikson coined the term *pseudospeciation* to describe this kind of mind-set. In *The Biology of Peace and War*,[672] Austrian ethologist Irenäus Eibl-Eibesfeldt showed how pseudospeciation is used to dehumanise enemies and opponents and justify inhumane treatment and atrocities.

Applied to a prehistoric standoff between two tribes glaring at each other across a clearing, it is not difficult to see that, with both sides hardwired with the same anthropocentric networks (predisposing them to perceive the other group as subhuman by virtue of some deviant characteristic), conflict was unavoidable.

These scenarios suggest that, from the extinction of the Neanderthals (around 28,000 years ago) through the Mesolithic Period and into the Late Neolithic period (2500 years ago), lethal violence between coalitions of armed Cro-Magnons was practically continuous.

Throughout this period, nomadic groups of Cro-Magnons attacked, raped, pillaged, tortured and killed each other in a bloodbath of indescribable proportions.

This hypothetical scenario may seem overly dramatic and judgmental towards men, but it is emphatically corroborated by a sizeable body of evidence from crushed skulls and arrow-riddled bodies from countless Neolithic and Mesolithic mass graves and massacre sites. The data confirm an unprecedented period of endemic intergroup and extragroup warfare from the Mesolithic onwards.[673,674,675,676,677,678]

The same palaeoanthropological data also identify who was behind this prehistoric wave of violence. They point squarely to male coalitions (or armies) competing for females and material resources. Stefan Bracha, research psychiatrist from the National Center for Posttraumatic Stress Disorder in Honolulu, and his team describe it in their paper "Evolution of the human fear-circuitry and acute sociogenic pseudoneurological symptoms":

> Neolithic inter-group warfare almost exclusively involved
> attacks against non-combatants in unsuspecting settlements
> by raiding parties of mateless young, post-pubertal males in
> search of material and especially reproductive resources.[679]

Although scholars originally took the view that intergroup warfare was not widespread enough to play a major role in prehistoric society, the latest archaeological data conclusively proves otherwise,[680] and the ubiquity and ferocity of this prehistoric conflagration is no longer in doubt. The debate now centres on the evolutionary origins of this prolonged period of intergroup conflict and what if any functional advantage it may have provided, given its seemingly maladaptive nature.

the day the men came

This is where NP theory comes in. It proposes that, although this attenuated period of violence appears haphazard, disorganised and ultimately
maladaptive, it achieved two functional evolutionary results. Firstly, it was
an expression of artificial selection which, as we have seen, can be a high-
speed, super-efficient form of natural selection. Secondly, it directed human evolution down a very narrow physical and behavioural path. The
reason for this becomes evident when examined through the perspective
of Teem theory. Although Cro-Magnons were now spread out all around
the world, their intergroup violence was guided by the same Neanderthal
derived teems and sign stimuli. This ensured that the artificial selection
occurred in virtually identical forms, all over the world. Guided by identical teems, widely dispersed Cro-Magnon tribes applied lethal violence
to exterminate exactly the same kind of people. For exactly the same
reasons.

This hypothesis proposes that top of the hit list for eradication on six
continents were deviants and those perceived to be the *others*. Theoretically,
this could mean anyone who triggered a Neanderthal teem. Pragmatically
though, it could include anyone who looked different. If your nose was
too flat, your eyeballs not white enough, your pupils not circular enough
or your lips too thin, you were at risk of being subconsciously perceived
as a Neanderthal—and treated as such. In a world where first impressions
were often a matter of life and death, coming across as dumb, crass,
humourless or gruff was likely to get you killed. And because nothing
creates a first impression better than posture, having a stooped (monkey-
like) gait, hunched shoulders or a head that jutted forward on your
shoulders was a recipe for a short life.

Because artificial selection was almost exclusively exercised by men,
females would be more prone to scrutiny than males. If girls were
considered too flat-chested, straight-waisted, wrinkled, thin-lipped, or if
the labia protruded beyond the vulva, they would be less likely to pass on
their genes.

It was as if these spontaneously self-forming death squads had all
been issued with the same orders. And the same hit list. From Spain to
eastern Mongolia, and from Alaska to Tierra del Fuego the same motley
collection of ill-formed deviants became the target of this sustained
campaign of lethal selection. Although it is sometimes argued that 'death
squads' only emerged in the 1970s and 1980s in South America, they have
existed under different guises since prehistoric times. The all too familiar

lament of 'the day men came with guns' to rape, murder and pillage has its antecedents in the Mesolithic, when men came with flint-tipped spears—to line up the innocents and make their lethal selection. But had a CSI unit of forensic pathologists examined the bodies, they would have seen a pattern to the victims. The selection was anything but random.

By this simple expedient, a unique homogeneous human physiology and behavioural repertoire began to emerge simultaneously around the world. This blunt, brutal but chillingly effective scenario is, along with mate selection derived from Neanderthal teems, the only evolutionary scenario that can explain how and why modern humans are today one species.

learning to dance

As a result of this lethal form of artificial selection, behaviours that had previously provided little or no contribution to fitness (like the ability to dance, hold a tune or laugh at a joke) now assumed an adaptive function. When a Cro-Magnon raiding party descended on a community, the villagers' ability to speak fluently, decorate their bodies or even crack a joke could mean the difference between living and dying. This brings new meaning to conformity—and to being 'human'. If Neanderthals were thought of as an artless, humourless, crass bunch, then art, tattoos, music, dancing, laughter and singing would become reliable indicators of *us*.

This generated pressure for everyone to acquire these external identifying signifiers. Men and women began wearing jewellery, tattooing their bodies and painting them with red ochre because they found these cultural accruements to be like passports—facilitating free and safe movement.

Cro-Magnons invented musical instruments and played them as a stamp of their humanity. They told stories, brewed alcoholic drinks and sang songs around the campfire. And they painted pictures on cave walls and fashioned ivory into figurines. Back in the Mesolithic, 'artistic' was not an affectation or indulgence—it was a

Intergroup violence is so pervasive in human history, we tend to take it for granted. (Right, from top) a prehistoric drawing of archers and victim from a cave in Castellón, Spain; the biblical massacre of the innocents; the shooting of Kiev Jews by Nazis; the My-Lai massacre by American troops in Vietnam; and skulls of the victims of the Rwandan genocide.

much admired survivalist skill that could very well save your life. Styling their locks, embellishing clothes, tools and weapons—in effect, 'making a fashion statement'—became ingrained in the human psyche as an adaptive behaviour. In a very real sense, the Cro-Magnons were the first slaves to fashion.

designer babies

There is every reason to believe that the relentless selection process included newborns. Neonates displaying atypical characteristics were 'soft targets' and infanticide was unquestionably the simplest, most cost effective application of artificial selection.

This tells us that the most dangerous time in the life of a Cro-Magnon was immediately after birth. That was when the males would inspect each baby and euthanise any infant they considered beyond the norm. This blunt policy of infanticide probably concentrated on conspicuous Neanderthaloid indicators such as the amount of body hair, facial wrinkles, head size and body fat.

For example, while birth is a challenge for most primate species because of the large size of the foetal head compared to the pelvis,[681] the wide birth canal in chimps and gorillas and the small head size of their babies normally allows safe, unassisted delivery.[682] This predicts that Neanderthal females also had wide hips and small-headed babies to make birth easier and safer.

Applying the *differentiation hypothesis* predicts that selection pressure would be generated for a larger head size in Cro-Magnon neonates. But even if a large head proclaimed to the tribe that a newborn was 'one of us', this reassurance came at a price. If the baby's head was too big, neither mother or infant would survive. It also meant that a normal isolated birth became much more dangerous.

The obvious solution would be for tribal females to assist the mother during the final stages of her delivery. By guiding the neonate from the birth canal, untangling the cord if necessary and starting the baby breathing, tribal females could neutralise the maladaptive impact of a larger head size. This kind of intelligent intervention was only possible because the assisting females now possessed the cognitive capacity to perform these tasks.

A review of the cross-cultural anthropological literature on human childbirth shows that today isolated birth is virtually unknown,[683] and that humans remain the only primate species to require assisted delivery.[684]

The amount of body fat a baby was born with may also have come under positive selection. Why? Because if, like all nonhuman primates, Neanderthal babies were born with almost no baby fat (antipodal tissue) to make birthing easier and safer, then skinny human babies (with minimal fat) may have triggered Neanderthal sign stimuli.

This equates to a simple protocol—the fatter the Cro-Magnon baby, the more chance it had of surviving. This would result in neonates getting fatter and fatter, until natural selection limited the maximum body size that a woman could deliver and survive. It would explain why a fat baby today is considered a bonny baby and its birth weight proudly announced.

eliminating the competition

The theory that blind senseless violence—that most loathsome of human proclivities—has played a pivotal role in the emergence of modern humans by eradicating vestigial Neanderthaloid remnants from the Cro-Magnon genome, may be disagreeable. However, the model now goes even further. It predicts that as Cro-Magnons colonised Africa and Asia, they inevitably encountered ancestral hominid populations such as 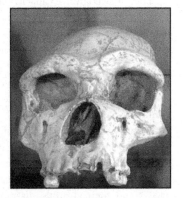 *Homo floresiensis (left)* and *Homo erectus (above)*. The model proposes that the perceived deviancy of these indigenous people would also trigger *them and us* teemic responses, that would predispose Cro-Magnons to treat them as if they were Neanderthals, even though they had never seen a real Neanderthal. In other words, the hotchpotch campaign of sexual selection and artificial selection that they applied to one another would now be applied to other species of *Homo* they came across.

Once labelled generically as *them*, indigenous hominid species would be subject to the full force of Cro-Magnon aggression. With inevitable consequences.

Could this explain what happened to all those pre-existing populations of hominids and early modern humans spread across Asia, Africa and the Americas? The archaeological evidence certainly confirms that, while there were numerous hominid species living from Africa to Asia before the arrival of Cro-Magnons, once the Cro-Magnons arrived, they all disappeared. The first to vanish were two species of *Homo erectus*—one in China, the other in Indonesia.

Until then, *erectus* had been probably the most successful hominid species of all, a tenacious hunter-gatherer who had survived for 1.75 million years and colonised half the globe.

For ages, it was believed that *Homo erectus*—thought to be the first hominid species to leave Africa—became extinct long before modern humans arrived in their areas. But we now know this is not the case. Recent dating of fossilised bones and artefacts reveals one population of *erectus* held out on the isolated island of Java until as recently as 25,000 years ago.[685] This coincides with the time humans reached Java. After that, *Homo erectus* disappears from the fossil record.

Their new cognitive capacity enabled Cro-Magnons to build seaworthy vessels and cross the Timor Sea to Australia. The earliest widely-accepted date for their arrival in Australia is around 38,000 years ago,[686] but a recent review of the data suggests occupation as early as 42,000–45,000 years ago.[687]

When Cro-Magnons arrived, there appears to have been at least one other hominid species already living in Australia—in the south of the continent. Known as the Kow Swamp people, they had relatively large and robust bodies and thick skulls indicating they were related to *Homo erectus*.[688] It's thought the Kow Swamp people arrived when there was still a land bridge between Australia and Asia.

The Kow Swamp people appear in the fossil record about 20,000 years ago,[689] and then abruptly disappear. Given that Cro-Magnons entered Australia from the north and the isolated Kow Swamp lived in the south, it is conceivable that the two groups did not make contact for thousands of years. NP theory suggests that when they finally did, the humans promptly wiped them out.

Whether humans were also responsible for the extinction of the diminutive *Homo floresiensis*—the 'Hobbits'—on the remote island of Flores in Indonesia about 13,000 years ago,[690,691,692] is also impossible to

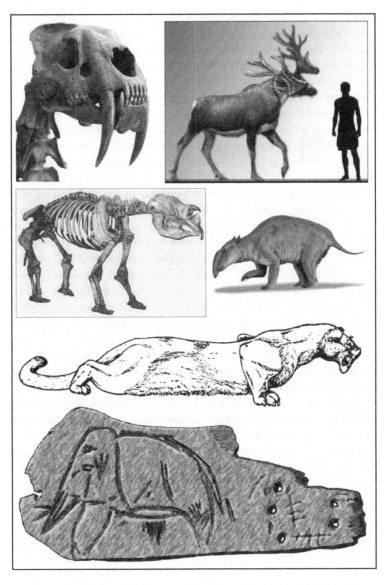

The size and lethality of many large animals (megafauna) encountered by hyper-aggressive humans as they spread across the globe may have triggered Neanderthal teems. The Cro-Magnons would then perceive them, not simply a food source, but a prey to be exterminated at every opportunity. This scenario could explain the rapid Late Pleistocene extinction of megafauna in regions colonised by humans.

confirm. But again, anthropologists Peter Brown, Michael Morwood and their Indonesian colleagues, who discovered and named *floresiensis*, argue that they were contemporaneous with modern humans on Flores. This makes them the longest-lasting hominid (apart from humans), outlasting the Neanderthals by about 12,000 years. It also highlights Peter Brown's claim that these resilient species of the genus *Homo* may have been direct descendants of *australopithecus* (like 'Lucy') one of the earliest African hominids. If so, then these resilient little fellows managed to survive in a unbroken line for a whopping five million years. Until, that is, modern humans arrived on their island. Once humans arrived, *floresiensis* abruptly disappeared.

This represents only circumstantial evidence of genocide and requires more proof, but some points are unequivocal. Firstly, by 13,000 years ago, of the at least seven—and possibly dozens, or even hundreds—of different sub-species of hominids which had inhabited the world, there remained only one. Secondly, their disappearance occurred only *after* the arrival of modern humans. Thirdly, because all other species became extinct, everyone living today can trace their ancestry to the original population of Cro-Magnons in the Levant. In effect, this 'purification' of the gene line was evolution by genocide. As an instrument of artificial selection, it was systematic, methodical and extremely efficient. Modern humans owe their present homogeneity to the thoroughness of the genocidal eradication of anyone considered too deviant to fit into the Cro-Magnon culture.

Finally, the hypothesis of a hyper-aggressive clade of Cro-Magnons sweeping across the planet killing anything that set off their hair-trigger Neanderthal sign stimuli is also consistent with the extinction of a number of large animal species (megafauna) in Australia and elsewhere coinciding with the appearance of modern humans.[693,694,695]

23 BACK TO AFRICA

A lthough the archaeological and genetic evidence tells us that all the competing hominid species of *Homo* disappeared, something very unusual happened in Africa.

Because the Skhul-Qafzeh were originally from Africa, when they returned as Cro-Magnons it was in a very real sense a homecoming. In the Levant all they had ever known were Neanderthals, but Africa was a different kettle of fish. Here, in the second largest continent on earth comprising over 11,700,000 square miles, they almost certainly encountered many new and varied species and sub-species of hominids.

At the time, Africa was home to a large, well-entrenched indigenous population of ancestral beings displaying a range of human and hominid traits that Cro-Magnons would have recognised in themselves. Some of the hominid species, like *Homo erectus* and *Homo floresiensis*, had migrated out of Africa, but remnants of the ancestral founding populations doubtlessly remained on that continent. The climate evidence indicates that Africa was at the time a fertile habitat, capable of supporting large populations of hominids. It has been estimated that as many archaic humans lived in Africa as in Europe and Asia combined.[696]

If these indigenous populations were ubiquitous throughout Africa at the time the Cro-Magnons returned, then we can say with considerable confidence that they encountered one another.

What would be the evolutionary implications of this interaction? For a start, there were such a large number of indigenous Africans. Secondly, the indigenous Africans, while archaic by Cro-Magnon standards, did not look like cold-adapted Neanderthals. They had evolved in the same equatorial, tropical and savannah environment as had the Cro-Magnons' own ancestors. And, while behaviourally some of them would be very primate-like, others would have been recognisably hominid and would even have used primitive stone tools. But as well as these populations, we know from the archaeology that a few Initial Upper Palaeolithic hominids also existed and that these people made complex tools and used red ochre to decorate themselves. In other words, Africa was large enough, and fertile enough to play host to potentially hundreds, if not thousands of isolated populations of hominids and early humans just as it plays host today to myriad populations of widely varied fauna.

Drawing on modern analogies, we can speculate that some hominid populations acquired minor regional adaptations to cope with the range of African ecosystems and habitats. We can also assume that some groups interbred, while others maintained isolated breeding populations which consolidated into separate hominid species and sub-species. We need to put aside the popular preconception that there were no other hominids in Africa when Cro-Magnons re-entered it. This acknowledges that the biological diversity we see today in Africa was apparent when Cro-Magnons returned to Africa 40,000 years ago, and that this model applied to hominid populations as much as it applied to other mammalian species.

How did the Cro-Magnons respond to these interactions? NP theory's Cro-Magnon behavioural model indicates that the more primitive of these hominid species would trigger the Cro-Magnons' Neanderthal teems and this would lead to the species' rapid extinction. Nothing unusual there.

However, the model also predicts that not every unfamiliar hominid the Cro-Magnons came across would necessarily generate a Neanderthal reaction. And the reason for this is sex. The desire of dominant Cro-Magnon males for fertile young females (which would maintain genetic diversity) suggests that Cro-Magnons would be open to the possibility of mating with some indigenous populations, provided they were not *too* different. The fossil evidence helps identify the most likely candidates— isolated populations of Initial Upper Palaeolithic cultures inhabiting southern Africa.

Cro-Magnon males would have mated with these Initial Upper Palaeolithic females only if they considered them, perhaps not exactly like themselves, but similar enough to strike an emotional chord. For example, the presence of red ochre at these sites suggests they may have decorated their bodies, which Cro-Magnons would have recognised as an indicator of *us*. So, where Initial Upper Palaeolithic indigenous populations presented no direct threat, sexual desire may have overcome Cro-Magnon xenophobia to allow a degree of interbreeding to occur.

This sub-hypothesis, while conjectural, recognises the highly sexualised nature of hyper-aggressive Cro-Magnon males. But it is also supported by considerable new genetic evidence. Mitochondrial DNA extracted from about 600 indigenous African populations in April 2008, by a team led by Doron Behar from the Rambam Medical Center in Israel, supports the view that Cro-Magnons returning 'back to Africa' did exchange genes with some existing African populations. The genetic evidence paints a more subtle picture of what happened. Doron Behar reports:

> We see strong evidence of ancient population splits beginning as early as 150,000 years ago, probably giving rise to separate populations localized to Eastern and Southern Africa. It was only around 40,000 years ago that they became part of a single pan-African population, reunited after as much as 100,000 years apart.

This scenario, of two long-separated human populations reuniting after many millennia apart, is consistent with the theory that Cro-Magnons returning to their ancestral homeland did in fact interbreed with some indigenous populations. While the genes of the indigenous African population were swamped by the 'invaders', faint traces of their genetic material can still be detected in modern humans.

the two-edged sword

In 1892, in *The Principles of Ethics*, English philosopher Herbert Spenser first described features of violent ethnocentrism and xenophobia in prehistoric tribes.[697] Charles Darwin, writing in 1871, argued that intergroup violence had been a significant factor in human evolution. "Natural selection," he wrote in *The Descent of Man*, "arising from the competition of tribe with tribe...would, under favourable conditions, have sufficed to raise man to his high position."[698]

Throughout the 20th century, the view that intergroup violence (or *intergroup competition* as academics began to call it) played a major role in modern human evolution gained widespread support.[699,700,701,702]

What NP theory adds to this paradigm is an understanding of the evolutionary origins of lethal intergroup competition. It shows that it was not resource driven, as some scholars believe, but motivated by innate behavioural responses originating from Neanderthal predation. In addition, it demonstrates how the massive scale of human intergroup violence (over 200 million dead in the last century alone)[703] has impacted on human evolution.

When social anthropologist Gregory Stanton analysed the contributing factors that lead to genocide—the most extreme form of group violence— he identified *The Eight Stages of Genocide.*[704] Among them are "them and us distinctions", and "dehumanisation"—both attitudinal prerequisites in the progression of genocide.

Given, too, the view of authors Paul Shaw and Yuwa Wong in *Genetic Seeds of Warfare: Evolution, Nationalism, and Patriotism,* that "xenophobia is the potent force behind out-group enmity, discrimination and nationalistic sentiments leading to war",[705] NP theory's value here is in helping understand the evolutionary origins of these behaviours. Indeed, it is hard to imagine how any other scientific theory could adequately explain these behavioural proclivities, or the evolutionary mechanisms that imprinted them into the human genome.

the proof is in the genome

The implications of the recent consolidation hypothesis derived from NP theory are significant. The most obvious corollary is that modern human physiology and behaviour were synthesised into their present final form relatively late, some time between 45,000 and 10,000 years ago. This is a very brief period of time (a veritable flash in the pan compared to normal evolutionary scenarios) and also very recent. It follows that we may expect to find evidence that the human genome continued to undergo major changes within the last 50,000 years. Genomic dating technology, whereby geneticists are able to chronologically date when alterations to the human genome occurred, can be used to test both these hypotheses.

And the results? Studies of changes in both mitochondrial and nuclear DNA categorically reveal that the human genome underwent just such a recent change. There's even a name for it. It's called a *recent selective sweep.*

Analysis of single-nucleotide polymorphisms in disparate modern human populations has identified a number of genomic locations that have experienced recent selective sweeps. Examination of 1.2 million such mutations in African-American, European-American, and Chinese populations identified over 100 regions of the human genome that had experienced recent selective sweeps.[706] It has now been estimated that up to ten percent of the human genome has been altered by recent selection, including genes involved in nervous system development and function, skin pigmentation, immune system, heat shock, and sense of smell. These are all genes predicted by NP theory to have come under selective pressure as a result of Neanderthal predation. But, most telling, the studies show that this recent sweep occurred during the last 15,000 to 100,000 years,[707] providing excellent concurrence with NP theory.

The prediction that body hair and colouration were among the most important divides—and therefore would come under concerted selection— is also confirmed by genetic analysis in two recent studies that show five genes regulating to skin pigmentation (OCA2, MYO5A, DTNBP1, TYRP1 and SLC24A5) all reveal evidence of recent selection.[708,709]

The journal *Evolution and Human Behavior* recently published a study by Canadian anthropologist Peter Frost, which claimed the genetic mutation in the hair colour gene that resulted in blonde hair occurred about 11,000 years ago and quickly spread through sexual selection.[710] Researchers at Copenhagen University have identified the single point mutation in the OCA2 gene that is responsible for all the blue-eyed people alive today. They calculated the mutation happened between 6,000 and 10,000 years ago in Europe.

This genetic data supports NP theory's argument that by 10,000 years ago, artificial selection and sexual selection of the nascent human phenotype was in full swing.

almost there

For 35,000 years the campaign of artificial selection (complemented by sexual selection) gradually amalgamated the disparate strands of human- ity on four continents into a single unified species. By the beginning of the Neolithic Period (about 10,000 years ago) almost all the physical and behavioural vestiges of the primate-Neanderthaloid past had been eradi- cated from the newly minted 'human' genotype.

It was this process, I suggest, that was responsible for the uniformity of the modern human genome. It is this that explains why 99.9 percent of everyone's DNA is identical, and it is only this that explains why there is just one human nature.

For example, so thoroughly had the genes for hairiness been expunged, rendered inoperative (turned into what are called *pseudogenes*) or silenced (which means they are no longer expressed) that today, anyone born with full body hair is considered a medical curiosity. Since records began in the Middle Ages, only about 34 cases of the condition, called congenital generalised hypertrichosis, have been described in the medical literature.[711]

CONGENITAL GENERALISED HYPERTRICHOSIS

Throughout history, people suffering from congenital generalised hypertrichosis were ostracised and persecuted— and so tended to stay indoors during the day. Because they ventured out only under cover of darkness, this led to the first werewolf myths. Even today, this condition is still usually referred to in the media as 'werewolf syndrome.' In 1995, researchers localised the gene responsible for the condition on the X-chromosome. Normally, the gene is silenced, but very occasionally, it is expressed and inherited by offspring. This has led researchers at the Baylor College of Medicine, in Houston, Texas to confirm what NP theory suggests—that hypertrichosis is an atavism—the reappearance of a dormant trait that was once common.

Because of its importance in differentiating the warring species, the Cro-Magnon human face received the full makeover. Faces became more symmetrical. Skin became wrinkle-free, clear and unblemished. The eye whites really were white, the lips fuller and the nose (petite by primate standards) protruded conspicuously from the face. Gone were the two forward-projecting gaping nostrils of the primate nose. Gone was the leathery skin. And gone too was the coating of protective body hair, even in hot tropical regions. Beauty became the prevailing guide to mate selection, and meant the opposite of what Neanderthals looked like.

I also suggest that the number of common birth abnormalities was severely reduced by artificial selection because infants born with congenital birth defects would be culled. This is confirmed by archaeological evidence from early Neolithic kill sites in Denmark, collected by Pia Bennike from the University of Copenhagen, that shows that victims of violence included people born with congenital abnormalities and disabling diseases.[712]

Further accentuating the divide were mutational alleles for novel hair and eye colours. Amongst some Northern European groups the new lighter colours became highly-prized. From a distance nothing stamped a person *one of us* better than blue eyes and a coiffure of blonde, brunette or red hair, especially if it was well-groomed and decorated—something *the others* never did.

The 35,000-year-long process of genetic pruning was so comprehensive that it rendered Cro-Magnons almost unrecognisable from their former selves. They were now much smarter, more artistic, more creative… more human. Behaviourally though, it was a different story. There was still one step to go—one final transition before you'd let one of these Neolithic men date your daughter or sit down with you to discuss the economic meltdown over a decaf cappuccino. The last challenge was to curb—or at least control—hyper-aggression in young males.

24 GETTING THE PSYCHOPATHS OFF THE STREETS

the mesolithic nightmare

It is difficult to imagine that Cro-Magnon males ever worried about their own aggression. After all, the most aggressive males were the ones who fought and bludgeoned their way to the top—to become the alpha males, chiefs, kings, 'big men' and rulers of rag-tag Neolithic armies and proto-nation states. By the Mesolithic, hyper-aggression was a ubiquitous male attribute. It reached fixation because it was essential to the transition from multiple populations of post-bottleneck, Upper Palaeolithic humans to a single homogeneous population of fully modern humans.

But by the late Mesolithic, hyper-aggression had become seriously maladaptive. Male coalitions had killed, maimed and displaced so many people that family life and child-rearing were becoming untenable, threatening the viability of the budding species.

This core NP hypothesis is supported by abundant skeletal evidence of mortal injuries, which bioarchaeologist and forensic anthropologist Phillip Walker from the University of California Santa Barbara interprets as strongly indicative of a marked increase in homicide from the Mesolithic onwards.[713] Bruce Knauft, a cultural anthropologist who has studied violence in prehistoric times, confirms that by the Mesolithic, the fear of becoming a victim of homicide was a fact of everyday life.[714]

But if the Mesolithic was dangerous, things were about to get even worse. The frequency of cranial injuries in a sample of Italian bones from massacre sites indicates the level of violence actually rises sharply during the Neolithic.[715] Walker points out that this escalation challenges the commonly held view that Neolithic agriculturalists were more peaceful.[716]

Neolithic men were not only extraordinarily violent, but the butchered human bones excavated from Neolithic sites like La Baume Fontbrégoua in south-eastern France tell us they sometimes also ate their victims.[717,718]

Male hyper-aggression was now out of control and threatened the viability of the entire human race.

But here's the catch. The more lives that male hyper-aggression claimed, the more selection pressure was generated for adaptations to curb it. NP theory identifies seven adaptations which appear to have emerged almost exclusively to rein in deleterious male aggression. While undoubtedly helping to curb the death toll, they also added seven new pieces to the complex web of human nature and human physiology. In this respect, they provided a 'last minute' fine-tuning of the species. They are some of the best things to come out of Neanderthal predation. It was these last seven modifications that transformed Cro-Magnons into humans beings.

pyrrhic victories

The first adaptation against male hyper-aggression, not surprisingly, was natural selection. Archaeologists digging at 11 eastern Mediterranean sites ranging from the Neolithic to modern times reported that the number of

King Pyrrhus of the Hellenistic kingdom of Epirus defeated the Romans in 280 BC, but suffered so many casualties, he reportedly said, "Another such victory and I shall be ruined". It's not difficult to envisage that the constant skirmishes between hyper-aggressive Cro-Magnons also ended in 'pyrrhic victories' because both sides were equally matched and armed with similar weapons.

head and neck injuries in males increased dramatically during the Neo-lithic, reflecting a marked intensification of intergroup male violence.[719] Several field studies from the European Iron Age confirm that trauma injuries of all kinds are strikingly more common in males than females.[720] These data show that not only were things getting more violent as humans entered the Neolithic Period, but that the violence was being perpetrated mainly by men against other men.

Applying simple Darwinian theory to this situation predicts that over time, the marauding gangs of testosterone-charged homicidal killers became too violent for their own good. Gradually, the constant intergroup warfare killed off many of the most aggressive young males—the very ones at the forefront of the fighting. And with them went some of the most virulent genes and teems predisposing hyper-aggression in post-pubertal males.

Archaeological data does not reveal what proportion of hyper-aggressive males were culled by natural selection, but research into warfare among modern hunter-gatherer societies provides some clues. In 1970, American anthropologist Karl Heider spent two years in the remote central highlands of West New Guinea studying the Dugum Dani (*right*), an isolated group of very aggressive hunter-gatherers. Heider reported that almost 30 percent of Dugum Dani men were killed in warfare.[721]

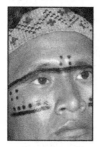

A similar story emerges from the highlands of southern Venezuela and northern Brazil, home to a large group of indigenous hunter-gatherers called the Yanomamö (*left*). According to anthropologist Napoleon Chagnon's field study, warfare between some 125 Yanomamö tribes is almost constant, and responsible for the deaths of one third of the total population.[722]

When anthropologists first studied the Huaorani (or Waorani) group of some 4000 hunter-gathers living at the base of the Andes in Ecuador in the fifties, they reported they were the fiercest, most bellicose ethnic group on earth. Huaorani society was characterised by unremitting intertribal warfare with lethal raiding a ubiquitous feature of their lives. Quarrels over marriage arrangements, accusations of sorcery and blood feuds arising from past killings were common causes of intertribal violence. The researchers estimated that inter-clan skirmishes were responsible for the deaths of a staggering 60 percent of all Huaorani.[723]

So deleterious was the murder rate that, not surprisingly, over the last 30 years the level of violence has dropped substantially, so that today the Huaorani lead relatively peaceful lives—a testament perhaps to the effectiveness of natural selection.

Given that the Dugum Dani, the Yanomamö and the Huaorani are modern humans and their Mesolithic ancestors were far more violent, we may expect the casualty rate among Mesolithic and Neolithic warriors to be significantly higher—and that those responsible for the killing, raping, razing, burning and pillaging would almost all be men.

These case studies support the contention that by removing or silencing some of the genes and teems regulating male hyper-aggression from the nascent human genome, life for family people in the Neolithic would have gained some much-needed breathing space.

looking for mister nice guy

During the period of Neanderthal predation, when human women and children came under concerted attack by Neanderthals because they were soft, sexy targets, women preferred—and selected—aggressive men to protect them. But in the post-Neanderthal era, it is likely that women began to change their attitudes towards aggression, and that this had a direct bearing on mate selection. Those burly, super-macho men with their violent hair-trigger tempers, ready to reach for their spears or axes at the slightest provocation, must have been hell to live with. Ironically, their aggressive behaviour meant that Neolithic men were behaving much like their former brutish adversaries.

This would have altered the women's choice of mating partners, which nominates sexual selection as the second major adaptation against male hyper-aggression.

For the first time, hyper-aggressive men were passed over by mate-seeking women in favour of more gentle men who, while protective, were also disposed to provide affection and parental support. In this way, sexual selection not only reduced the number of hyper-aggressive men, but also promoted better fathers. In the unimaginably violent Mesolithic and Neolithic periods, choosing a kind man became a proactive adaptive female strategy—providing women with the best chances of surviving long enough to raise their children to adulthood.

let's be logical about this

Hyper-aggression is derived from the emotional centres of the 'reptilian brain.' This means that Cro-Magnon fixed action patterns would have been inflexible, emotional responses. The non-cognitive nature of these behavioural responses is reflected today in psychological attitudes like racism, colourism, xenophobia, ethnocentrism, chauvinism, pack rape mentality, vigilantism, hooliganism and vandalism.

For the most part, these are not specific behaviours. They are emotional states and psychological mindsets that, under certain circumstances, may predispose violent behaviour such as lynching, gang rapes and ethnic cleansing. Once they are triggered, these behaviours are normally resistant to cognitive constraint. A lynch mob in the full frenzy of hatred is rarely responsive to rational argument or persuasion.

Vestiges of this emotional thinking can be seen today in societies besieged by military threats, political upheavals and economic uncertainties—circumstances that discourage rational debate.

Back in the Mesolithic, this suggests that once Cro-Magnons killed the menfolk of a village, there would be no debate about whether to enslave the women and girls. Silent instructions were being parlayed uncensored from primitive neural networks in their Cro-Magnon brains. That's what made them so dangerous. They were 'mindless' and their violence was 'mindless violence'.

This kind of senseless violence—this kind of man—was ultimately maladaptive, and would have generated selection pressure for new cerebral networks to curb and control Neanderthal fixed action patterns. The massive mammalian brain was already there, it just needed some judicious rewiring—a patch.

So the third mechanism used to counter hyper-aggression was, I suggest, the emergence of cognitive networks able to consciously appraise Neanderthal sign stimuli and, when appropriate, modify or even negate their expression. It was not perfect—but it was a start. Once selected, logic, rationality, objectivity and other higher order cognitive functions would prove adaptive—not only in moderating aggressive fixed action patterns, but in a wide range of other social interactions, such as diplomacy and mediation—and consequently would creep inexorably towards fixation.

Women would quickly recognise the benefits of a smarter man—able to exercise a degree of self-control over his primal instincts and make rational decisions based on information rather than emotional impulses and prejudices. They would increasingly be repulsed by 'mindless' men—preferring intelligent fathers for their children.

Indeed, neurobiologist David Neill believes that these kinds of cognitive advances were essential to the emergence of fully modern humans.[724] They also fit with the fact that the cognitive and emotional networks in the prefrontal cortex (which controls higher central executive levels of consciousness and rationality)[725] are among the most recent neural networks acquired by *sapiens*.

These networks were important because they not only supported consciousness and self-awareness, but also self-directed autonomous behaviour in the absence of external stimulation.[726] Complex forward thinking and behaviour were no longer reliant on sign stimuli. "The result", Neill writes, "could be that thoughts, acting independent of input from the external environment, could direct behaviour."[727]

These upper echelon levels of brain function—possibly for the first time—found fruitful expression vetting, verifying, controlling and negating potentially lethal (maladaptive) fixed action patterns of behaviour.

For example, if a Neolithic mob came across a boy out foraging for fruit, any unusual physical feature, (like the shape of his nose) would normally trigger a fixed action response—with potentially deadly consequences. However, if 'gut instincts' could be overridden or even negated by cerebral networks based on logic, self interest, social protocols or long-term objectives, and a rational evaluation ensued, the mob might conclude that, despite the size of the boy's nose, he was nevertheless *one of us* and would not be harmed. In the long term, this kind of rational intervention would almost certainly reduce personal violence.

ethnicity and the evolution of tolerance

When small hunter-gatherer groups—spreading across Asia, Europe, Africa and the Americas—encountered other groups, they would be acutely aware of the minor physical and cultural differences that had accumulated between them. If the differences were considered too great, each group would perceive the other as *them*—with predictable consequences—until one group eliminated the other.

This dynamic had a direct impact on evolution by removing the most pronounced regional characteristics, and leaving only groups whose acquired regional characteristics were generally (often marginally) accepted by other Cro-Magnon groups as emblematic of *us*. While they remained acutely aware of differences, they could nevertheless acknowledge their commonality. Those foreigners may decorate their bodies differently, but they do decorate their bodies. And while their clothes were different, they at least wore them.

Sometimes this would be enough to prevent Neanderthal teems being triggered and avoid hostilities between groups. It was also an important step in the gradual homogenisation of humanity, presaging the late emergence of a new and important human adaptation—a degree of tolerance of deviancy.

While the emergence of tolerance may seem paradoxical in the grand scheme of Cro-Magnon evolution and the antithesis of NP theory, it was nonetheless a highly adaptive trait that contributed considerably to their survival rates. As well as reducing intergroup conflicts, tolerance enabled sexual contact with outside groups, which reduced the deleterious impact of inbreeding, such as congenital birth defeats, low fertility rates and so on. For nomadic Cro-Magnon tribes, periodically replenishing their gene pool was a necessity rather than a luxury.

Tolerance between isolated regional groups was also adaptive because it allowed people who were slightly different to trade, socialise and exchange ideas and technologies. In addition, it prevented isolated groups from solidifying into a plethora of new species and sub-species.

For Cro-Magnons, swapping genes and intergroup exchange of sexual partners involved families, co-parenting and falling in love, so the capacity to be sexually attracted to someone from an outside group became a kind of litmus test. Because people had to feel enough commonality with each other to form romantic attachments and raise children together, interbreeding occurred only between groups who were divided by only minor physical, behavioural and cultural differences. And it's here that tolerance played a major role—in accepting superficial differences in others.

Tolerance provided an evolutionary alternative to speciation. It allowed Cro-Magnons to coalesce into something that may be unique to humanity—hundreds, then thousands of slightly variable regional populations that overlooked their differences to occasionally interbreed. These tribes developed their own cultural identify and while they mostly chose mates from within their group, enough periodically chose partners from outside to replenish their gene stocks. Today, we know these separate but sexually compatible populations as *ethnic groups*.

Ethnicity describes populations that share similar cultural, religious, physical and linguistic traditions,[728] and who mostly (but not always) marry within the group.[729] It is so much part of the cultural landscape we tend to take it for granted, yet ethnicity must have emerged somewhere, at some point in our evolutionary history, to fill an adaptive niche. This new theory of the evolution of ethnicity appears to demonstrate that adaptive functionality. It shows why a primary function of ethnicity is the group's recognition of its own distinctiveness,[730] and as a means of distinguishing *us* from *outsiders*.[731] This places ethnicity in the ambit of *them and us*—as yet another mechanism of selection against Neanderthal traits and in favour of human traits.

To function adaptively, ethnicity requires acceptance of deviancy—tolerance—at both a group and individual level, something that would not have come naturally to Late Pleistocene humans. It may have been dependent on the emergence of specialist neuronal networks able to rationally examine sign stimuli and, if necessary, consciously repress fixed action responses.

It follows then that ethnicity was a precarious adaptation—inherently unstable and likely to vaporise into maladaptive responses. Tolerance was the oil that lubricated the machinery of budding ethnicity but, during the Mesolithic and Neolithic, that attribute would often be in short supply. Famine, droughts, warfare, population densities and other capricious social stresses could affect the interpretation of Neanderthal sign stimuli, so that inconsequential ethnic variations—like clothes, speech patterns and hairstyles—that normally would not trigger Neanderthal teems, now triggered them, sparking violent tribal conflicts which periodically escalated into 'ethnic cleansing'.

shoulder to shoulder

Until now, the adaptations against male hyper-aggression and evolutionary violence have all been biological, and therefore take time. They do not begin to change things until they are close to fixation. For example, it would not be much use if only 20 percent of the women opted for less macho men, or if only 30 percent of men acquired genes that predisposed rational decision-making or tolerance.

This indicates that in the short to medium term, the biological protocols listed would have created a divided society, which included a range of aggressive tendencies. This would gradually coalesce into two camps— one composed mainly of hyper-aggressive young men, aggregated into large 'proto-armies', and a second camp, of less aggressive men and women aggregated into families and small tribes for the purposes of raising children. At this stage, both these stone-age groups were nomadic so chance encounters between them would be frequent, and doubtlessly filled with trepidation for the family groups.

During this transitional period, family life and child-rearing would have been possible, but only under extreme duress. Throughout the Mesolithic, and up to the middle Neolithic, the threat of violence to peaceful tribes from pugnacious warrior clans remained destabilising and maladaptive.

If collective violence was as detrimental as suggested by the archaeological evidence, then additional cultural protocols would have been employed to stem the tide of blood. Cultural (non-biological) protocols could impose short-term didactic solutions to bridge the gap—until biological protocols spread to enough of the population to significantly reduce the death toll.

25   SAFETY IN NUMBERS

In my view, the single most effective cultural mechanism against collective violence in the Neolithic was the principle of safety in numbers: the ability to form large defensive groups which would outnumber male raiding parties and withstand their assaults.

Evolutionary ecologist Richard Alexander, from the University of Michigan, arrived at this conclusion in the 1970s. Alexander's analysis of the Neolithic period convinced him that the emergence of extended family groups was not driven by the need for protection against nonhuman predators, but because large groups provided protection against human aggression and intergroup competition.[732]

Alexander's hypothesis aligns with NP theory, which attempts to place collective violence into a plausible evolutionary context. But his suggestion that Neolithic humans grouped together in large numbers for mutual protection against the rampaging hordes of bloodthirsty savages presents a few problems.

Firstly, Mesolithic people didn't possess the hierarchical, organisational and logistical strategies to support significant population intensification. The small groups of less than 50 people, in which they lived for millions of years, could not have increased to several thousand people—or several hundred thousand—without their acquiring a raft of new social and organisational skills. Realistically, large aggregations of people (society) require certain skill sets—such as social intelligence, leadership, common identity, reciprocity and good communications—to function effectively.

The Mesolithic people would have had to introduce organisational systems to store and protect food surpluses, as well as political systems to resolve intergroup conflicts and distribute shared resources. They would also have required stringent protocols to prevent hyper-aggressive males from dominating the group.

So it is very likely that, as the adaptive demands of population intensification mounted, increased selection pressure was generated for neural networks that would facilitate the hierarchical, linguistic, cognitive, organisational and socialisation protocols needed to sustain unprecedented population expansions. In other words, fear drove Mesolithic and Neolithic people together into artificially large cultural groups, and natural selection provided the glue that allowed these unnaturally large formations to stick. By the second millennium BC, according to Paul Bairoch in *Cities and Economic Development: From the Dawn of History to the Present*, the population of Babylon was more than 200,000.[733]

Sure, there are plenty of sociologists and cultural anthropologists who would argue that even today humans haven't perfected the art of living together in super-sized groups. But, without the impetus for population intensification generated by hyper-aggression, we would probably still be members of small tribal groups scratching out a living hunting deer and digging for tubers.

Despite acquiring the necessary psychological, organisational, political and social protocols to support population intensification, these early humans had to overcome some serious practical problems, and this brings us to the sixth adaptation.

if you build it, they won't come

There are limits to the size of an economically viable nomadic hunter-gatherer group. Today, most consist of between ten to thirty individuals.[734] At times, such as when prey animals are in large supply, larger temporary seasonal aggregations of 100 people or more may form. Throughout the Mesolithic, 100 was probably the upper limit to what traditional hunter-gatherer procurement strategies could sustain.[735]

Central to the hunter-gatherer lifestyle was its nomadic nature, driven by the need to follow seasonal migrations of prey and find fresh hunting grounds. This raised the likelihood of groups coming into contact with marauding gangs of wild young men also roaming the countryside in search of fresh quarry.

Archaeologist Allen Johnson and economic anthropologist Timothy

Earle, authors of *The Evolution of Human Societies: From Foraging Group to Agrarian State*, estimate that during the Neolithic, there were more than 100,000 small extended family groups.[736] The chances are high that these groups would come into contact with each other at waterholes, on animal migration routes, and in rich foraging regions.

The prospect of violent encounters between family units and bachelor groups simply had to be addressed if childrearing in the Mesolithic was to remain viable. People encircled by pugnacious warriors could not rely on their large numbers or existing tactics such as threats, negotiation or pleas for mercy. They needed something else. Ultimately, only a physical barrier—something solid and impenetrable like a fortress—could provide any real protection. Ultimately, only tall sturdy walls could offer a defence against the hordes of males who were making their lives a misery.

Yet, as logical as this solution seems, it wasn't feasible at the time because fortresses are fixed in the landscape and the Mesolithic people were nomadic. Even if they invented fortresses, how would they feed themselves? Hunting and foraging were simply incompatible with a sedentary existence within the walls of a fortress.

As a precursor to developing a stockade, our ancestors had to resolve the issue of food procurement and I suggest they achieved this by inventing agriculture. Agriculture was immediately adaptive because it allowed Neolithic hunter-gatherers to live in fortified compounds, while providing sufficient food for their group.

The theory that Neolithic people were forced to abandon their traditional lifestyle to reluctantly embrace agriculture and a sedentary lifestyle because it provided a buffer against male hyper-aggression is a radical hypothesis. But it does offer some answers to what has been described as the most intractable mystery of the Neolithic—what caused the agricultural revolution[737]—the extraordinary transition from hunting and gathering to farming.

Writing in the *Journal of Anthropological Archaeology*, Brian Hayden from the University of Southampton observes, "Few topics in prehistory have engendered as much discussion and resulted in so few satisfying answers as the attempt to explain why hunter/gatherers began to cultivate plants and raise animals."[738] Applying the male hyper-aggression model to this truculent anthropological and historical problem is for me one of the most exciting applications of NP theory.

the fortress theory

The only thing anthropologists agree on is that there is no consensus on what caused the agricultural revolution.[739,740,741]

Brian Hayden says:

> Climatic change, population pressure, sedentism, resource concentration from desertification, girls' hormones, land ownership, geniuses, rituals, scheduling conflicts, random genetic kicks, natural selection, broad spectrum adaptation and multicausal retreats from explanation have all been proffered to explain domestication. All have major flaws... the data do not accord well with any one of these models.[742]

Current opinions include that the "Neolithic revolution was opportunistic";[743] that it was the result of extinction of large herbivores,[744] that it resulted from the "emergence of socioeconomic inequalities and competition among complex, economically specialised hunter/gatherers,"[745] and various other causes.[746,747,748]

For a while, because the shift to a settled agricultural lifestyle appeared to coincide with a period of climate warming (known as the Bølling-Allerød Interstadial), it was believed that agriculture was made possible by the improved climate. But carbon dating of pollen from ice core samples proves this wasn't the case.

Another theory argues that the invention of agriculture caused the shift to new settlement patterns, but this too has been disproved. Nicholas Wade explains in *Before the Dawn*, "the reverse is true: it was not agriculture that led to settlement, but rather sedentary life came first, well before the Neolithic age began, and agriculture followed in its train."[749]

Yet another theory argues that sedentism was a response to overpopulation,[750] but we now know that populations increased only after the shift to agriculture.

One reason for this lack of consensus is that the shift to agriculture doesn't seem to make sense. Palaeopathological and comparative studies show the health of populations that adopted cereal agriculture actually deteriorated.[751] The spread of infections in crowded cities was a real problem—costing thousands of lives—as was the deterioration in the quality of food that accompanied cereal farming.[752]

Professor of Anthropology at State University of New York Mark Cohen asks, "If agriculture provides neither better diet, nor greater dietary reliability, nor greater ease, but conversely appears to provide a poorer diet, less reliably, with greater labour costs, why does anyone become a farmer?"[753]

This question has never been satisfactorily answered. Even after a lifetime studying the causes of the Neolithic revolution, archaeologist Richard MacNeish declares, "...after all these years of work on the problem of how and why agriculture began, I see no final answers."[754]

The theory that humans invented agriculture (and adopted it grudgingly) because it allowed them to live in walled compounds for protection against hyper-aggressive men, can be tested against the archaeological record. For a start, it predicts there should be a sudden proliferation of walled compounds and forts at the same time as agriculture took off, which is the case. The earliest settlements of the Middle East—at Jericho, Uruk, Kadesh-Barnea, Troy, Aphek, Rehman Dheri, Tell Hamourkar, Asikli and Kalibangan—were all fortified with high walls and defensive trenches. The Syrian Neolithic settlement of Tell Hamoukar, for instance, which dates to around 4000 BC, was over 500 acres in size, and yet the entire settlement was enclosed by a defensive stone wall 4 metres (13 ft) thick and 3 metres (10 ft) high.

The concept of a walled fortress probably evolved through a process of trial and error. Consider, for example, Çatal Hüyük in modern day Turkey. Built about 8500 years ago, Çatal Hüyük (*left*) is thought to be the oldest human settlement on Earth. An analysis of its distinctive architecture reveals

what I believe to be the first stage in the cultural evolution of the fortress. The city did not have an external defensive wall as such, possibly because it still hadn't been conceived or that its inhabitants did not possess the political, social and logistical systems to organise and communally build something as complex as an encircling wall. Eventually though, the need to protect themselves against male coalitions led to what, at the time, must have seemed an ingenious solution. Families built their individual houses next to each other in a cluster, so tightly packed together that there weren't even any streets or passageways between them. That meant that the outside walls of the houses on the periphery formed a single unbroken barrier around the whole settlement, creating a de facto stockade wall.

This earliest attempt to build a defensive fortress would explain why the inhabitants of Çatal Hüyük did not put doors in their houses. And except for a few small air vents, there were no windows either—nothing big enough for an invader to climb through.

To enter their houses, the inhabitants had to climb down a ladder extending up through a small hole in the roof, making the houses dark, hot and airless. About 10,000 people crammed into the 10 acre site and, during its 1000 year occupation, they kept building on top of each other until they created a veritable warren 20 metres high. This design was hardly conducive to a healthy lifestyle but would have been worth it because it provided the citizens with a sense of security.

Ultimately, though, this clustered, doorless, windowless, airless, sunless concept of town planning proved too inconvenient, and it was up to the Neolithic city of Jericho (in the West Bank of the Palestinian Territories) to take the next creative step—a separate free-standing wall enclosing the whole settlement.

Jericho is a milestone in the history of human achievement. The entire 10 acre settlement was encircled by an embankment and two stone walls 15 metres (47 ft.) high and three metres (10 ft.) thick, surrounded by a dry moat and stone towers.[755] This formidable wall (built 5000 years before the pyramids) represents an unprecedented engineering achievement and reflects the insecurity and anxiety of its ancient builders. That this three metre thick wall was built over 11,000 years ago is truly extraordinary.

The NP theory of the origins of agriculture makes another claim that can be tested. It asserts that Neolithic people did not want to give up their traditional hunter-gatherer lifestyle. They did it only in order to live behind tall protective walls—where they could feel safe, and where they could raise their children in relative peace. In all likelihood, they probably initially loathed living in such close confines, until it became a way of life.

Apart from new neighbours to push *them and us* buttons, a settled lifestyle also brought vermin and disease. Smallpox, measles and influenza were originally animal diseases but spread to the first human farmers with catastrophic consequences.[756,757]

*Today, little remains of Jericho but its two massive stone walls, that predate the
pyramids by 5000 years, are one of humanity's greatest engineering achievements.*

Food waste, garbage, flies, rats and maggots had not been a problem
for nomadic people, neither had raw sewage or the problem of fresh
drinking water. Settled people not only took on these social hygiene
problems but also had to make new social accommodations and com-
promises. As Nicholas Wade puts it, Neolithic people "had to trade
their prized freedom and equality for hierarchy, officials and chiefs and
other encumbrances."[758]

And farming was hard work. Archaeological data consistently shows
that not only did farmers spend more time than hunter-gatherers procuring
the same amount of food, but that their diet was less healthy and more
prone to famine than hunter-gatherers.[759,760]

When archaeologist Andrew Moore excavated the Syrian Neolithic
settlement of Abu Hureyra in the 1970s, he found evidence that the 'daily
grind' of cereal grains was much more strenuous and labour-intensive
than previously thought. Because seeds deteriorate once they are de-
husked, this—and grinding—had to be done daily. But it took so long
and placed such a strain on their bodies that, in many cases, the bones and
muscles of the inhabitants became deformed.

The sacrifice and inconvenience were justified only by the measure of
safety that such a sea-change afforded. For a while at least, it is likely that
the first farmers continued to hunt to supplement their meagre agricultural
efforts, and this too is confirmed by the latest archaeological evidence. It
shows that in many cases, people (like the Natufians who occupied Jordan

and Palestine) continued their reliance on hunting for some time after the shift to sedentism.[761]

In conclusion, while the ostensible cause of the Neolithic revolution was the need for walled enclaves to protect settled family populations, the underlying cause was male hyper-aggression, which has its evolutionary antecedents in Neanderthal predation.

The counter argument would come from scholars who interpret evidence of early walls, ditches, banks and palisades in a different light. Robert Evans and Judith Rasson's review of the corpus of Neolithic research in southeast Europe devotes only two paragraphs to defensive structures, and mostly quotes scholars who argue the "identification of a community by a wall or fence may be symbolic (to create a sense of community) or functional (to keep animals in or out, for instance)".[762] A related argument holds that Neolithic walls, banks and ditches were not built as fortifications at all, but as a method of community 'demarcation'.[763]

It is difficult to see why you would need a three metre thick wall to keep the goats in. It is equally difficult to resist the view that this interpretation of the evidence reflects an anthropocentric bias—that humans are too noble, intelligent, and courageous to hide behind walls and palisades. However, the weight of archaeological evidence supporting widespread intertribal conflict during the Neolithic is overwhelming.

what's behind the wall?

From the Neolithic onwards, the construction of fortified settlements dramatically increased, driven by technological innovation and increased social organisation. But the need to construct these massive edifices also drove the technological advances and the complex social systems needed to fund and organise these ever-increasing constructions.

Today, the wall remains humanity's most enduring architectural legacy. For the entire recorded history of humankind, we have built fortresses and walls with unbridled enthusiasm—as if our lives depended on them. Our obsession with wall building lies ultimately in our genetic fear of Neanderthals. (Right from top):

Hadrian's Wall, England

The Great Wall of China took 1200 years to build, is 6350 km long, and the largest engineering task ever undertaken

The Berlin Wall was torn down in 1989

Although condemned by the UN, Israel has recently built a wall twice as high as the Berlin Wall, through the West Bank and Jerusalem. Paradoxically, these walls don't assuage the feelings of insecurity and paranoia—they exacerbate them.

Wooden palisades were replaced with stone forts, surrounded by water-filled moats, with drawbridges and towers from which invaders could be seen approaching. Castles, citadels, and fortified cities became a ubiquitous feature of the landscape from the Bronze Age onwards, peaking in the Middle Ages when almost every European city, port, monastery and rural settlement was fortified.

By the Late Iron Age, the threat no longer came from small nomadic gangs. It came from barbarian hordes or large invading armies, which changed the function of castles. They gradually became sanctuaries for farming folk from surrounding areas during times of conflict. The other change was that, as human culture spread across the globe and diversified, walled fortresses reflected emerging cultural identities.

At first glance, walled enclosures seem to be solely cultural artefacts. Their enormous cultural variety and form has obfuscated the evolutionary imperatives that motivated their construction. It could be argued, for instance, that the reason Byblos Castle in Lebanon (*below left*) was built by the Crusaders in the 12th century was simply as a defence against the armies of Saladin, the Sultan of Egypt. Or that the medieval moated Bodiam Castle in East Sussex (*below right*) was specifically built to defend the surrounding area from a feared French invasion. And while that's correct, the ubiquity of fortress building around the world suggests it is also part of human nature. The anthropologist Lee Cronk has argued that when humans express a strong cultural attitude or when an aspect of culture is universal (such as gossip, dancing and belief in deities), it may have a biological origin.[764]

If, as NP theory argues, these constructions are subliminal expressions of teems that were encoded by the trauma of Neanderthal predation and Cro-Magnon hyper-aggression, then they are not just cultural. Although the fears humans inherited have been subsumed, redirected and concealed within cultural protocols, they nevertheless have their evolutionary origins in biology. The fear of *the others* is in our genes.

This would explain why, as munitions development rendered fortresses redundant in the eighteenth and nineteenth centuries and people stopped building castles, the innate fears simply found a new expression—in locked houses, burglar alarms, security guards, reinforced doors, grilled windows, padlocks, police, and guard dogs.

To understand why this nebulous biological fear of *them* inculcates culture to such an extent, it is important to understand the nature of teems.

Teems are inheritable packages of emotion, and provide only an emotional memory of a traumatic incident. Teems derived from Neanderthals and Cro-Magnons present only half the picture—and no details. They describe what *the others* felt like but not what they specifically looked like. To flesh out the details, Mesolithic and Neolithic humans had to use their imagination, or draw on their storytellers and mythographers (all aspects of culture) to give form to the demons, monsters and satanic creatures they believed lurked in the darkness beyond their walls. In other words, culture gives form to teems.

Even today, when modern humans attempt to identify the source of residual anxieties, they too must draw on their imagination, just as their ancestors did, or project their feelings onto one of the monsters from mythology, literature or the movies. Alternatively, they can select a convenient scapegoat from ethnic minorities, migrant groups, gays, women, members of religious communities and other minority groups and dress them in the feelings of their teems. The tragedy is that in each case, the real culprit has long gone.

These futile attempts to identify the invisible *others* that lurk just beyond the firelight continued unabated throughout the Neolithic, Mesolithic, Bronze Age, the Iron Age and finally into recent recorded history. In each culture, capricious vicissitudes nominated expedient scapegoats and personified them as monsters, fiends and demons.

In Europe, *the others* were identified as witches, warlocks, heretics, incubuses and werewolves—creatures who came out only under cover of darkness to wreak havoc on righteous people everywhere. At other times, *the others* included any and all foreigners. Often they were labelled barbarians—a subhuman race that sprang from dark satanic places to kill the innocents, defile virtuous women and eat babies.

Ammianus Marcellinus, a fourth century Roman historian, described how "a race of men, hitherto unknown, had suddenly

A marble relief depicting a Roman victory over the barbarians. Although 'barbarians' were known as a race of wild and uncivilised people, the term was only ever a pejorative cultural label applied, I suggest, to any group that triggered 'them and us' teems.

descended like a whirlwind from the lofty mountains, as if they had risen from some secret recess of the earth, and were ravaging and destroying everything which came in their way."

The Greek historian, Herodotus was no less kind:

> Barbarians can neither think nor act rationally, theological controversies are Greek to them... Under the assault of their horrible songs the classic meter of the ancient poet goes to pieces... Barbarians are driven by evil spirits; 'possessed by demons', who force them to commit the most terrible acts... Barbarians are without restraint... they are given to gross personal hygiene... they run dirty and barefoot, even in the winter... They grease their blond hair with butter and care not that it smells rancid...Their reproductive energy is inexhaustible; the Northern climate of their native land, with its long winter nights favours their fantastic urge to procreate.

It would not concern these finger-pointing ancients that no such race as the barbarians ever existed. As historian David Willis McCullough points out, "there was no one group called 'barbarian' and no ancestral home-land of Barbaria."[765] They certainly didn't refer to themselves as barbarians. That was a pejorative term first used by the Greeks and Romans, and simply meant anyone who could not be understood, either because they stammered, or their rudimentary language was so guttural and animal-like, no decent 'civilised' person could comprehend it.

To the ancients, barbarians included everyone they feared—Thracians, Egyptians, Persians, Berbers, Indians, Celts, Germans, Phoenicians, Etruscans, Romans, Carthaginians, Macedonians, Eleans and Epirotes. Later, Huns, Vandals, Saracens, Mongols, Scythians, Celts, Goths, Tartars, Christians and Vikings were added to the list

Much to the chagrin of Herodotus, the barbarians used basically the same term to express their own xenophobic perception of foreigners. The ancient Indians, for example, referred to foreigners as 'Mlechcha'— barbarians. When the Portuguese sailors first arrived in Japan, they were called nanban, which means 'barbarians from the south'. Not to be left out, the Persians considered Roman and Arab cultures to be so inferior to their own, they called them 'Soosk'—'barbarian' in Farsi. In the east, the Han Chinese bestowed the term on Europeans, Mongols, Koreans, Japanese, Manchu, Tartars and Turks, while the cultural elite of the Italian Renaissance used it to describe anyone born outside Italy. Until recently, the Chinese used the pejorative term 'yangguizi' (which means 'foreign devil') to describe all foreigners.

While the term 'barbarian' lives on as a term of abuse to describe the typical suite of Neanderthaloid-Cro-Magnon attributes, the barbarians of those times have long gone. They morphed into solid, law-abiding farmers and denizens of the new cities that mushroomed around the world. But consistent with NP theory's thesis that barbarians were only ever a cultural surrogate for deeper anxieties, new barbarians have resurfaced to take their place. They are sometimes real aggressors, reflecting the last vestiges of male hyper-aggression. But more likely, they are the alienated and marginalised victims of pogroms, persecutions and genocides, suggesting the cultural projection of innate fears remains a salient feature of human affairs.

26 CIVILISING THE SAVAGES

The seventh and final constraint on male hyper-aggression was ostensibly cultural. It was the uniquely human collection of laws, edicts, philosophies, conventions and collected wisdom we call civilisation. Civilisation and the rule of law are normally used by sociologists to describe socially complex agricultural societies with large cities and developed economies. But from the perspective of NP theory, civilisation and the rule of law are much more. They are functional adaptations that contributed to fitness.

Civilisation and the rule of law involve such complex social, political, artistic and organisational systems, they require specialist neural networks and cerebral modules which, I argue, came under positive selection because civilisation was so effective in constraining male coalitionary violence. The cerebral modules that support civilisation spread rapidly because they allowed humans to apply cultural constraints to moderate maladaptive innate behaviours that had previously been all but immune from cultural control.

Like a Guttenberg printing press, civilisation churned out for the first time a plethora of moral and religious codes, laws, decrees and proto-governmental edicts to regulate social behaviour and, in particular, inappropriate violent behaviour by men. Prior to this, there was no formal mechanism for punishing offences against persons and property. It was left to tribesmen or relatives to punish the culprit, a practice which often escalated into broader conflicts.

The earliest example of coercive cultural management of male violence is probably the set of 57 laws, guidelines and edicts preserved on a small clay tablet by the king of Ur, Ur-Nammu (2112–2095 BC). Known as the Ur-Nammu law code, it begins:

> Then did Ur-Nammu, the mighty man, the king of Ur, the king of Sumer and Akked, by the power of Nanna, the city's king, and by the..., establish justice in the land, and by force of arms did he turn back evil and violence.

The Ur-Nammu code (*right*) provides the first real social antidote to collective senseless violence. One law, for example, reads, "If a man has severed with a weapon...bone of another man, he shall pay one mana of silver."

Three centuries later, in 1760 BC, King Hammurabi, the sixth Babylonian king enacted his own sets of laws—the famous Code of Hammurabi. It not only provided citizens with guidelines for acceptable behaviour,

plus a detailed list of criminal offences and punishments, it also stipulated procedures for settling disputes peacefully. The code was carved onto a black stone stele (*left*), 2.4 metres (8 ft) tall, and was on constant public display, so no one could plead ignorance of the law.

For Babylonians contemplating a flirtation with villainy, a cursory glance at the stele might prompt a rethink. Examples include:

- If a man has stolen goods from a temple, or house, he shall be put to death; and he that has received the stolen property from him shall be put to death.

- If any one take a male or female slave of the court, or a male or female slave of a freed man, outside the city gates, he shall be put to death.

- If a man has stolen a child, he shall be put to death.

In all, there are 282 edicts, enough to cover most social situations and, while they may seem draconian by today's standards, they didn't hold a candle to the laws promulgated by the 7th century BC Greek legislator Draco. By imposing the death sentence for practically every offence, no matter how trivial, he gave his name to the word 'draconian'.

While the Jewish Torah includes hundreds of commandments, the Judeo-Christian tradition condensed these into the Ten Commandments (or Decalogue) which incorporated several religious prohibitions along with its moral directives.

Central to all these cultural regulations is an unequivocal prohibition against gratuitous violence. And, in every case, the edicts are enforced by physical coercion. The punishments listed in the Yasa (or law) of Genghis Khan, the infamous Mongolian warlord, include:

- An adulterer is to be put to death without any regard as to whether he is married or not.
- Whoever is guilty of sodomy is also to be put to death.
- Whoever urinates into water or ashes is also to be put to death.
- Whoever finds a runaway slave or captive and does not return him to the person to whom he belongs is to be put to death.

For the three millennia following their introduction, cultural prohibitions continued to rein in male violence. When a group of rebellious English lords forced King John to sign the Magna Carta in 1215, they not only curtailed the worse excesses of his violent nature, they introduced several revolutionary new concepts into the campaign, including protection of the law, freedom, and a citizen's right to feel safe:

> No freeman shall be taken, or imprisoned, or disseised [dispossessed], or outlawed, or exiled, or in any way destroyed, nor will we go upon him, nor will we send upon him, except by legal judgement of his peers or by the law of the land…
> All persons are to be free to come and go, except outlaws and prisoners.

From a 21st century perspective, it is difficult to comprehend the social and political impact these edicts had. After five million years of the law of the jungle, with all its hostile connotations, here was a radical new concept that meant, for the first time in human history, people were not constantly looking over their shoulders.

Of course there was the massive gulf between intention and reality, exemplified by the English lords themselves whose motives for Magna Carta remained steadfastly those of self interest. But despite the glacially slow progress, by 1790 the *Declaration of the Rights of Man* of the French Revolution was empowered in a genuine attempt to curb the devastation of barbarism, anarchy and mob rule.

Not all the rules of law were written down. Indigenous Australians, custodians of the oldest continuous culture in the world, incorporated an holistic set of social and spiritual laws into a complex oral tradition, disseminated by 'law men' and tribal elders. Central to the law was the concept of *payback* which includes procedures for redressing grievances through ritual ceremony, gift-giving, corporal punishment, or even killing.[766]

In practical terms, it means that if an offence is committed by an individual, only the offender is punished, which prevents escalation into larger tribal conflicts. So successful was the law, Indigenous Australians remain one of the few nomadic people who did not need to construct walled cities and so could maintain their hunter-gatherer existence.

Whatever form they took, cultural mechanisms of control generally proved an effective means of curbing male violence. I see three main reasons for this:

- Most of the codes used violence to curb violence, with violators more often than not facing the death sentence. While this 'eye for an eye' may seem paradoxical, it doesn't contradict human nature. Punishment, chastisement, reprisal, violence, ostracism, victimisation and marginalisation are all endemic to the human condition. We're biologically *au fa*it with them. They're part of our inherited biology.

- The laws were edicts of 'big men'—chiefs, kings, tribal elders and warlords—all surrogates of the ancestral alpha male who dictated behaviour in early human groups and, before that, in ancestral primate troops. Humans are genetically inclined to obey the alpha male—to comply with his dictates—particularly during times of stress because, historically, such obedience proved adaptive.

- The rule of law appealed to people's altruistic, civil,

generous, intellectual and familial sides. This was the
carrot to complement the big stick. The philosophies of
Socrates, Plato, Aristotle, Lao Tzu, Confucius, the pre-
Socratic philosophers and the Pax Romana are prime
examples of the appeal to reason and lucidity, as were
the moral teachings attributed to Jesus of Nazareth and
Mohammad.

This reassessment of civilisation argues that its greatest achievement was
not art, language or the spread of technology. It was the rule of law. It
functioned as an antidote to male hyper-aggression. The incorporation of
both coercive measures and appeal to newly acquired reason and rationality allowed humanity to reach a tipping point where, despite continual
warfare and intergroup hostilities, family life finally became sustainable.

This new appreciation of civilisation also illuminates its fragility.
Civilisation is a bulwark between our arduous evolutionary legacy and
viable continuance. In this book, space precludes a detailed discussion of
the social, political and personal implications of NP theory for modern
humans, but I feel an obligation to at least highlight both the tenuous
nature of civilisation and the indispensable role it played in human
evolution.

NP theory suggests that seven mechanisms emerged to mitigate the
worst excesses of male coalitionary violence:

- Natural selection: the most violent men killed each
  other off and their genes were lost.
- Sexual selection: women preferred less violent men to
  father their children.
- The development of cognitive networks enabled logic
  and rationality to control innate aggressive tendencies.
- The evolution of a degree of tolerance of individual
  and cultural variability.
- The emergence of neural networks that supported
  complex society, and the aggregation of people into
  large groups for mutual protection.
- The invention of agriculture which enabled people to
  live in walled compounds.
- The advent of civilisation and the rule of law to
  culturally inhibit gratuitous interpersonal violence.

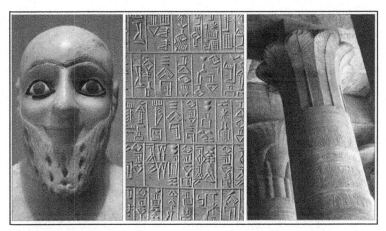

When we think of civilisation we normally think of art, language, architecture, agriculture and industrialised societies—but one of the most important aspects of civilisation was the rule of law that significantly reduced male violence.

Scrolling down the seemingly endless lists of victims of human violence over the last few millennia begs the question—did these seven adaptations against male hyper-aggression do any good at all? They may have removed the 'hyper-', but we are still an undeniably aggressive species. Researchers have calculated that over the last thousand years, 11 European countries have been engaged in some form of warfare 47 percent of the time. The devoutly Catholic nation of Spain tops the list having spent 67 percent of the last millennium at war.[767]

To appreciate just how ingrained these predation imperatives are, we need only note that—despite the attrition of the most virulent male aggression genes throughout the Neolithic, despite the controls imposed by rules, laws and commandments, and despite the civilising influence of religion and philosophy—two global conflagrations, a holocaust, and countless genocides have occurred within living memory.

Humans remain a violent species and the prevalence of weapons of mass destruction ensures that our continuance as a species cannot be guaranteed. However, without these seven adaptations, humankind would have torn itself to pieces years ago.

THE ORIGINS OF
WORLD MYTHOLOGY

the sledgehammer and the walnut

I mention in the preface that I first became interested in human evolution and, in particular, the innate aspects of human behaviour as a result of researching a book on myths and movies. I became intrigued with how cultures on different continents, often with no contact with each other, created myths with unerringly similar themes and storylines.

As early as the nineteenth century, the universality of myths and folkloric stories began to become apparent. Andrew Lang, the famous Scottish folklorist, discovered that the story of the Argonauts—which was thought to have originated in Greece—also appeared in Samoan, Japanese, Finnish and his own Scottish mythology in almost identical forms.

In the Pacific, Polynesian cultures like that of the Maori feature snake-headed creatures almost identical to the Grogan's head of Etruscan, Roman and Greek mythology. Winged serpents and dragons appear in a range of mythologies from Egypt and Europe to Australia and both Americas. Among the most common are tales of valiant heroes venturing into terrifying underworld realms to rescue beautiful maidens abducted by demonic monsters. And everywhere, epic journeys to strange lands by intrepid adventurers are ubiquitous.

Anthropologist Joseph Campbell's *The Hero with a Thousand Faces* analyses world mythologies and finds a consistent preoccupation with the same story, plot points and characters, which he calls 'The Hero's Journey'.

The journey begins when the hero accepts the call to adventure, which usually involves confronting evil monsters of unimaginable brutality. The mythological odyssey progresses to the most dangerous phase, 'the approach to the innermost cave'—often a subterranean cavern where the forces of darkness reside, but it may be a dragon's lair or a sinister castle in the middle of a dark forest. It may be a witch's hovel, or hell or an underworld fortress, or it may be Darth Vader's death star.

Entering the innermost cave is often the hero's final test before 'the supreme ordeal', when he comes face-to-face with his greatest fear. He is now within the 'belly of the beast'—locked in mortal combat of the physical or metaphysical kind. By passing the supreme ordeal, either by stealth, intelligence, strength or creativity, the hero earns his reward, the gratitude of a beautiful maiden, the approbation of his clan or an elixir to heal a wounded land.

These recurrent themes highlight the ubiquity of imaginary monsters and mythic creatures in world mythology. From the Babylonian Alü, a demon who crushed humans with his enormous bulk, to the Xanthus, a talking horse from Greek mythology, there are literally thousands of diverse monsters, dragons, angels, gods, demons and half humans whom millions of people from an eclectic mix of cultures have believed in with an absolute and resolute conviction.

Sex-crazed satyrs, the appeal of vampire films like *Twilight*, the plethora of supposed Bigfoot sightings, and the number of reports involving alien abduction and sexual probing hint to common evolutionary origins. It was this commonality that provided the first clue, that in turn led to Teem theory, and subsequently to NP theory. Now, ten years later, as I apply Teem theory and NP theory to explain the evolutionary origins of human mythology I feel I am perhaps using a sledgehammer to crush a walnut.

mythic monsters

During the Cro-Magnon conquest of Europe and the protracted 20,000 year battle to rid the continent of their historic enemies, Cro-Magnons would gather around the campfire and eagerly describe their adventures, including their dramatic encounters with Neanderthals. Narrating these first-hand accounts helped Cro-Magnons cope with the psychological stress of armed conflict. As well as entertaining the group, the cathartic tales would also boost morale and disseminate invaluable survival lessons.

Following the Neanderthal extinction, it may be confidently speculated that first-hand accounts of these nightmarish creatures and the heroic humans who fought them would proliferate culturally. Gradually, they would be embellished and supplemented by third-person accounts, exaggerated depictions and quasi-mythologised rewrites—fused snippets of reality and fiction—until the line was so blurred, no-one knew what was real and what was myth.

In the mythological tradition, Neanderthal-like creatures took centre stage—attributed with mythic, magical and demonic powers. The myths reflected the transitional phase between actual encounters with Neanderthals, second-hand accounts and finally mythologised tales. Because these accounts started out as first-person reports, they carried that credibility down through the generations. If a Cro-Magnon male asserted around the campfire that his ancestor had slain one of these demonic creatures with a single blow from his stone axe, there would be no reason to doubt that story.

Newly equipped with formidable powers of imagination, plus new linguistic and narrative skills, the humans turned storytelling into an art form. They had always experienced those strange emotions that surfaced periodically—activated by specific circumstances. Now they began to create stories to match the emotions of their teems. If Neanderthal teems made them afraid of the dark, or of monsters with superhuman strength, or of hairy strangers, they invented stories to give form to their fears and help express them. In this way, they found stories could produce a cathartic release from pent-up teemic emotions.

The best of these cathartic tales were so therapeutic and so exciting, they were retold by storytellers and shamans through the generations. Their redemptive power earned these fabled tales and their valiant heroes a revered place in early human society. And of course, the weavers of these tales—the storytellers, shamans, sages and priests—were venerated for their gifts.

This 17th century English manuscript typically depicts a wildman abducting a woman—a subliminal expression of our innate fear of sexual predation.

Because the stories were acts of imagination, they were drawing from the same subliminal wellspring that fed their Neanderthal instincts and innate behaviours. In other words, they were tapping into their repertoire of Neanderthal teems and giving flesh to the emotional memories they evoked. The monsters they imagined looked and acted a lot like Neanderthals. Their plots mostly followed the recurring theme of conflict between *them and us*.

If early Greek, Roman, Norse and Chinese mythologies are anything to go by, the legends spun by early humans centre around an heroic human (almost always a man) who is pitted against an ugly, evil, cruel monster with superhuman strength, so vile it has the capacity to destroy the virtuous.

This universal mythic monster is usually male, invariably wild, hairy, dangerous, and uncouth. Often, it is half man-half animal, and tends to live in dank forests or dark caves, or emerge from the 'underworld' under cover of darkness to wreak havoc on decent folk. The monster is also frequently a sexual fiend who kidnaps and ravishes innocent maidens and fair princesses whom he drags back to his shadowy lair. It commonly feeds on human flesh, devours children and stalks by night.

The bestiary from western cultures includes satyrs, fauns, giants, Minotaurs, Cyclopes, Lamias, ghouls, ghosts, hydras, Leszis, chimeras, gorgons, harpies, dragons, woodwodes, green men, forest ogres and vampires. It is no coincidence that the two earliest sculptures ever discovered, 30,000-year-old ivory carvings from Hohlenstein-Stadel cave (*right*) and Hohle Fels Cave (in Germany) both depict half human-half animal creatures.[768] The sheer preponderance and consistency of folkloric narratives about half man-half beasts residing in forest and caves and emerging from the 'underworld' to abduct and ravish females,[769,770,771,772] cannot easily be dismissed.

In some scenarios, the human hero uses his superior intelligence, courage and strength to defeat these subterranean creatures. At other times, he uses guile, wit and cunning to get the upper hand. The outcome is always the same. These uniquely human strategic attributes enable the hero to rescue the princess and vanquish the monster.

As the best of these oral tales were passed down from one generation to the next, they consolidated into the antecedents of the earliest Mesopotamian, Egyptian, Phoenician, Sumerian and Minoan mythologies. In other words, humanity (according to anthropologist Joseph Campbell) has a unique and cherished repository of universal myths, legends and fairy tales,[773,774] which NP theory asserts were forged in the furnace of Neanderthal predation.

This hypothesis is supported by the rich canon of folkloric literature from around the world. Everywhere, the same bias is evident—the stories are overwhelmingly about two things. The first is Neanderthal-like monsters—vile creatures with super-human powers and lascivious sexual appetites.

The other ancient preoccupation is with the human heroes who vanquished these monsters—like the Greek heroes Hercules, Bellerophon, Jason, Odysseus, Perseus, Theseus and Achilles. Every human culture, from Incas to Inuit, from Cambodians to Cameroonians have similar monsters and similar heroes.

Of course, it may be argued that the monsters of mythology and folklore are derived from nonhuman predators like wolves, lions and

World mythologies are replete with tales of rape and abduction to underworld domains. The abductor is often a deity, satyr, centaur or some other wild creature. The rape of Persephone by Hades, from Greek mythology (left), is an typical example.

leopards. That may be the case. But in *The Thematic Guide to World Mythology* Lorena Stookey stresses an important distinction between real animals and the imaginary creatures that haunt the popular imagination:

> Whereas large predatory animals—often including the lion, the jaguar, or the wolf—are represented as terrifying creatures in some cultural traditions, it is nevertheless telling that myths' imaginary beasts are among the most dreadful of the animals described in peoples' stories. Indeed, accounts of frightening creatures composed of parts from various animals, appear in narratives from around the world.[775]

where the wild things are

NP theory goes on to claim that the Levantine humans' innate responses to predation live on in modern humans. Although they are now vestigial and subliminal, the innate fears, vigilance and identification modules of our Levantine ancestors still find expression through our modern emotions, imagination, dreams, nightmares, reverie, superstition and paranoia. And, of course, through various genres of storytelling..

Obviously, today no one believes in dragons, cannibalistic cyclopes, or minotaurs. They are what cryptozoologists call *cryptids*—animals or creatures that were claimed to have existed, but have not been proven to exist. But it seems that the same hardwired emotions that predisposed ancient civilisations to imagine such creatures and that peopled mythology with epic heroes are no less active today.

If the Romans believed that half-goat half-human deities called Satyrs roamed their forests and mountains with permanent erections looking for young girls, we can pass that off as sheer ignorance. And if people in the Middle Ages were convinced that ogres, goblins, greenmen, trolls and other nasty creatures were living in the surrounding woods, again we can say, "That was the dark ages". But, while it is amusing to hear that Mesopotamians 4000 years ago believed in a legendary crocodile-like dragon with wings, claws and fiery breath called an Enuma Elish, it is somewhat more disconcerting to realise that up to 3 million Americans believe they have had a personal encounter with an alien. And, despite scientific investigations that have produced not one actual yeti, sasquatch or abominable snowman, millions of people around the world still firmly believe in their existence.

The mythologies of almost every culture on earth have a variant of these hairy forest-dwellers, yet not one has ever been proven unequivocally to exist, which suggests that they reside in our collective unconscious—as much a part of human nature as our love of music and dance.

Does the yeti exist in reality, or simply in the mind, as one old Sherpa homily suggests: "There is a yeti in the back of everyone's mind; only the blessed are not haunted by it".[776]

Is it a coincidence that so many cryptids, like the collection of greenmen (*left*) look unerringly like Neanderthals? Are these reports based on eye-witness accounts of remnant Neanderthal populations? Do Neanderthals still cling on in the Himalayas, Mongolia and other geographically remote outposts?

A brief sample includes almas (Mongolian for 'wild men'), who are meant to inhabit the Caucasus and Pamir Mountains of central Asia and the Altai Mountains of southern Mongolia. They are described as "human-like bipedal animals, between five and six and a half feet tall, their bodies covered with reddish-brown hair, with anthropomorphic facial features including a pronounced brow ridge, flat nose, and a weak chin."[777]

The mountainous regions of Afghanistan and Northern Pakistan are said to be the home of the barmanu, a bipedal primate "supposed to possess both human and apelike characteristics and which is said to abduct women and attempt mating with them."[778]

Half way across the world, in New Zealand, many Maori still believe in the moehau, or 'hairy moehau'. They are described as, "wild men in the forests of New Zealand they were thought to live on the South Island and be solitary creatures, occasionally kidnapping people."[779]

Cross the Pacific to the northwest region of the United States and Canada and you will come across stories of sasquatch, or bigfoot. Wikipedia describes this creature as "a large, hairy bipedal hominid" covered in dark brown or dark reddish hair and said to inhabit remote forests. Its head "seems to sit directly on the shoulders, with no apparent neck. Alleged witnesses have described large eyes, a pronounced brow ridge, and a large, low-set

A motley collection of yetis, abominable snowmen and sasquatch from popular culture and mythology, all bear a striking similarity to Neanderthal physical characteristics.

forehead; the top of the head has been described as rounded and crested, similar to the sagittal crest of the male gorilla."[780]

Meaning 'forest man' in Vietnamese, the người rừng is rumoured to be a hominid living deep in the jungle "approximately six feet tall and completely covered with hair except the knees, the soles of the feet, the hands and the face. The hair ranges in color from gray to brown to black. The creature walks on two legs and has been reported both solitary and moving in small clans."[781]

Siberia is supposed to be the home of the tjutjuna or chuchunaa, a six to seven feet tall bipedal hominid cryptid covered with dark hair.[782] In Malaysia, locals believe the rainforest of Johor is inhabited by bipedal hominids called orang mawas, that are covered in black fur,[783] while the jungles of South America are thought to be the home of the Maricoxi— "extremely hairy...large apelike creatures that speak in grunts".[784]

While no rock-solid scientific evidence has emerged to prove any of these bipedal, forest-dwelling cryptids actually exist (although cryptozoologists remain hopeful that proof will some day emerge) their sheer ubiquity across disparate cultures on different continents and separated by thousands of years has long puzzled ethnographers and anthropologists.

This adds weight to the proposition that Neanderthal teems are encoded in human ncDNA, supplying each generation with an innate emotional memory of these ancient predators. These teems guide and inform the imagination of artists, myth-makers, story-tellers and movie-makers, and provide emotionally receptive audiences for such alien, yet familiar creatures.

the struggle between good and evil —the new spin

Central to my thesis is that Neanderthal teems, and the Neanderthal sign stimuli they engender, created a genetic distinction between *them* and *us*. It is axiomatic that this *them and us* duality equates to *good and evil* respectively. Because the division operates at a genetic, psychological and cultural level, it not surprisingly found its way into Cro-Magnon mythology—and from there into all the world's mythologies. Within this cultural context, the Cro-Magnon campaign of genocide was spin-doctored into an heroic struggle between the forces of 'good and evil'.

The Cro-Magnon hero myth did not speak of merciless violence, rape, sadism or mutilation. It spoke of valiant men engaged in selfless struggles against irredeemably evil entities. By claiming the moral high ground, Cro-Magnon mythology clarified and simplified the divide—and the conflicts. It defined violence in terms straightforward enough for Palaeolithic audiences to understand and relate to. Good and evil became a powerful motivational force, emboldening men to take risks and to undergo any hardship, even sacrificing their own lives.

With *them and us* now redefined as the righteous battle between good and evil, innumerable atrocities could be rationalised. Vanquished, raped and mutilated enemies could be blithely consigned to dust while the victors were ennobled as virtuous heroes. No one ever pitied the dragon slain by Saint George, the minotaur that Theseus put to the sword, or the multi-headed hydra that Hercules dispatched.

As modern humans spread across the globe, the mythic concept of *them and us* found a natural home in nascent religious cults. Humans were now mentally equipped to contemplate their own deaths—something no species had done before. They could comprehend oblivion—with all its associated fears—and they quickly invented shamanistic beliefs to help them cope, not only with their own mortality, but with the many vicissitudes of life they faced as they dispersed across the globe. In these new quasi-religious beliefs, the concept of good and evil found fertile ground.

By virtue of their membership of a religious sect, adherents were placed on the side of the angels in struggles against sinful, and invariably ugly, miscreants such as demons, incubi and succubi. Because the Christian crusaders saw their conquest of the Holy Lands as a beneficent expression of piety against the heretical forces of Satan, they were able to massacre 30,000 Jewish and Muslim inhabitants of Jerusalem without a moment's hesitation. Once they had turned the streets into rivers of blood they congregated at the Church of the Holy Sepulchre to give thanks. In 16th century France, the Catholic church slaughtered thousands of Protestant Huguenots on St Bartholomew's Day, prompting Pope Gregory XIII to write to the French king, "We rejoice with you that with the help of God you have relieved the world of these wretched heretics".

Religion provided such a fertile medium for the dissemination of good versus evil that it became the quintessential myth of modern humans—and remains so to this day. How it became so may seem a bagatelle compared to other aspects of human evolution, but it goes to the heart of who we are as a species. And no other theory of human origins comes even close to explaining it.

28   ARE WE THERE YET?

a bit worse for wear

By a precarious and traumatic path, the human race has spread across the earth to become the most successful of all mammalian species. Our achievements are extraordinary and yet, despite the pyramids, the enigmatic smile on Leonardo's masterpiece and our footprints on the moon, modern humans still carry the emotional, physical and psychological scars from long-dead predators. Our genetic cellars still harbour behaviours and maladies, including depression, phobias, warfare and sexism as well as paranoia, racism, genocide and homicide, all of which have their evolutionary genesis in Neanderthal predation.

The theory argues that all the great empires of antiquity—Phoenician, Persian, Greek, Roman, Mongol, Egyptian, Byzantine, Mogul and Aztec—engaged in expansionist re-enactments of the first great conquistadorial campaign by Cro-Magnons against the Neanderthals. Their strategies and techniques have uncannily mimicked Cro-Magnon tactics—classifying the alien enemy as inferior and sub-human; killing the men and raping the women; subjugating, pillaging and enslaving; occupying enemy lands; and showing no mercy.

The same innate Neanderthal responses that find expression in ethnic cleansings and internecine conflicts have also been intuitively applied by dictators and unscrupulous politicians. In the 1950s, Senator

Joseph McCarthy tapped into this primordial fear to whip America into a fervour of anti-communist hysteria. Israeli descriptions of Palestinians as 'two-legged animals' and 'lice',[785] Hutus labeling Tutsis as 'inyenzi' (cockroaches) and the Nazi's classification of Jews as 'worse than animals' all have their antecedents in the prehistoric *them and us* mindset. George W. Bush's deft association of 'Muslim' with 'terrorist' in the minds of post 9/11 Americans is a recent example. Beyond politics, the same tendencies can turn a husband's suspicion of his wife's infidelity into homicidal rage They supply the emotions that legitimise stoning women for adultery and are behind the disturbing rise of acid attacks on women and girls in Pakistan, Cambodia (*below*) and other third-world countries.

Because young Palaeolithic girls were at increased risk of Neanderthal sexual predation once they began menstruating, the onset of menstruation was inevitably associated with increased anxiety, stress and depression. Could this explain modern statistics that show the likelihood of severe depression in modern teenage girls doubles in the year after the onset of menstruation?[786] Psychiatric epidemiologist Patricia Cohen from the New York State Psychiatric Institute found that severe depression in girls peaks around 13 and 14. "There's a tremendous risk for depression in girls in the years following puberty," she says.[787]

While paranoia is generally considered to be a mental illness suffered by individuals, NP theory argues that innate Neanderthal identification triggers render humans paranoid—as a species. At a cellular level, we are genetically imprinted with a belief that *they* are still out there, waiting

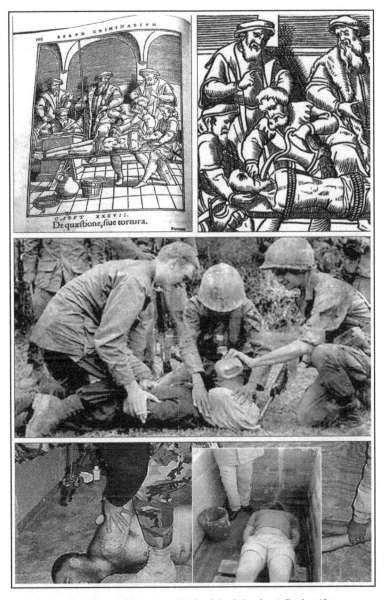

The capacity to deny the humanity of 'others' (and therefore inflict horrific tortures like waterboarding on them) does not appear to have diminished over time. Humanity must become cognisant of the evolutionary imperatives underlying 'them and us' behaviours in order to control them.

to strip the flesh from our bones, ravish our daughters and devour our infants. As part of our inborn anti-predator defence, we instinctively develop weaponry, stockpile armaments, fortify borders, impose pass laws and enforce inhumane restrictions on refugees. We watch films like *The Terminator, Independence Day, I Am Legend,* and *Jurassic Park* because they tap into our residual fears and satisfy our instinctive desire to vanquish what we now define as 'the forces of evil'.

We separate ourselves into races, religions, sects, classes and ethnic groups in the hope of distinguishing *us* from *them*. We enslave Neanderthal surrogates, burning them as witches and denouncing them as communists, reactionaries, homosexuals, Christians, Muslims, Jews or ethnics but, even so, there are not enough stockpiled nuclear devices to make us feel secure. There are not enough submarines to protect our shores, not enough B52s to protect our skies, and not enough locks to keep out the nightmares. Despite decades of unprecedented wealth and prosperity, the citizens of the developed world seem as fearful and anxious as at any time in history.

How can we reconcile our 21st century perception of ourselves as 'masters of the universe'—beings Shakespeare eulogised as "noble in reason, infinite in faculty—how like an angel", with the image of a frightened, angry, even demonic species springing half-formed from our evolutionary cauldron and spoiling for a fight?

The tragedy of Shakespeare's King Lear, his daughter Regan said, was that "he hath ever but slenderly known himself". If this is also our curse, it is easy to see why. Just as individuals suffering from post-traumatic stress disorder often repress all memory of the trauma, as a species, we have repressed the collective memory of Neanderthal predation. It's simply too painful and, strangely, too embarrassing. Our challenge is to honestly and openly acknowledge where we came from, and to look back with compassion and understanding at the travails our ancestors endured to get us here. We owe our existence to their courage and resilience, but we must also acknowledge the mind virus we have inherited that can turn a sensible man into a rapist or wife beater, transform gentle societies into armies, religions into inquisitions and clear-headed villagers into fanatical witch burners.

And what of the Neanderthals? We can begin by acknowledging that, despite almost wiping us out, Neanderthals were themselves just trying to survive. But more than this, we can recognise that they were responsible for the spurt of evolution that transformed us into modern humans. Without them, we would still be rubbing sticks together to light fires.

The need to identify ourselves as human is responsible for the rich cultural diversity we see today. We have a need to declare, "These adornments prove I am one of Us." It is this evolutionary imperative that fuels issues of identity, particularly among teenagers.

Despite their legacy of violence, we owe them our beautiful minds. We owe them the joy of music, art, literature, dance, comedy and culture. Thanks to them, we can fall in love. To them we owe our dualistic nature. We are hardwired with a propensity towards mindless violence, but we are also sentient beings who can contemplate the future and consider the impact we are having on the biosphere. Drawing on that intelligence, we may even negate the environmental catastrophe that threatens our planet.

All that's left of our former predator—one solitary footprint in a Romanian cave. But despite being extinct for over 28,000 years, Neanderthals remain part of our everyday lives—and will continue to influence us, and the course of human history.

potential problems with the theory

I have used three scientific theories to develop NP theory. The first two, Darwin and Wallace's theory of natural selection and Darwin's theory of sexual selection are widely respected and form the backbone of biological orthodoxy. The third theory, Teem theory is in its infancy, but nevertheless has provided insights into how emotional responses of early humans towards Neanderthal predation became innate and surreptitiously influenced our evolutionary trajectory. However, my interpretation of these theories and their specific application to the circumstances under discussion may not always be correct. Others may interpret these theories differently or draw other conclusions.

One problem with NP theory is the sheer scope of the hypothesis. The number of sub-hypotheses alone almost guarantees there will be errors of both fact and theory. Some of these may be corrected in future editions as a result of feedback. But if Darwin wrote six editions of *The*

Origin of Species to correct errors and placate his critics (even if some scholars, myself included, believe the First Edition was actually the best), then it will take more time than I have left to fine-tune the theory.

And here is another problem. As an independent scholar and autodidact, I lack the resources to substantiate the hypothesis, except in the most perfunctory manner. My research methodology is almost certainly flawed by current academic standards and I have probably not given enough consideration to alternative explanations. In addition, my decision to write the book for a general audience rather than as an academic treatise may have compromised the argument because it is 'neither fish nor fowl'.

The question of testability may also have a bearing on the theory's credibility. Throughout the book, I have continually tested aspects of the hypothesis by the hypothetico-deductive method—an hypothesis is proposed, its consequences are deduced, and these are tested against available evidence. But because the predicted events took place up to 100,000 years ago, the archaeological evidence is often sparse and equivocal. In a recent email, anthropologist and archaeologist Mark Aldenderfer, from the University of Arizona, reminded me that "many topics of the deep past may never be tested in a comprehensive manner" (*personal correspondence, September 2008*). It will be up to academics to extract further predictions from the model and test them against reliable datasets.

When trying to evaluate his own theory, Darwin was buoyed by the fact that natural selection provided cogent explanations for a large number of different phenomena. After the publication of *The Origin of Species* he wrote to a friend, "I cannot persuade myself that a theory which explains (as I think it certainly does) several large classes of facts, can be wholly wrong."[788]

In other words, even if some of the details were wrong, his theory explained so many important facts and resolved enough problematical issues that it was unlikely to be wrong overall. However, he also added, "Any one whose disposition leads him to attach more weight to unexplained difficulties than to the explanation of a certain number of facts will certainly reject my theory."

Applying this criteria, there can be little doubt that NP theory appears to explain many 'large classes of facts' relating to human evolution, physiology, psychology and human nature. In fact, it has been called a unified field theory—a simple explanation of the workings of nature that holds true over a wide range of exploration.

And yet, while this seems its greatest strength, some may see it as a negative. How can the evolution of the most complex being on the planet be reduced to one simple theory? Surely the magnificent complexity of humanity cannot be the result of prosaic animalistic forces. Compare this new picture of humanity's humble and cowed beginnings to the heroic versions in world mythology and religion. The *King James Bible*, for example, tells us that "God created man in his own image". If imitation is the greatest form of flattery, this elevates humanity to a kind of ultimate masterpiece creation—the pinnacle of a divinity's frenetic week of creation.

The same reverence for humanity as the pinnacle of life is also evident in Islam. The Qur'an singles out Allah's creation of Adam and Hawwa (Eve) from clay as a special case of creation.

Religious, cultural and anthropocentric dichotomies create a subtle resistance to NP theory that will not easily be allayed by rational argument. Similarly, for many mid-career anthropologists who have spent their working lives subscribing to (and defending) the 'out of Africa' or 'regional continuity' models of human evolution, NP theory may be challenging. The history of science tells us that, initially, revolutionary new scientific ideas are almost always treated with scepticism by the scientific community. In his paper *Peer Review for Journals: Evidence on Quality Control, Fairness, and Innovation*,[789] Scott Armstrong, from the University of Pennsylvania, reports that, while "trivial new findings threaten no one and are unlikely to offend reviewers", innovative papers (which he describes as "those with evidence that existing beliefs are incorrect") are more likely to be judged as defective. Similarly, science historian Thomas Kuhn in *The Structure of Scientific Revolutions* shows that resistance to innovative findings is likely to be strong and continuing when those findings conflict with established beliefs.[790] And psychologist Michael J Mahoney demonstrates that reviewers tend to reject the methodology of controversial papers while accepting identical methodology in papers supporting the orthodox view.[791]

An anonymous reviewer of a paper on NP theory I submitted to *Current Anthropology* wrote, "If CA wants to generate a veritable firestorm of commentary, this is the paper to do it!"

They didn't.

Ironically, Darwin predicted this kind of *a priori* response to his *The Origin of Species*. In the last chapter, he wrote, "I by no means expect to convince experienced naturalists whose minds are stocked with a multitude of facts all viewed, during a long course of years, from a point of view directly opposite to mine."

There is no clear-cut solution to this intellectual conservatism except, as Darwin said, "to look with confidence to the future,- to young and rising naturalists, who will be able to view both sides of the question with impartiality".[792] And that is what NP theory may need—a new generation of young anthropologists, palaeontologists and archaeologists just out of university, who have not already made up their minds about the crucial issues of recent human evolution and who will be able to evaluate the arguments with greater objectivity.

Eventually, a furry, bug-eyed Neanderthal may emerge from a melted glacier and provide physical evidence to prove or disprove NP theory but, until then, it will retain speculative elements.

This, of course, does not mean the theory is flawed. It simply reflects that, by its nature, it is a theory. And history tells us that new scientific theories often take years to be verified or refuted. For example, although Darwin and Wallace first put forward their theories of natural selection in 1859, it was not until the 1950s that the molecular mechanisms of natural selection, (such as point mutations, DNA, RNA, proteins, polypeptides and genes) were fully understood and accepted. Similarly, although Gregor Mendel published his theory of inheritance in 1865, it took another 50 years to identify and articulate the molecular-genetic mechanisms of inheritance.

While this version of NP theory appears to explain a raft of diverse biological and behavioural phenomena, the final version is yet to be written. That will come only after experimenters, clinicians and hands-on researchers have vigorously critiqued and, where necessary, corrected or refuted it. In the interim, this book will hopefully provide a conceptual framework to guide new lines of enquiries.

a personal reflection

Although I have not explored the implications of NP theory in detail in this book, clearly they are many and varied. The theory can be applied to resolve a large number of issues relating to human evolution, physiology, behaviour and history. It can be used to identify the evolutionary puppet master behind personal behaviours such as why someone would pay $245 for a bottle of Chanel No 5, why newborn babies tend to look like their fathers, why some people suffer panic attacks, get jealous or become addicted to post-apocalypse video games.

Or it can be applied to understanding deeper issues of the human condition; what is really behind racial discrimination, genocide, stock market panics, the belief in bigfoot, yetis, UFO abductions or the proliferation of weapons of mass destruction. It may help psychologists understand the behaviour of cults, youth gangs, monasteries and other isolated and introspective groups. Analysis of predation stress may provide new insights into depression, pessimism, school shootings, social anxiety and youth suicide. For examples of the enduring legacy of Neanderthal predation, you need only switch on the six o'clock news.

Knowing the secret history of our ancestors becomes a burden of sorts, like hearing painful news about someone we love. For me, the theory occasionally slips from its scientific moorings to overwhelm me with a profound sense of sadness. How many innocent souls have been turned to unlamented dust by hard-eyed men who came with clubs, then spears, then bows and arrows, guns, napalm, tanks and, finally, nuclear bombs? How many have dreaded the fickle gesture that directed them to the left, and survival—or right, to the gas ovens, to be casually exterminated like a cellar of rats.

Just as tragic is the realisation that the wars humanity has waged on itself since the Stone Age are so arbitrary, irrational and so horribly misconstrued. The leader of the murderous Ugandan LRA rebels Joseph Kony is convinced he is on a God-given mission to "cleanse the Acholi people"—ironically something he gleaned from biblical references.[793] The Nazi terror was inspired by the concept of an Aryan race and the need to prevent its adulteration by *them*—Jews and other non-Aryans.

But intuitively we all know it could be sparked by anything. For the victims of firing squads, bayonet charges, scorched earth policies, ethnic cleansings and naval bombardments, the justification is irrelevant. Surely there was only one question in the minds of the victims—how can men be so heartless?

Them and us not only refers to the prehistoric confrontation in the Levant but also acknowledges the ongoing divide amongst modern humans. Understanding and overcoming the redundant *them and us* mindset looms as the greatest challenge facing humanity today—because in its deadly circuitry lies the potential destruction of our planet.

However, sometimes there is a flash of sanity. On Christmas Eve in 1914, on the western front, English and German troops (*above*) came out of their trenches and briefly fraternised. They walked across no man's land and came face to face. For a moment, as they shared a cigarette and posed for photos, the virulent great divide evaporated and they saw the awful truth—we are all humans. There is no *them and us*. It's all an illusion. There is only us.

GLOSSARY

ACCULTURATION: Cultural change that occurs in response to extended firsthand contacts between two or more previously autonomous groups.

ADAPTATION: Any heritable characteristic of an organism that improves its ability to survive and reproduce in its environment.

ADMIXTURE: Transfer of genes between two populations that had previously been isolated from each other.

AGONISTIC BEHAVIOUR: Aggressive, negative behaviours, such as fighting, threatening and fleeing.

ALLELE: One of the alternative forms of a gene.

ANCIENT DNA: A DNA sequence retrieved from a biological sample of a dead organism.

ANTHROPOLOGY: The study of humanity: divisions are physical anthropology, archaeology, ethnology, and anthropological linguistics.

ANTHROPOMORPHIC: 'Human-like'—used to describe artifacts or art work decorated with human features or with a human-like appearance.

APEX PREDATOR: A predator which is not itself preyed upon as a species.

ARTIFACT: Any object manufactured, used or modified by humans. Common examples include tools, utensils, art, food remains, and other products of human activity.

ARTIFICIAL SELECTION: The process by which humans breed animals and cultivate crops to ensure that future generations have specific desirable characteristics. It can also include 'lethal selection'—killing individuals to remove an unwanted trait or characteristic.

ASSEMBLAGE: A group of artifacts recurring together at a particular time and place, and representing the sum of human activities.

ATLATL: A wood or bone shaft implement, held in one hand, and used to propel a spear. The tool functions as a lever, giving greater thrust and distance.

BC: Before Christ.

BP: Before Present.

BEHAVIOURAL ECOLOGY: The study of the ecological and evolutionary basis for animal behaviour, and the role of behaviour in enabling an animal to adapt to its environment.

BIG-MAN: A form of leadership in tribes where the leader achieves power and influence based on ability.

CANNIBALISM: Consuming the flesh of the same species. Among humans, this can occur in the context of warfare, as part of a funeral rite or, rarely, in cases of extreme dietary stress.

CARNIVOROUS: Eating only meat. Carnivorous animals are carnivores.

CENTRAL NERVOUS SYSTEM: An organ system, composed of a network of cells called neurons, that allows an animal to monitor its internal and external environment, and to move voluntarily or in response to stimulation.

CHERT: A fine-grained rock formed in ancient ocean sediments. It can be shaped into arrowheads by chipping. It has often been called 'flint', but true flint is found in chalk deposits and is blackish in color.

CLADE: A group comprising a single common ancestor and all the descendants of that ancestor.

COEVOLUTION: Evolution in two or more species, such as a predator and its prey or a parasite and its host, in which evolutionary changes in one species influence the evolution of the other species.

COGNITIVE: Relating to cognition, the mental processes involved in the gathering, organisation, and use of knowledge, including aspects such as awareness, perception, reasoning, and judgment. The term refers to any mental 'behaviours' where the underlying characteristics are abstract in nature and involve insight, expectancy, complex rule use, imagery, use of symbols, belief, intentionality, problem-solving, etc.

COMMON ANCESTOR: The most recent ancestral form or species from which two different species evolved.

CULTURE: The learned patterns of behaviour and thought that help a group adapt to its surroundings.

CUNEIFORM: A style of wedge-shaped writing common in the Middle East which pre-dates letters by 1500 years. Writing was scribed into soft clay using a specially shaped tool.

DARWINISM: Darwin's theory that species originated by evolution from other species and that evolution is mainly driven by natural selection.

DEMOGRAPHY: The study of the distribution, density, and vital statistics of populations.

ECOLOGY: The study of interrelationships of organisms and their environment.

ELECTRON SPIN RESONANCE (ESR): A chronometric dating technique based upon the behaviour of electrons in crystals exposed to naturally occurring radioactivity; used to date limestone, coral, shell, teeth, and other materials.

ETHNOCENTRISM: Judging other cultures by the standards of your own, which you believe to be superior.

ETHNOLOGY: A subset of cultural anthropology concerned with the comparative study of contemporary cultures, with a view to establishing general principles about human society.

ETHOLOGY: The branch of zoology that studies the behaviour of animals in their natural habitats.

FIXATION: A gene has achieved fixation when its frequency has reached 100 percent in the population.

FLAKE: A fragment removed from a core or nucleus of fine-grained rock by percussion.

FOSSIL: Most commonly an organism, a physical part of an organism, or an imprint of an organism that has been preserved from ancient times in rock, amber, or by some other means.

FOUNDER EFFECT: The loss of genetic variation when a new colony is formed by a very small number of individuals from a larger population.

GENE POOL: All the genes in a population at a particular time.

GENE: A sequence of nucleotides coding for a protein (or, in some cases, part of a protein); a unit of heredity.

GENETIC DRIFT: Changes in the frequencies of alleles in a population that occur by chance, rather than natural selection.

GENETIC: Related to genes. A gene is a sequence of nucleotides coding for a protein (or, in some cases, part of a protein); a unit of heredity.

GENETICS: The study of genes and their relationship to characteristics of organisms.

GENOME: The full set of DNA in a cell or organism.

GENOTYPE: The genetic profile of an individual.

GRAVE GOODS: Tools, weapons, food, or ceremonial objects placed with a burial.

HEREDITY: The process by which characteristics are passed from one generation to the next.

HERITABLE: Partly or wholly determined by genes; capable of being passed from an individual to its offspring.

HOLOCENE: The post-glacial period, beginning about 10,000 years ago.

HOMO ANTECESSOR: An extinct hominin species dating from 1.2 million to 800,000 years ago,

HOMO ERECTUS: A species of hominid that lived between 1.8 million and 30,000 years ago; the first Homo species to migrate beyond Africa.

HOMO: The genus in which all humans are classified.

HOMOLOGOUS STRUCTURES: The structures shared by a set of related species because they have been inherited, with or without modification, from their common ancestor. For example, the bones that support a bat's wing are similar to those of a human arm.

HOMOLOGY: A character shared by a set of species and present in their common ancestor.

HYBRID: The offspring of two separate species.

HYPOTHESIS: An explanation of one or more phenomena in nature that can be tested by observations, experiments, or both. In order to be considered scientific, an hypothesis must be falsifiable, which means that it can be proven to be incorrect.

HYPOTHETICO-DEDUCTIVE EXPLANATION: A form of explanation based on the formulation of hypotheses and the establishment from them by deduction of consequences which can then be tested against the archaeological data.

IN SITU: In its original place.

INDUSTRY: All the artifacts in a site that are made from the same material, such as the bone industry.

INHERITANCE OF ACQUIRED CHARACTERS: Historically influential but incorrect theory that an individual inherits physical traits that its parents acquired during their lifetimes.

ISOTOPIC ANALYSIS: An important source of information on the reconstruction of prehistoric diets, this technique analyses the ratios of the principal isotopes preserved in human bone; in effect the method reads the chemical signatures left in the body by different foods

KILL SITE: A type of special activity site where large game animals were killed and butchered.

LINEAGE: A unilineal descent group composed of people who trace their genealogies through specified links to a common ancestor.

LITHIC TECHNOLOGY: The process of manufacturing tools etc. from stone. Most frequently refers to stone flaking.

LUMBAR LORDOSIS: An inward curving of the lumbar spine (just above the buttocks).

MANDIBLE: A part of the bony structure of a jaw. In vertebrates, it is the lower jaw.

MESOLITHIC: An Old World chronological period beginning around 10,000 years ago, situated between the Palaeolithic and the Neolithic, and associated with the rise to dominance of microliths.

MITOCHONDRIAL DNA: DNA found in the mitochondrion, a small round body found in most cells. Because mitochondria are generally carried in egg cells but not in sperm, mitochondrial DNA is passed to offspring from mothers, but not fathers.

MORPHOLOGY: The form, shape, and structure of organisms.

MOUSTERIAN CULTURE: Flaked hand axes and tools from the Middle Palaeolithic period that appeared throughout Europe after 250,000 and before

30,000 years ago. Mousterian artefacts are associated with Neanderthals.

MUTATION: A change in genetic material that results from an error in replication of DNA. Mutations can be beneficial, harmful, or neutral.

NATIONAL CHARACTER: Studies based on the assumption that collectively members of a society have a distinctive set of psychological qualities.

NATURAL SELECTION: The differential survival and reproduction of organisms that differ from one another in one or more heritable characteristics. Through this process, the forms of organisms in a population that are best adapted to their local environment increase in frequency relative to less well-adapted forms over a number of generations.

NEOLITHIC REVOLUTION: A term coined by VG Childe in 1941 to describe the origin and consequences of farming (i.e. the development of stock raising and agriculture), allowing the widespread development of settled village life.

NICHE: The ecological role of a species; the set of resources it consumes and habitats it occupies.

NONPROTEIN-CODING DNA (ncDNA): DNA that does not carry the information necessary to make a protein.

PALAEOANTHROPOLOGY: The study of the fossil record and archaeology.

PALAEOECOLOGY: The study of the relationship of extinct organisms or groups of organisms to their environments.

PALAEOLITHIC: The archaeological period before c.10,000 BC, characterised by the earliest known stone tool manufacture.

PANGENESIS: Charles Darwin's flawed theory of heredity that proposes an organism's physical traits are passed on from one generation to the next in the form of particles called 'pangenes' given off by all parts of an organism, and which get passed on to offspring via sperm or egg.

PHENOTYPE: The physical or functional characteristics of an organism, produced by the interaction of genotype and environment during growth and development.

PHEROMONE: A chemical substance produced by organisms and emitted into the environment to communicate with others of the same species. They are used to mark out territories, attract mates, lay trails, and promote social cohesion and coordination in colonies. Pheromones are usually volatile organic molecules which are effective at very low concentrations, as little as one part per million.

PHYLOGENY: The study of ancestral relations among species, often illustrated with a "tree of life" branching diagram, which is also known as a phylogenetic tree.

PHYSICAL ANTHROPOLOGY: The scientific study of the physical characteristics, variability, and evolution of the human organism.

PLEISTOCENE EPOCH: The sixth geological epoch of the Cenozoic Era. The Pleistocene occurred approximately 1.81 million to 10,000 years ago. This was mostly a time of world cooling punctuated by three or four major ice ages. Most human evolution took place during the Pleistocene.

PREHISTORY: The period of human history before the advent of writing.

PROTEIN: A molecule made up of a sequence of amino acids. Many of the important molecules in a living thing—for example, all enzymes—are proteins.

PROVENIENCE: The three-dimensional location of an artifact or feature within an archaeological site, measured by two horizontal dimensions, and a vertical elevation.

RADIOCARBON DATING: A process that provides absolute dates by counting the radioactive decay of carbon in the remains of once living plants and animals (i.e., charcoal, wood, bone, shell).

REPRODUCTIVE ISOLATION: Two populations are considered reproductively isolated from one another if they cannot together produce fertile offspring.

SEDENTARY: A term applied to human groups leading a settled, non-migratory lifestyle.

SELECTIVE PRESSURE (SELECTION PRESSURE): Environmental forces such as scarcity of food or extreme temperatures that result in the survival of only certain organisms with characteristics that provide resistance.

SETTLEMENT PATTERN: The spatial distribution of cultural activities across a landscape at a given moment in time.

SEXUAL SELECTION: A selection of mating behaviour, either through competition among members of one sex (usually males) for access to members of the other sex; or through choice by members of one sex (usually females) of certain members of the other sex.

SPECIATION: the study of the layers of deposits at archaeological sites.

SPECIES: An important classificatory category, which can be variously defined by the biological species concept, cladistic species concept, ecological species concept, phenetic species concept, and recognition species concept.

STRATIGRAPHY: The archaeology definition of spatial evidence is the cultural remains and natural deposits form layers over time. Stratigraphic excavation is the digging out of an Area by completely clearing each strata layer before going any deeper.

SYMPATRY: Living in the same geographic region.

THEORY: A well-substantiated explanation of some aspect of the natural world that typically incorporates many confirmed observations, laws, and successfully verified hypotheses.

THERMOLUMINESCENCE DATING (TL): A chronometric dating method based on the fact that some materials, when heated, give off a flash of light. The intensity of the light is proportional to the amount of radiation the sample has been exposed to and the length of time that has elapsed since the sample was heated. It has much in common with electron spin resonance (ESR).

TOOL KIT: The set of all weapons and tools that was created and used by a person or group of people.

ZOOLOGY: A branch of biology that is concerned with the scientific study of animals, including their biology, distribution, and identification.

REFERENCES

1   Vendramini, D 2005, 'Noncoding DNA and the Teem theory of inheritance, emotions and innate behaviour', *Medical Hypotheses* 64, pp.512–519.

2   Zimmer, C 2003, 'Great Mysteries of Human Evolution', *Discover*, Sept.

3   Mellars, P 2005, 'The Impossible Coincidence. A Single-Species Model for the Origins of Modern Human Behavior in Europe', *Evolutionary Anthropology* 14, pp.12–27.

4   McBrearty, S & Brooks, A 2000, 'The revolution that wasn't: a new interpretation of the origin of modern human behavior', *J Human Evolution* 39, pp.453–563.

5   Henshilwood, C & Sealey, JC 1997, 'Bone artefacts from the Middle Stone Age at Blombos Cave, Southern Cape, South Africa', *Current Anthropology* 38, pp.890–895.

6   Jacobs, Z et al. 2008, 'Ages for the Middle Stone Age of Southern Africa: Implications for Human Behavior and Dispersal', *Science* 322, pp.733–735.

7   Quoted in: Deborah Smith, 2008, 'Tools linked to stone age exodus', *Sydney Morning Herald*, 30 October.

8   Kaufman, D 2002, 'Re-evaluating Subsistence Skills of Levantine Middle and Upper Palaeolithic Hunters: A Comparison of the Faunal Assemblages', *Oxford Journal of Archaeology* 21 (3), pp.217–229.

9   Grayson, DK & Delpech, F 1994, 'The Evidence for Middle Paleolithic Scavenging from Couche VIII, Grotte Vaufrey (Dordogne, France)', *Journal of Archaeological Science* 21, pp.359–75

10   Stiner, MC 1994, *Honor among thieves: A zooarchaeological study of Neandertal ecology*, Princeton University Press, Princeton.

11   Patterson, N, Richter, DJ, Gnerre, S, Lander ES & Reich, D 2006, 'Genetic evidence for complex speciation of humans and chimpanzees'. *Nature* 441, pp.1103–1108, 29 June.

12   Bar-Yosef, O 2002, 'The Upper Paleolithic Revolution', *Annual Review of Anthropology* 31.

13   Bar-Yosef, O 1996, 'Modern humans, Neanderthals and the Middle/Upper Paleolithic transition in Western Asia' in: The Lower and Middle Palaeolithii, Bar-Yosef, O, Cavalli-Sforza, LL, March, RJ and Piperno, M (eds), (Colloquia of the XIII International Congress of Prehistoric and Protohistoric Sciences, no. 5), *ABACO Edizion Forlì*, Italy pp.175–190.

14   Kozlowski, J 1982, *Excavations in the Bacho Kiro Cave (Bulgaria): Final Report*, Panstwowe Wydawnictwo Naukowe, Warsaw.

15   Kozlowski, J 2000, in Bar-Yosef, O & Pilbeam, D, Harvard (eds), *The Geography of Neandertals and Modern Humans in Europe and the Greater Mediterranean*, University Press, Cambridge, MA, Peabody Museum Bulletin 8, pp.77–106.

16   Bar-Yosef, O 1998, 'On the nature of transitions: the Middle to Upper Palaeolithic and the Neolithic revolution', *Cambridge Archaeological Journal*, 8, pp.141–163.

17   Noble, W & Davidson, I 1991, The evolutionary emergence of modern human behaviour: language and its archaeology, *Man* 26, pp.223–253.

18   Klein, RG 2000, 'Archaeology and the evolution of human behavior', *Evolutionary Anthropology* 9, pp.7–36.

19   Bar-Yosef, O 2002, 'The Upper Palaeolithic revolution', *Annual Review of Anthropology* 31, pp.363–393.

20   Kuhn, SL, Stiner, MC, Reese, DS & Gulec, E 2001, 'Ornaments of the earliest Upper Paleolithic: new insights from the Levant', *Proceedings of the National Academy of Sciences* 98 (13), pp.7641–6.

21   Bar-Yosef, O & Vandermeersch, B 1993, Modern Humans in the Levant, *Scientific American Magazine*, April.

22   Bickerton, D 1995, *Language and human behaviour*, University of Washington Press, Seattle.

23   Noble, W & Davidson, I 1996, *Human evolution, language and mind*, Cambridge University Press.

24   Neville, MC 1983, 'Regulation of Mammary Development and Lactation', in Neville, MC & Neifert, MR (eds), *Lactation, Physiology, Nutrition, and Breast Feeding*, Plenum, New York.

25   Pawlowski, B 1999, 'Loss of Oestrus and Concealed Ovulation in Human Evolution', *Current Anthropology*, 40 (3), p. 257.

26   Morris, D 1968, *The Naked Ape*, McGraw-Hill.

27   Pinker, S 1997, *How the Mind Works*, Penguin Books.

28   Rummel, RJ 1994, *Death By Government*, Transaction Publishers, New Brunswick, NJ.

29   French, M 1992, *The War Against Women*, Summit Books.

30 Daly M & Wilson M 2001, An assessment of some proposed exceptions to the phenomenon of nepotistic discrimination against stepchildren, *Annales Zoologici Fennici* 38, pp.287–296.

31 Perrett, DI, May, KA & Yoshikawa, S 1994 'Facial shape and judgments of female attractiveness', *Nature* 368, 17 March, pp.239–242.

32 Leopold, LB 1969, Landscape esthetics, *Natural History*, October, pp.37–44.

33 Abello, RP, Bernaldez, FG & Galiano, EF 1986, 'Concensus and contrast components in landscape preference', *Environment and Behavior* 18 (2), pp.155–178.

34 Hagerhall CM 2001, 'Consensus in Landscape Preference Judgements', *Journal of Environmental Psychology* 21, (1), March, pp.83–92 (10)

35 Pyszczynski, TL 2002, 'Gender differences in the willingness to engage in risky behavior: A terror management perspective' *Death Studies* 26, pp.117–142.

36 Wagner, MK 2001, 'Behavioral characteristics related to substance abuse and risk-taking, sensation-seeking, anxiety sensitivity and self-reinforcement', *Addictive Behaviors* 26, Jan./Feb. pp.115–120.

37 Singh, D (1993) 'Adaptive significance of female physical attractiveness: Role of waist-to-hip ratio', *Journal of Personality and Social Psychology* 65, 293–307.

38 Singh, D 1995, 'Female judgment of male attractiveness and desirability for relationships: Hip-to-waist ratio and financial status', *Journal of Personality and Social Psychology* 69, pp.1089.

39 Klein RG 1999, *The human career: human biological and cultural origin*, 2nd edn, University of Chicago Press, Chicago.

40 Klein, Richard G 2000, 'Archeology and the Evolution of Human Behavior', *Evolutionary Anthropology* 9, pp.17–36.

41 Klein, RG & Edgar, B 2002, *The Dawn of Human Culture*, John Wiley and Sons.

42 Morgan, TH, Sturtevant, AH, Miller, HJ & Burges, CG 1915, *The Mechanics of Mendelian Heredity*, Holt, Reinhart and Winston.

43 Inlow, JK & Restifo, LL 2004, 'Molecular and Comparative Genetics of Mental Retardation', *Genetics* 166, pp.835–881.

44 Gallagher, R, & Aenzeller, T 1999, 'Beyond Reductionism', *Science* 284 (5411), p. 79.

45 Fisher, RA 1922. 'On the dominance ratio', *Proc. Roy. SOC. Edinb.*

46 Otto, SP & Whitlock, MC 1997, 'The Probability of Fixation in Populations of Changing Size', *Genetics* 146 (2), pp.723–733.

47 Haldane, JBS 1927, 'A mathematical theory of natural and artificial selection. V. Selection and mutation', Proceedings of the Cambridge Philosophical Society, 23, pp.838–844.

48 Wright, S 1931, 'Evolution in Mendelian populations', *Genetics* 16, pp.97–159.

49 Haldane, JBS 1932, 1990, *The Causes of Evolution*, Princeton Science Library, Princeton University Press.

50 Schmalhausen, II 1949, *Factors of Evolution: The Theory of Stabilizing Selection*, University of Chicago Press, Chicago.

51 Hoffman, AA & Parsons, PA 1997, *Extreme Environmental Change and Evolution*, Cambridge University Press.

52 Dillon, LS 1970, 'Speciation and Changing Environment', *American Zoologist* 10 (1), pp.27.

53 Grant, PR & Grant, BR 2002, 'Unpredictable evolution in a 30-year study of Darwin's finches', *Science* 296, pp.707–711.

54 Binet, D. & Marchael, E 1993, 'The large marine ecosystems of shelf areas in the Gulf of Guinea: Long-term variability induced by climatic changes', in Sherman, K, Alexander, LW & Gould, B, *Large Marine Ecosystem: Stress, Mitigation and Sustainability*, AAAS Pub. pp.92–39S, pp.104–118.

55 Rampino, MR & Ambrose, SH 2000, 'Volcanic winter in the Garden of Eden: The Toba super-eruption and the Late Pleistocene human population crash', in McCoy, FW & Heiken, G (eds), *Volcanic hazards and disasters in human antiquity*, Special Paper 345, Geological Society of America, Boulder, Colorado, pp.71–82.

56 Ambrose, SH 2003, 'Did the super-eruption of Toba cause a human population bottleneck? Reply to Gathorne-Hardy and Harcourt-Smith', *Journal of Human Evolution* 45, pp.231–237.

57 Lahr, M & Foley, RA 1998, 'Toward a theory of modern human origins: geography, demography, and diversity in recent human evolution', *American Journal of Physical Anthropology* 41, pp.137–176.

58 Oppenheimer, C 2002, 'Limited global change due to the largest known Quaternary eruption, Toba ~74kyr BP?', *Quaternary Science Reviews* 81, pp.1593–1609.

59 Shea, JJ 2001, 'The Middle Paleolithic: EMHs and Neandertals in the Levant', *Near Eastern Archaeology* Mar/Jun 64, ½, Academic Research Library, pp.38–64.

60 Jacobs, Z et al. 2008, 'Ages for the Middle Stone Age of Southern Africa: Implications for Human Behavior and Dispersal', *Science*, 322, pp.733–735.

61 Darwin, C 1859, *The Origin of Species*, John Murray, London.

62 Wallace, AR 1858, 'On the Tendency of Varieties to Depart Indefinitely From the Original Type', *Journal of the Proceedings of the Linnean Society, Zoology* 3 (20) Aug. pp.53–62.

63 Kuhn SL, Stiner MC, Reese DS & Gulec E 2001, 'Ornaments of the earliest Upper Paleolithic: new insights from the Levant'. *Proceedings of the National Academy of Sciences* 98 (13), pp.7641–6.

64 Bar-Yosef, O 1998, 'On the nature of transitions: The Middle to Upper Palaeolithic and the Neolithic revolution', *Cambridge Archaeological Journal* 8, pp.141–163.

65 Klein, RG 2000, 'Archaeology and the evolution of human behavior', *Evolutionary Anthropology* 9, pp.7–36.

66 Bar-Yosef, O 2002, 'The Upper Palaeolithic revolution', *Annual Review of Anthropology* 31, pp.363–393.

67 Vermeij, GJ 1977,'The Mesozoic marine evolution: Evidence from snails, predators, and grazers', *Paleobiology* 3, pp.245–258.

68 Vermeij, GJ 1987, *Evolution and Escalation: An Ecological History of Life*, Princeton University Press.

69 Taylor, RJ 1985, *Predation*, Chapman and Hall, New York.

70 Ardrey, R 1977, *The Hunting Hypothesis*, Bantam Books, New York.

71 Devore, I, & Lee, R (eds), 1968, *Man the Hunter*, Aldine Transaction.

72 Peterson, D & Wrangham,R 1997, *Demonic Males: Apes and the Origins of Human Violence*, Mariner Books.

73 Megarry, T 1995, *Society in Prehistory: The Origins of Human Culture*, MacMillan Press.

74 O'Connell, JF, Hawkes, K, Lupo, KD & Blurton Jones, NG 2002, 'Male strategies and Plio-Pleistocene archaeology', *Journal of Human Evolution* 43 (6), December, pp.831–872.

75 Sussman, RW 1999, 'The Myth of Man the Hunter, Man the Killer and the Evolution of Human Morality', *Zygon* 34 (3), pp.453–471.

76 Hart, D & Sussman, RW 2005, *Man The Hunted: Primates, Predators, and Human Evolution*, Westview Press.

77 Clarke, J 1969, *Man is the Prey*, Andre Deutsch.

78 Shea, JJ 1998, 'Neandertal and EMH Behavioral Variability: A Regional-Scale Approach to Lithic Evidence for Hunting in the Levantine. Mousterian'. *Current Anthropology* 39 (2), Supplement: Special Issue: The Neanderthal Problem and the Evolution of Human Behavior, June S45–S78.

79 Ronen, A 2006, 'The oldest human groups in the Levant', *Comptes Rendus Palevol* 5, pp.343–351.

80 Turville-Petre, F 1927, *Researches in Prehistoric Galilee, 1925–26*, British School of Archaeology in Jerusalem, London.

81 Vandermeersch, B 1989,'The evolution of modern humans: Recent evidence from Southwest Asia', in Mellars, P and Stringer, C (eds), *The human revolution: Behavioural and biological perspectives on the origins of modern humans*, Princeton, Princeton University Press.

82 Vanhaeren, M et al. 2006, 'Middle Paleolithic Shell Beads in Israel and Algeria', *Science* 312, June, pp.1785–1788.

83 Walter, RC et al. 2000, 'Early human occupation of the Red Sea coast of Eritrea during the last interglacial', *Nature* 405, pp.65–69.

84 Stringer, C 2000, 'Palaeoanthropology: Coasting out of Africa', *Nature* 405, 4 May, pp.24–27.

85 Valladas, H, Mercier, N, Joron, J & Reyss, J 1998, 'GIF Laboratory dates for Middle Paleolithic Levant', in Akazawa, T, Aoki, K & Bar-Yosef, O (eds), 1998, *Neandertals and Modern Humans in Western Asia*, Plenum Press, New York, pp.69–75.

86 Walter, RC et al. 2000, 'Early human occupation of the Red Sea coast of Eritrea during the last interglacial', *Nature* 405, pp.65–69.

87 Stringer, C 2000, 'Palaeoanthropology: Coasting out of Africa', *Nature* 405, 4 May, pp.24–27.

88 Tchernov, E 1981, 'The biostratigraphy of the Middle East', in Cauvin, J & Sanlaville, P (eds), *Pr'ehistoire du Levant*, Comptes rendus de l'Académie des sciences, Paris, pp.67–98.

89 Tchernov, E 1998, 'The faunal sequences of the Southwest Asian Middle Paleolithic in relation to Hominid dispersal events', in Akazawa, T, Aoki, K, and Bar-Yosef, O (eds), *Neandertals and Modern Humans in Western Asia*, Plenum, New York, pp.77–90.

90 Shea, JJ 2003, 'Neandertals, competition, and the origin of modern human behavior in the Levant', *Evolutionary Anthropology* 12, pp.173–187.

91 Blondel, J, and Aronson, J 1999, *Biology and Wildlife of the Mediterranean Region*, Oxford University Press, New York.

92 Cheddadi, R, and Rossignol-Strick, M 1995, 'Eastern Mediterranean quaternary paleoclimates from pollen isotope records of marine cores in the Nile cone area', *Paleoceanography* 10, pp.291–300.

93 Blondel, J and Aronson, J 1999, *Biology and Wildlife of the Mediterranean Region*, Oxford University Press, New York.

94   Zohary, M 1973, *Geobotanical Foundations of the Middle East*, Gustav Fischer Verlag, Stuttgart.

95   Gilead, I 1991, 'The Upper Paleolithic Period in the Levant', *Journal of World Prehistory* 5 (2), pp.105–154.

96   Jelinek, AJ 1982, 'The Tabun Cave and Paleolithic Man in the Levant', *Science* 216, pp.1369–1375.

97   Bar-Yosef, O 1996, 'Modern humans, Neanderthals and the Middle/Upper Paleolithic transition in Western Asia'. In Bar-Yosef, O, Cavalli-Sforza, LL, March, RJ, Piperno, M (eds), *The Lower and Middle Palaeolithic* (Colloquia of the XIII International Congress of Prehistoric and Protohistoric Sciences, no. 5). Forlì, Italy, ABACO Edizioni, pp.175–190.

98   Tchernov, E 1998, 'The faunal sequences of the Southwest Asian Middle Paleolithic in relation to Hominid dispersal events', in Akazawa, T, Aoki, K, and Bar-Yosef, O (eds), *Neandertals and Modern Humans in Western Asia*, Plenum, New York, pp.77–90.

99   Arensburg B & Belfer-Cohen, A 1998, 'Sapiens and Neanderthals: Rethinking the Levantine Middle Paleolithic hominids', in Akazawa, T, Aoki, K & Bar-Yosef, O, *Neanderthals and Modern Humans in West Asia*, Plenum, New York, pp.391–322.

100 Shea, JJ 2001, 'The Middle Paleolithic: EMHs and Neandertals in the Levant', *Near Eastern Archaeology*, Mar/Jun 64, (1/2), Academic Research Library, pp.38–64.

101 Kaufman, D 2001, 'Comparisons and the case for interaction among Neanderthals and EMHs in the Levant', *Oxford Journal of Archaeology* 20, pp.219–240.

102 Arensburg, B 2002, 'Human remains from Geula Cave, Haifa', *Bulletins et Mémoires de la Société d'Anthropologie de Paris* 14, Fascicule 1–2.

103 Kramer, A, Crummett, TL & Wolpoff, MH 2001, 'Out of Africa and into the Levant: replacement or admixture in Western Asia?', *Quaternary International* 75, v 51–63.

104 Schwarcz, HP, Simpson, JJ, Stringer, CB, 1998, 'Neanderthal skeleton from Tabun: U-series data by gamma-ray spectrometry', *Journal of Human Evolution* 35, pp.635–645.

105 Alperson, N, Barzilai, O, Dag, D, Hartman, G, Matskevich, Z 2000, 'The age and context of the Tabun I skeleton: a reply to Schwarcz et al.', *Journal of Human Evolution* 38, pp.849–853.

106 Arensburg, B 2002, 'Human remains from Geula Cave, Haifa', *Bulletins et Mémoires de la Société d'Anthropologie de Paris* 14, Fascicule 1–2.

107 Shea, JJ 2003, 'The Middle Paleolithic of the East Mediterranean Levant', *Journal of World Prehistory* 17 (4) December, pp.313–394.

108 Grün, R and Stringer, CB 1991, 'Electron Spin Resonance Dating and the Evolution of Modern Humans', *Archaeometry* 33, pp.153–199.

109 Valladas, H et al. 1987, 'Thermoluminescence dates for the Neanderthal burial site at Kebara in Israel', *Nature* 330, 18 Nov, pp.159–160.

110 Trinkaus, E 1991, 'Les Hommes fossiles de la grotte de Shanidar, Irak: évolution et continuité parmi les Hommes archaïques et tardifs du Proche-Orient', *L'Anthropol* (Paris) 95, pp.535–572.

111 Shea, JJ 2003, 'The Middle Paleolithic of the East Mediterranean Levant', *Journal of World Prehistory* 17 (4) December, pp.313–394.

112 Bar-Yosef, O 1998, 'The Chronology of the Middle Paleolithic of the Levant', in *Neandertals and Modern Humans in Western Asia*, Akazawa, T, Aoki, K & Bar-Yosef, O (eds), Plenum, New York.

113 Trinkaus, E & Shipman, P 1993, *The Neanderthals; Changing the Image of Neanderthals*, Pimlico.

114 Shea, JJ 2003b, 'Neandertals, competition, and the origin of modern human behavior in the Levant', *Evolutionary Anthropology* 12, pp.173–187.

115 Shea, JJ 2003, 'The Middle Paleolithic of the East Mediterranean Levant', *Journal of World Prehistory*, 17(4) December, pp.313–394.

116 Grün R, and Stringer C 2000, 'Tabun revisited: Revised ESR chronology and new ESR and Useries analyses of dental material from Tabun C1', *Journal of Human Evolution* 39, pp.601–612.

117 Shea, JJ 2003b, 'Neandertals, competition, and the origin of modern human behavior in the Levant', *Evolutionary Anthropology* 12, pp.173–187.

118 Shea, JJ 2003, 'The Middle Paleolithic of the East Mediterranean Levant', *Journal of World Prehistory* 17 (4), December.

119 Darwin, C 1859, *The Origin of Species*, Chapter IV: 'Natural Selection; Or the Survival of the Fittest', John Murray, London.

120 Gause, GF 1934, *The struggle for existence*, Williams & Wilkins, Baltimore, MD.

121 Currat, M and Excoffier, L 2004, 'Modern Humans Did Not Admix with Neanderthals during Their Range Expansion into Europe', *PLoS Biol* 2 (12), December.

122 Serre, D, Langaney, A, Chech, M, Teschler-Nicola, M, Paunovic, M, et al. 2004, 'No evidence of Neandertal mtDNA contribution to EMHs', *PLoS Biol* 2 (3), E57.

123 Krings, M, Capelli, C, Tschentscher, F, Geisert, H, Meyer S et al. 2000, 'A view of Neandertal genetic diversity', *Nature Genetics* 26, pp.144–46.

124 Krings M, Stone A, Schmitz RW, Krainitzki H, Stoneking M et al. 1997, 'Neandertal DNA sequences and the origin of modern humans', *Cell* 90, pp.19–30.

125 Schmitz, RW, Serre D, Bonani G, Feine S, Hillgruber F et al. 2002, 'The Neandertal type site revisited: interdisciplinary investigations of skeletal remains from the Neander Valley, Germany', *Proceedings of the National Academy of Sciences* 99, pp.13342–47.

126 Bischoff, JL et al. 2003, 'Neanderthals', *Journal of Archeological Science* 30, pp.275.

127 Noonan JP et al. 2006, 'Sequencing and analysis of Neanderthal genomic DNA', *Science* 314, pp.1113–1118.

128 Green RE et al. 2006, 'Analysis of one million base pairs of Neanderthal DNA', *Nature* 444, pp.330–336.

129 Beerli P, and Edwards, SV 2002, 'When did Neanderthals and modern humans diverge?' *Evolutionary Anthropology* 11, S1, pp.60–63.

130 Trinkaus, E 1978, 'Hard Times among the Neanderthals', *Natural History* 87, p.10.

131 Shreeve, J 1995, 'The Neanderthal Peace', *Discover* 16 (09), September.

132 Shea, JJ 2008, quoted in Viegas, J 2008, 'Early Weapon Evidence Reveals Bloody Past', *Discovery News*, 31 March, [online].

133 Stiner, MC 1994, *Honor Among Thieves: A Zooarchaeological Study of Neandertal Ecology*, Princeton University Press, Princeton.

134 Jaubert, J, Lorblanchet, M, Laville, H, Slott-Moller, R, Turq, A & Brugal, J-P 1990, 'Les Chasseurs d'Aurochs de La Borde: Un Site du Paléolithique Moyen (Livernon, Lot)' *Maison des Sciences de l'Homme*, Paris.

135 Gardeisen, A 1999, 'Middle Palaeolithic Subsistence in the West Cave of 'Le Portel' (Pyrénées, France)', *Journal of Archeological Science* 26, pp.1145–1158.

136 Trinkaus, E 2000, quoted in 'Neanderthals likely were skilled hunters', *The Japan Times*, 14 June.

137 Wynn, T and Coolidge, FL 2004, 'The expert Neandertal mind', *Journal of Human Evolution* 46, pp.467–87.

138 Kolen, J 1999, 'Hominids without homes: On the nature of Middle Palaeolithic settlement in Europe', in Roebroeks,W & Gamble, C (eds), *The Middle Palaeolithic occupation of Europe*, University of Leiden Press, Leiden, pp.39–75.

139 Vaquero, M, Chacón, G, Fernández, C, Martinez, K & Rando, JM 2001, 'Intrasite spatial patterning and transport in the Abric Romaní Middle Paleolithic site (Capellades, Barcelona, Spain)', in Conard, NJ (ed), *Settlement dynamics of the Middle Palaeolithic and Middle Stone Age*, pp.573–95.

140 Marean, CW & Assefa, Z 1999, 'Zooarcheological evidence for the faunal exploitation behavior of Neandertals and EMHs', *Evolutionary Anthropology* 8, pp.22–37.

141 D'Errico, F, et al. 2003, 'Archaeological evidence for the emergence of language, symbolism, and music: An alternative multidisciplinary perspective', *Journal of World Prehistory* 17, pp.1–70.

142 Adler, DS, Bar-Oz, G, Belfer-Cohen, A & Bar-Yosef, O 2006, 'Ahead of the Game; Middle and Upper Palaeolithic Hunting Behaviors in the Southern Caucasus', *Current Anthropology* 47 (1), February.

143 Steegmann, Jr A, Cerny, FJ and Holliday, TW 2002, 'Neandertal Cold Adaptation: Physiological and Energetic Factors', *American Journal of Human Biology* 14, pp.566–583.

144 Shea, JJ 2001, 'Modern Human Origins and Neanderthal Extinctions in the Levant', *Athena Review* 2, (4) 'Neanderthals Meet Modern Humans'.

145 Kuhn, SL, Stiner, MC 2006, 'What's a mother to do? The division of labor among Neandertals and modern humans in Eurasia', *Current Anthropology* 47, pp.953–980.

146 White, MJ 2006, 'Things to do in Doggerland when you're dead: surviving OIS3 at the northwestern-most fringe of Middle Palaeolithic Europe', *World Archaeology* 38 (4), pp.547–575.

147 Houston, DC 1979, 'The Adaptations of Scavengers', in Sinclair, ARE & Norton-Griffiths, M (eds), *Serengeti: dynamics of an ecosystem*, Univ. of Chicago Press, Chicago, pp.263–286.

148 Trinkaus, E 2000, quoted in 'Neanderthals likely were skilled hunters', *The Japan Times*, 14 June.

149 Bar-Yosef, O 2004, 'Eat What is There: Hunting and Gathering in the World of Neanderthals and their Neighbours', *International Journal of Osteoarchaeology*, 14, pp.333–342.

150 Bocherens, H, et al. 1999, 'Palaeoenvironmental and palaeodietary implications of isotopic biogeochemistry of last interglacial Neanderthal and mammal bones in Scladina cave, Belgium', *Journal of Archaeological Science* 26 (6), pp.599–607.

151   Fizet, M, Mariotti, A, Bocherens, H, Lange-
      Badré, B, Vandermeersch, B, Borel, J & Bel-
      lon, G, 1995, 'Effect of diet, physiology and
      climate on carbon and nitrogen isotopes of
      collagen in a late Pleistocene anthropic pa-
      leoecosystem, France, Charente, Marillac)',
      Journal of Archaeological Science 22, pp.67–79.

152   Michael P. Richards, Paul B. Pettitt,
      Trinkaus, E, Fred H. Smith, Maja Paunovi,
      and Ivor Karavani, 2000. 'Neanderthal diet
      at Vindija and Neanderthal predation: The
      evidence from stable isotopes', *Proceedings of
      the National Academy of Sciences USA* 97, (13),
      pp.7663–7666.

153   Balter V, Person A, Labourdette N, Drucker
      D, Renard M, and Vandermeersch, B, 2001,
      'Les néandertaliens étaient-ils essentielle-
      ment carnivores? Résultats préliminaires sur
      les teneurs en Sr et en Ba de la paléobiocé-
      nose mammalienne de Saint-Césaire' - Were
      Neandertalians essentially carnivores? Sr
      and Ba preliminary results of the mam-
      malian palaeobiocoenosis of Saint-Césaire.
      *Comptes rendus de l'Académie des sciences. Série
      2. Sciences de la terre et des planètes* 332, (1),
      pp.59–65.

154   Pettitt, PB 2000, 'Odd man out: Neander-
      thals and modern humans', *British Archaeol-
      ogy* 51, February.

155   Eaton, SB 2006, 'The ancestral human diet:
      what was it and should it be a paradigm for
      contemporary nutrition?' *Proceedings of the
      Nutrition Society*, 65 (1), February, pp.1–6.

156   Trinkaus, E 1986, 'The Neandertals and
      Modern Human Origins', *Annual Review of
      Anthropology* 15, pp.193–218.

157   White, R 1982, 'Rethinking the Middle/Up-
      per Paleolithic transition', *Current Anthropol-
      ogy* 23, pp.177–181.

158   Binford, LR 1984, *Faunal Remains from Klasies
      River Mouth*, Academic, New York.

159   Klein, RG 1976, 'The mammalian fauna
      of the Klasies River Mouth sites, Southern
      Cape Province, South Africa', *South African
      Archeological Bulletin* 31, pp.75–98.

160   Klein, RG 1978, 'Stone age predation on
      large African bovids', *Journal of Archeological
      Science* 5, pp.195–217.

161   Lee RB 1968, 'What hunters do for a living,
      or how to make out on scarce resources', in
      Lee RB and DeVore, I (eds), *Man the hunter*,
      Aldine Publishing Co, Chicago, pp.30–48.

162   Jacob-Friesen, KH 1956, *Jahrb. Röm.-German.
      Zentralmuseums Mainz* 3, pp.1–22.

163   Beyries, S 1987, in Stordeur, D (ed), *La
      Main et l'Outil: Manches et Emmanchements
      Préhistoriques*, Travaux de la Maison de
      l'Orient, Lyon, pp.55–64.

164   Oakley, K, Andrews, P, Keeley, LH, & Clark,
      JD 1977, 'A Re-appraisal of the Clacton
      Spearpoint'. *Proceedings of the Prehistoric Society*
      43, pp.13–30.

165   Boëda, E, Geneste, J M, Griggo, C, Mer-
      cier, N, Muhesen, S, Reyss, J L, Taha, A
      & Valladas, H 1999, 'A Levallois Point
      Embedded in the Vertebra of a Wild Ass
      (Equus africanus): Hafting, Projectiles and
      Mousterian Hunting Weapons', *Antiquity* 73,
      pp.394–402.

166   Geist, V 1981, 'Neanderthal the hunter',
      Natural History 90, pp.26–36.

167   Trinkaus, E 1978, 'Hard Times among the
      Neanderthals', *Natural History* 87(10).

168   P B Pettitt 2000, 'Neanderthal Lifecycles:
      Developmental and Social Phases in the
      Lives of the Last Archaics', *World Archaeol-
      ogy* 31, (3) Human Lifecycles, February,
      pp.351–366.

169   Trinkaus, E & Zimmerman, MR 2005,
      'Trauma among the Shanidar Neandertals',
      American Journal of Physical Anthropology 57
      (1), pp.61–76.

170   Trinkaus, E 2005, 'The Shanidar 3 Neander-
      tal', *American Journal of Physical Anthropology*
      57 (1), pp.37–60.

171   Berger, TD and Trinkaus, E 1995, 'Patterns
      of trauma among the Neandertals', *Journal
      of Archaeological Science* 22 (66), pp.841–852.

172   Zollikofer, CPE, Ponce de León, MS,
      Vandermeersch, B & Lévêque, F 2002,
      'Evidence for interpersonal violence in the
      St. Césaire Neanderthal', *Proceedings of the
      National Academy of Sciences USA*, 23 April.

173   Berger, TD & Trinkaus, E 1995, 'Patterns
      of trauma among the Neandertals', *Journal
      of Archaeological Science* 22, pp.841–852.

174   Trinkaus, E 1983, *The Shanidar Neanderthals*,
      Academic Press, New York.

175   Zollikofer, CPE, Ponce de Leo´n, MS,
      Vandermeersch, B & Le´ve´que, F 2002,
      'Evidence for interpersonal violence in
      the St. Ce´saire Neanderthal', *Proceedings
      of the National Academy of Sciences USA* 99,
      pp.6444–6448.

176   Caspari, R, and Lee, S-L 2004, 'Older age
      becomes common late in human evolution',
      *Proceedings of the National Academy of Sciences
      USA* 101, 10895e10900.

177   Shea, JJ 2001, 'Modern Human Origins and
      Neanderthal Extinctions in the Levant',
      Athena Review 2, (4), 'Neanderthals Meet
      Modern Humans'.

178   Parson, A 2006, 'Neandertals Hunted as
      Well as Humans, Study Says'. *National Geo-
      graphic News, 25* January.

179   Trinkaus, E 2000, quoted in 'Neanderthals
      likely were skilled hunters', *The Japan Times*,
      14 June.

180 Russell, MD 1986, 'Mortuary practices at the Krapina Neandertal site', *American Journal of Physical Anthropology* 72 (30), pp.381–397.

181 Malez, M and Ullrich, H 1982, 'Neue paläanthropologische Untersuchungen am Material aus der Höhle Vindija (Kroatien, Jugoslawien)', Zagreb: *Palaeontologia Jugoslavica* 29 (1).

182 Vandermeersch, B 1980, 'Circonscription de Poitou-Charentes', *Gallia Prehistoire* 23 (20), pp.301–316.

183 Hughes, CS, Garimond, S, Gagnière, S & Marcellin, P 1951, 'La grotte de la Verrerie à Macassargues,. Montmirat (Gard)', *Ann. Paléont, T.* 37, pp.155–174.

184 Mort, F Le 1989, 'Traces de décharnement sur lesossements néandertaliens de Combe-Grenal (Dordogne)', *Bulletin de la Société préhistorique française*, n°spécial:, Paris, 86 (3), pp.79–87.

185 Mann, A, et al 2005, 'Carnivore and Neandertal interactions at the Les Pradelles site (Charante, Southwest France)', *Paleoanthropological Society Abstracts*, April.

186 Hublin, JJ, Barroso, RC, Medina Lara P., Fontugne M, Reyss J-L 1995, 'The Mousterian site of Zafarraya (Andalucia, Spain): dating and implications on the palaeolithic peopling processes of Western Europe', *Comptes rendus de l'Académie des sciences*, Paris, 321 (IIa), pp.931–937.

187 Rosas, A et al. 2006, 'Paleobiology and comparative morphology of a late Neandertal sample from El Sidron, Asturias, Spain', *Proceedings of the National Academy of Sciences*, USA, 19 Dec.,103 (51), pp.19266–71.

188 Defleur, A, White, T et al. 1999, 'Neanderthal cannibalism at Moula-Guercy, Ardèche, France', *Science*, 286, 1 Oct., p. 128.

189 Lukaschek, K 2000/2001, *The History of Cannibalism*, thesis submitted in fulfilment of the MPhil Degree in Biological Anthropology, University of Cambridge, UK, Lucy Cavendish College.

190 Cook, J, Radovčić, J, & Frayer, DW 2005, 'New evidence for symbolic behavior by the Krapina Neandertals', Paleoanthropology Society Annual Meeting, Milwaukee, *PaleoAnthropology*, A46, reported in *Science News* 167, pp.244.

191 Gorjanović-Kramberger, D 1906, *Der Diluviale Mensch von Krapina in Kroatien*, C. W. Kreidel Verlag, Weisbaden.

192 Fernandez-Jalvo Y, Carlos Diez J, Caceres I & Rosell J 1999, 'Human cannibalism in the Early Pleistocene of Europe (Gran Dolina, Sierra de Atapuerca, Burgos, Spain)', *Journal of Human Evolution* 37 (3–4), pp.591–622.

193 Shea, JJ 2003b, 'Neandertals, competition, and the origin of modern human behavior in the Levant', *Evolutionary Anthropology*, 12, pp.173–187.

194 Cole, J 2006, 'Consuming Passions: Reviewing the Evidence for Cannibalism within the Prehistoric Archaeological Record', *Assemblage* 9, June.

195 Goodall, J 1977, 'Infant Killings and Cannibalism in Free-Living Chimpanzees', *Folia Primatologica* 28, pp.259–282.

196 Bartlett, TQ, Sussman, RW, Cheverud, JM, 1993, 'Infant Killings in Primates: A Review of Observed Cases with Specific Reference to the Sexual Selection Hypothesis', *American Anthropologist* 95, pp.958–990.

197 Turk, I (ed.) 1997, 'Mousterian "Bone Flute"? and Other Finds from Divje Babe I Cave Site in Slovenia', *Institut za Arhaeologijo*, Ljubljana, Slovenia.

198 Turka, I, Blackwellb, BAB, Turkc, J & Pflaum, M 2006, 'Results of computer tomography of the oldest suspected flute from Divje babé I (Slovenia) and its chronological position within global palaeoclimatic and palaeoenvironmental change during Last Glacial', *L'Anthropologie* 110 (3) July–September, 'Paléolithique supérieur', pp.293–317.

199 Morley, I 2006, 'Mousterian Musicianship? The Case Of The Divje Babe I Bone', *Oxford Journal of Archaeology* 25 (4), pp.317–333.

200 Solecki, RS 1975, 'Shanidar IV, a Neanderthal flower burial in northern Iraq', *Science* 190 (28), p.880.

201 Sommer, JD 1999, 'The Shanidar IV "Flower Burial": A Reevaluation of Neanderthal Burial Ritual', *Cambridge Archæological Journal* 9, pp.127–129.

202 Wrangham, RW 1999, 'Evolution of coalitionary killing', *Yearbook of Physical Anthropology* 42, pp.1–30.

203 van der Dennen, JMG, 1995, *The origin of war: The evolution of a male-coalitional reproductive strategy*, Origin Press, Groningen, pp.1–861.

204 Schmalhausen, II 1949, *The factors of evolution*, Blakeston, Philadelphia.

205 Mayr, E 1959, 'The emergence of evolutionary novelties', in Tax, S (ed.), *Evolution after Darwin*, University of Chicago Press, Chicago, pp.349–380.

206 Plotkin, HC 1988, 'Behaviour and evolution', in Plotkin, HC (ed.), *The role of behaviour in evolution*, MIT Press, Cambridge, Mass. pp.1–17.

207 Polis, GA, Myers, CA & Holt, RD 1989, 'The ecology and evolution of intraguild predation: potential competitors that eat each other', *Annual Review of Ecology and Systematics* 20, pp.297–330.

208 Laurenson, MK 1995, 'Implications of high offspring mortality for cheetah population dynamics', in Sinclair, ARE, Arcese, P (eds), *Serengeti II: Dynamics, Management and Conservation of an Ecosystem*, University of Chicago Press, Chicago.

209 Rosenzweig, ML 1966, 'Community structure in sympatric carnivora', *Journal of Mammalogy* 47, 602–612.

210 Palomares, F, Caro, TM 1999. 'Interspecific killing among mammalian carnivores', *The American Naturalist* 153, pp.492–508.

211 Eaton, RL 1979, 'Interference competition among carnivores: a model for the evolution of social behavior', *Carnivore* 2, pp.9–16.

212 Kimbrella, T, Holta, RD & Lundberg, P 2007, 'The influence of vigilance on intraguild predation'. *Journal of Theoretical Biology* 249, pp.218–234.

213 Wrangham, RW 1999, 'Evolution of Coalitionary Killing', *Yearbook of Physical Anthropology* 42, pp.1–30.

214 Kruuk, H 1972, *The spotted hyena: A study of predation and social behavior*, Chicago University Press, Chicago, pp.1–335.

215 Wrangham, RW 1999, 'Evolution of Coalitionary Killing', *Yearbook of Physical Anthropology* 42, pp.1–30.

216 Packer, C, Herbst, L, Pusey, AE, Bygott, JD, Hanby, JP, Cairns, SJ, & Mulder, MB 1988, 'Reproductive success of lions', in Clutton-Brock, TH (ed.), *Reproductive success: Studies of individual variation in contrasting breeding systems*, University of Chicago Press, Chicago, pp.363–383.

217 Caro, TM, & Collins, DA 1986, 'Male cheetahs of the Serengeti', *National Geographic Research* 2, pp.75–86.

218 Wrangham, RW 1999, 'Evolution of Coalitionary Killing', *Yearbook of Physical Anthropology* 42, pp.1–30.

219 Goodall, J 1986, *The chimpanzees of Gombe: Patterns of behavior*, The Belknap Press of Harvard University Press, Cambridge, MA, pp.1–673.

220 De Waal, FBM 1989, 'Peacemaking Among Primates', Harvard Univerity Press, p.65.

221 Wrangham, RW 1999, 'Evolution of Coalitionary Killing', *Yearbook of Physical Anthropology*, 42, pp.1–30.

222 Mech, LD, Adams, LG, Meier, TJ, Burch, JW & Dale, BW 1998, *The Wolves of Denali*, University of Minnesota Press, Minneapolis, MN, pp.1–225.

223 Goodall, J 1986, *The chimpanzees of Gombe: Patterns of behavior*, The Belknap Press of Harvard University Press, Cambridge, MA, pp.1–673.

224 Wrangham, RW 1999, 'Evolution of Coalitionary Killing', *Yearbook of Physical Anthropology* 42, pp.1–30.

225 Ibid.

226 Goodall, J 1986, *The chimpanzees of Gombe: Patterns of behavior*, The Belknap Press of Harvard University Press, Cambridge, MA.

227 van der Dennen, JMG 1995, *The origin of war: The evolution of a male-coalitional reproductive strategy*, Origin Press, Groningen, pp.1–861.

228 Manson, JH, & Wrangham, RW 1991, 'Intergroup aggression in chimpanzees and humans', *Current Anthropology* 32, pp.369–390.

229 Goodall, J 1986, *The chimpanzees of Gombe: Patterns of behavior*, The Belknap Press of Harvard University Press, Cambridge, MA, pp.528.

230 Ghiglieri, MP 1987, 'Sociobiology of the great apes and the hominid ancestor', *Journal of Human Evolution* 16, pp.319–357.

231 Boehm, C 1992, 'Segmentary 'warfare' and the management of conflict: comparison of East African chimpanzees and patrilineal-patrilocal humans', in Harcourt AH, de Waal FBM (eds), *Coalitions and alliances in humans and other animals*, Oxford University Press, Oxford pp.137–173.

232 Manson, JH, Wrangham, RW 1991, 'Intergroup aggression in chimpanzees and humans', *Current Anthropology* 32 pp.369–390.

233 Wilson, ML, Wallauer, WR, Pusey, AE 2004, 'New cases of intergroup violence among chimpanzees in Gombe National Park, Tanzania', *International Journal of Primatology* 25, pp.523–549.

234 Bygott, JD 1979, 'Agonistic behavior, dominance, and social structure in wild chimpanzees of the Gombe National Park', in Hamburg & McCown (eds), *Great Apes*, pp.405–28.

235 Mohnot, SM 1971, 'Some aspects of social changes and infant-killing in the Hanuman langur Presbytis entellus (Primates: Cercopithecidae) in western India', *Mammalia* 35, pp.175–98.

236 Turney-High, HH 1949, *Primitive war: Its practice and concepts*, University of South Carolina Press, Columbia, SC, pp.1–288.

237 Chagnon, NA 1992, *Yanomamo: The last days of Eden*, Harcourt Brace Jovanovich, New York, pp.1–309.

238 Keeley, LH 1996, *War before civilization*, Oxford University Press, New York, pp.1–245.

239 Trudeau, MB, Bergmann-Riss, E, Hamburg, DA 1981, 'Towards an evolutionary perspective on aggressive behavior: the chimpanzee evidence', in Hamburg, DA, Trudeau, MB (eds), *Biobehavioral aspects of aggression*, Alan Liss, New York, pp.27–40.

240 van Hoof, J 1990, 'Intergroup competition and conflict in animals and man', in Dennen, JMG van der & and Falger, VSE (eds), *Sociobiology and Conflict: Evolutionary perspectives on competition, cooperation, violence and warfare*, Chapman and Hall, London, pp.23–54.

241 Ghiglieri, M 1988, 'Sociobiology of the great apes and the hominid ancestors', *Journal of Human Evolution* 16, pp.319–358.

242 Manson, JH, Wrangham, RW 1991, 'Intergroup aggression in chimpanzees and humans', *Current Anthropology* 32, pp.369–390.

243 Alexander, RD 1989, 'Evolution of the human psyche', in Mellars P, Stringer C, (eds), *The human revolution: Behavioral and biological perspectives on the origins of modern humans*, Princeton University Press Princeton, NJ, pp.455–513.

244 Otterbein, KF 1997, 'The origins of war', *Crit Rev* 11, pp.251–277.

245 Sack, RD 1987, 'Human Territoriality: Its Theory and History', *Geographical Review*, 77 (4), October, pp.486–488.

246 Herbinger, I, Boesch, C, & Rothe, H 2001, 'Territory characteristics among three neighboring chimpanzee communities in the Taï National Park, Côte d'Ivoire', *International Journal of Primatology*, 22(2), pp.143–167.

247 Wilson, ML, Wallauer, RW & Pusey, AE 2004, 'New Cases of Intergroup Violence Among Chimpanzees in Gombe National Park, Tanzania', *International Journal of Primatology* 25 (3) June, pp.523–549.

248 Hamburg, D 1974, 'Recent Observations of Aggressive Behavior in Great Apes', Louis Leaky Memorial Lecture, Philadelphia, 27 October.

249 Teleki, G 1975, 'Primate subsistence patterns: collector-predators and gatherer-hunters', *Journal of Human Evolution* 4, pp.125–184.

250 Goodall, J 1986, *The chimpanzees of Gombe: Patterns of behavior*, The Belknap Press of Harvard University Press, Cambridge, MA, p.528.

251 Wrangham, R 1999, 'Evolution of coalitionary killing', *Yearbook Physical Anthropology* 42, pp.1–30.

252 Schaller, GB & Lowther, GP 1969, 'The relevance of carnivore behavior to the study of early hominids', *Southwestern Journal of Anthropology* 25, pp.307–341.

253 Thompson, PR 1975, 'A cross-species analysis of carnivore, primate and hominid behavior', *Journal of Human Evolution* 4, pp.113–124.

254 Schenkel, R 1966, 'Play, exploration and territoriality in the wild lion', *Symposium of the Zoological Society of London* 18, (1), pp.1–22.

255 Goodall, J 1977, 'Infant killing and cannibalism in free-living chimpanzees', *Folia Primatol* (Basel) 28(4), pp.259–89.

256 Watts, DP, Muller, M, Amsler, SJ, Mbabazi, G, & Mitani, JC 2006, 'Lethal intergroup aggression by chimpanzees in Kibale National Park, Uganda', *American Journal of Primatology* 68 (2), pp.161–80.

257 Milliken, S 2007, 'Neanderthals, Anatomically Modern Humans, and 'Modern Human Behaviour' in Italy', *Oxford Journal Of Archaeology* 26 (40), pp.331–358.

258 Tchernov, E 1998, 'The faunal sequences of the southwest Asian Middle Paleolithic in relation to hominid dispersal events', in Akazawa, T, Aoki, K, Bar-Yosef, O (eds), *Neandertals and modern humans in western Asia*, Plenum Press, New York, pp.77–90.

259 Shea, JJ 2003, 'The Middle Paleolithic of the East Mediterranean Levant', *Journal of World Prehistory* 17 (40), December, pp.313–394.

260 Tchernov, E 1988, 'The biogeographical history of the southern Levant', in Yom-Tov, Y, & Tchernov, E (eds), *The Zoogeography of Israel*, Dr W Junk Publishers, pp.159–250.

261 Klein, RG 1998. 'Why anatomically modern people did not disperse from Africa 100,000 years ago'. In: Akazawa, T, Aoki, K, Bar-Yosef, O (eds), *Neandertals and modern humans in western Asia*, Plenum Press, New York, pp.509–522.

262 Foley, RA 1989,'The causes of sociality', in Standen, V & Foley, RA (eds), *Comparative Socioecology: the Behavioural Ecology of Humans and other Mammals*, Blackwell Scientific Publications, Oxford, pp.37–40.

263 Wrangham, RW 1987, 'The significance of African apes for reconstructing human social evolution', in Kinzey, WG (ed.), *The Evolution of Human Behavior: Primate Models*, SUNY Press, Albany, NY, pp.51–71.

264 Dixson, AF 1998, *Primate Sexuality: Comparative Studies of the Prosimians, Monkeys, Apes, and Human Beings*, Oxford University Press, Oxford.

265 Deschner, T, Heistermann, M, Hodges, K & Boesch, C 2004, 'Female sexual swelling size, timing of ovulation, and male behavior in wild West African chimpanzees', *Hormones and Behavior* 46, pp.204–215.

266 Girolami, L, Bielert, C 1987, 'Female perineal swelling and its effect on male sexual arousal: an apparent sexual releaser in the chacma baboon (Papio ursinus)', *International Journal of Primatology* 8, pp.651–661.

267 Singh, D & Bronstad, PM 2001, 'Female body odour is a potential cue to ovulation', *Proceedings of the Royal Society of London B, Biological Sciences* 268, pp.797–801.

268 Boesch, C, Kohou, G, Néné, H & Vigilant, L 2006, 'Male Competition and Paternity in Wild Chimpanzees of the Taï Forest', *American Journal of Physical Anthropology* 130, pp.103–115.

269 Smutts, B 1995, 'Apes of Wrath', *Discover*, August, pp.35–37.

270 Wrangham, R & Peterson, D 1997, *Demonic Males: Apes and the Origins of Human Violence*, Mariner Books, p.142.

271 Goodall, J 1986, *The chimpanzees of Gombe: patterns of behavior*, The Belknap Press of Harvard University Press, Cambridge, MA.

272 Palmer, CT 1989b, 'Rape in Nonhuman Animal Species: Definitions, Evidence, and Implications', *Journal of Sex Research* 26 (3), pp.355–374.

273 Galdikas, BMF 2005, 'Subadult male orangutan sociality and reproductive behavior at Tanjung Putting', *American Journal of Primatology* 8 (2), pp.87–99

274 Thornhill, R & Palmer, CT 2000, *A Natural History of Rape: Biological Bases of Sexual Coercion*, MIT Press.

275 Kilpatrick, DG, Edmunds, CN and Seymour, AK 1992, *Rape in America: A report to the nation*, National Victim Center, Arlington, Virginia.

276 Russell, DEH 1984, *The Politics of Rape*, Scarborough House, p.35.

277 Wrangham, R & Peterson, D 1997, *Demonic Males: Apes and the Origins of Human Violence*, Mariner Books, p.137.

278 Sillen-Tullberg, B & Moller, AP 1993, 'The Relationship between Concealed Ovulation and Mating Systems in Anthropoid Primates: A Phylogenetic Analysis', *The American Naturalist* 141 (1), Jan, pp.1–25.

279 Fisher, H 2004, *Why We Love: The Nature and Chemistry of Romantic Love*, Henry Holt.

280 Trinkaus, E 2006, 'Late Neandertals & Early Modern Humans: Biology, Behavior and Population Dynamics', *Terra Nostra; 150 Years of Neanderthal Discoveries*, 21–26 July, 2006, Congress, Bonn, pp.74–83.

281 Jolly, CJ 2001, 'A proper study for mankind: Analogies from the Papionin monkeys and their implications for human evolution', *American Journal of Physical Anthropology* 116, S33, pp.177–204.

282 Brauer, G 2008, 'The Origin of Modern Anatomy: By Speciation or Intraspecific Evolution?' *Evolutionary Anthropology* 17, pp.22–37.

283 Muller, MN & Wrangham, RW 2004, 'Dominance, aggression and testosterone in wild chimpanzees: a test of the 'challenge hypothesis', *Animal Behaviour*, 67, pp.113–123.

284 Simeons, AT 1960, *Man's Presumptuous Brain*, Longmans, Green, London.

285 Scott, JP 1981, 'The evolution of function in agonistic behaviour', in Brain, PF & Benton, D (eds), *Multidisciplinary Approaches to Aggression Research*, Elsevier, Amsterdam, pp.129–58.

286 Bittles, AH & Neel, JV 1994,'The costs of human inbreeding and their implications for variations at the DNA level', *Nature Genetics*, 8, pp.117–121.

287 Greenwood, PJ 1980, 'Mating systems, philopatry and dispersal in birds and mammals', *Animal Behaviour* 28, pp.1140–1162.

288 Pusey, A & Wolf, M 1996, 'Inbreeding avoidance in animals', *Trends in Ecology and Evolution* 11, pp.201–206.

289 Ingham, JM & Spain, DH 2005, 'Sensual attachment and incest avoidance in human evolution and child Development', *Journal of the Royal Anthropological Institute*, V11(4), pp.677–701.

290 Boesch, C & Boesch-Achermann, H 2000, *The Chimpanzees of the Taï Forest*, Oxford University Press, Oxford.

291 Vigilant, L, Hofreiter, M, Siedel, H & Boesch, C 2001. 'Paternity and relatedness in wild chimpanzee communities', *Proceedings of the National Academy of Sciences USA*, 6 November, 98 (23) pp.12890–12895.

292 Goodall, J 1986, *The Chimpanzees of Gombe*, The Belknap Press of Harvard University Press, Cambridge, MA.

293 Boesch, C & Boesch-Achermann, H 2000, *The Chimpanzees of the Taï Forest*, Oxford University Press, Oxford.

294 Resnick, HD, Kilpatrick, DG, Dansky, BS, Saunders, BE & Best, CL 1993, 'Prevalence of civilian trauma and posttraumatic stress syndrome in a representative national sample of women", *Journal of Consulting and Clinical Psychology*, 61 (6), pp.984–981.

295 Strauss, WL, Jr and Cave, AJE 1957, 'Pathology and the Posture of Neanderthal Man', *Quarterly Review of Biology* 32 (4), pp.348–363.

296 Lieberman, DE 2007, quoted in: 'Stone Age feminism? Females joining hunt may explain Neanderthals'end', Colin Nickerson *Boston Globe*, 10 November.

297 Berman, JC 1999, 'Bad Hair Days in the Paleolithic: Modern (Re)Constructions of the Cave Man', *American Anthropologist*, New Series, 101 (2) June, pp.288–304.

298 Trinkaus, E 1981, 'Neanderthal limb proportions and cold adaptation', in Stringer, CB, (ed.) *Aspects of Human Evolution*, Taylor & Francis, London, pp.187–224.

299 Weaver, TD 2003, 'The shape of the Neandertal femur is primarily the consequence of a hyperpolar body form', *Proceedings of the National Academy of Sciences USA* 100, pp.6926–6929.

300 Ruff, CB 1994, 'Morphological adaptation to climate in modern and fossil hominids', *Yearbook of Physical Anthropology* 37, pp.65–107.

301 Trinkaus, E 1983a, *The Shanidar Neanderthals*, Academic Press, London.

302 Trinkaus, E, 1986. 'The Neanderthals and modern human origins', *Annual Review of Anthropology* IS, pp.193–217.

303 Trenton, WH 1997, 'Postcranial Evidence of Cold Adaptation in European Neandertals', *American Journal of Physical Anthropology* 104, pp.245–258

304 Guthrie, RD 1966, 'Pelage of Fossil Bison: A New Osteological Index', *Journal of Mammalogy* 47 (4), November, pp.725–727.

305 Ling, JK 1970, 'Pelage and Molting in Wild Mammals with Special Reference to Aquatic Forms', *The Quarterly Review of Biology* 45 (1), March, pp.16–54.

306 Stiner, MC 1999, 'Cave bear ecology and interactions with Pleistocene humans', *Ursus* 11, pp.41–58.

307 Nagel, D, Hilsberg, S, Benesch, A & Scholz, J 2003, 'Functional morphology and fur patterns in Recent and fossil Panthera species', *Scripta Geology* 126.

308 Gamble, CS 1986, *The Palaeolithic Settlement of Europe*, Cambridge University Press, Cambridge, p.256.

309 Perlès, C 1977, *Préhistoire du Feu*, Masson, Paris.

310 Straus, LG, Clark, GA, Altuna, J & Ortea, JA 1980, 'Ice-Age subsistence in northern Spain', *Scientific American* 242, pp.142–152.

311 Gilligan, I 2007, 'Neanderthal extinction and modern human behaviour: the role of climate change and clothing', *World Archaeology* 39(4), pp.499–514.

312 Aiello, LC and Wheeler, P 2003, 'Neanderthal thermoregulation and the glacial climate', in Van Andel, T & Davies, T (eds), *Neanderthals and Modern Humans in the European Landscape during the Last Glaciation:Archaeological Results of the Stage 3 Project* McDonald Institute, Cambridge, pp.147–166.

313 White, MJ 2006, 'Things to do in Doggerland when you're dead: surviving OIS3 at the northwestern-most fringe of Middle Palaeolithic Europe', *World Archaeology* 38 (4), pp.547–575.

314 Gilligan, I 2007, 'Neanderthal extinction and modern human behaviour: the role of climate change and clothing', *World Archaeology* 39 (4), pp.499–514.

315 Johanson, D and Edgar,B 1996, *From Lucy to Language*, Simon and Schuster Editions, p99.

316 Ibid. P99.

317 Osborn, AJ 2004, 'Adaptive responses to cold stress on the periglacial Northern Great Plains', in Crothers, GM & Carbondale, IL (eds), *Hunters and Gatherers in Theory and Archaeology*, Southern Illinois University Occasional Paper 31, pp.10–47.

318 Stenton, DR 1991, 'The adaptive significance of Caribou winter clothing for arctic huntergatherers', *Inuit Studies* 15, pp.3–28.

319 Hoffecker, JF 2004, 'Human evolution and the colonization of the higher latitudes', 34th International Conference of Arctic Workshop, Institute of Arctic and Alpine Research, Boulder Colorado.

320 Davies, W and Gollop, P 2003, 'The human presence in Europe during the Last Glacial period II: climatic tolerance and climatic preference of Mid- and Late Glacial hominids', in Van Andel, T and Davies, W (eds), *Neanderthals and Modern Humans in the European Landscape during the Last Glaciation:Archaeological Results of the Stage 3 Project*, McDonald Institute, Cambridge, pp.131–46.

321 Lalueza-Fox, C, et al. 2007, 'A Melanocortin 1 Receptor Allele Suggests Varying Pigmentation Among Neanderthals', *Science* 318, pp.1453–1455.

322 Caro, T 2005, 'The adaptive significance of coloration in mammals', *Bioscience* 55, pp.125–136.

323 Cott, HB 1940, *Adaptive colouration in animals*, Methuen, London.

324 Hershkovitz, P 1977, *Living New World monkeys*, University of Chicago Press, Chicago.

325 Bradley, BJ & Mundy, NI 2008, 'The Primate Palette: The Evolution of Primate Coloration', *Evolutionary Anthropology* 17, pp.97–111.

326 Ibid.

327 Czarnetzki, A 1995, 'Morphological evidence of adaptive characters in the genus Homo', in Ullrich, H (ed.), *Man and environment in the Palaeolithic*, Proceedings of the Symposium Neuwied , Germany, May 2–7, 1993, Études et Recherches Arch. de l'Univ. de Liège 62, Liège, S pp.97–110.

328   Meyer, MR, Chang, ML & Lewis, J 2005, 'Functional morphology of the Neandertal nose', Seventy-Fourth Annual Meeting of the American Association of Physical Anthropologists, April 6–9, Milwaukee.

329   Franciscus, RG & Trinkaus, E 1988, 'The Neanderthal nose', *American Journal of Physical Anthropology* 75, pp.209–210.

330   Lehmuskallio, E, Lindholm, H, Sarna, S & Friberg, O 1995, 'Frostbite of the face and ears: epidemiological study of risk factors in Finnish conscripts', *British Medical Journal* 311, pp.1661–1663.

331   Wright, PC 1995, 'The neotropical primate adaptation to nocturnality', in Norconk, MA, Rosenberger, AL & Garber, PA (eds), *Adaptive Radiations of Neotropical Primates*, Plenum Press, New York.

332   Stander, PE 1991, 'Cooperative hunting in lions: the role of the individual', *Behavioural Ecology and Sociobiology* 29, pp.445–454.

333   Charles-Dominique, P 1974, 'Nocturnality and diurnality: an ecological interpretation of these two modes of life by an analysis of the higher vertebrate fauna in tropical forest ecosystems', in Luckett, WP & Szalay, FS (eds), *Phylogeny of the Primates*, Plenum Press, New York.

334   Yates, CC 1964, 'The relationship of nose size to smelling prowess in mammals', *Mammalia* 101, pp.23–34.

335   Boule, M 1921, *Les hommes fossils*, Masson, Paris.

336   Tattersall, I & Schwartz, JA 1998, 'Morphology, Paleoanthropology, and Neanderthals', *The Anatomical Record* (New Anat.) 253, pp.113–117.

337   Cartmill, M 1972, 'Arboreal adaptations and the origin of the order Primates', in Tuttle, R (ed.) *The Functional and Evolutionary Biology of Primates*, Aldine, Chicago, pp.97–122.

338   Heesy, CP 2003, 'The evolution of orbit orientation in mammals and the function of the primate postorbital bar', PhD Dissertation, Stony Brook University.

339   Ravosa, MJ & Savakova, DG 2004, 'Euprimate origins: the eyes have it', *Journal of Human Evolution* 46, pp.355–362.

340   Goldsmith, TH 1990 'Optimization, constraint, and history in the evolution of eyes', *Quarterly Review of Biology* 65 (3), pp.281–322.

341   Ross, CF & Kirk, EC 2007, 'Evolution of eye size and shape in primates', *Journal of Human Evolution* 52, pp.294–313.

342   Cartmill, M 1972, 'Arboreal adaptations and the origin of the order Primates', in Tuttle, R (ed.) , *The Functional and Evolutionary Biology of Primates*. Aldine, Chicago, pp.97–122.

343   Allman, JM 1977, 'Evolution of the visual system in the early primates', in Sprague, JM & Epstein, AN (eds), *Progress in Psychobiology and Physiological Psychology* 7, Academic Press, New York, pp.1–53.

344   Kirk, EC 2006b, 'Effects of activity pattern on eye size and orbital aperture size in primates', *Journal of Human Evolution* 51, 159–170.

345   Malmström, T and Kröger, RHH 2006, 'Pupil shapes and lens optics in the eyes of terrestrial vertebrates' *Journal of Experimental Biology* 209, pp.18–25.

346   Geist, V 1978, *Life Strategies, Human Evolution, Environmental Design*, Springer-Verlag, New York.

347   Lieberman, DE, Mowbray, KM, Osbjorn, PM 2000, 'Basicranial influence on overall cranial shape', *Journal of Human Evolution* 38, pp.291–315.

348   Smith, FH & Green, MD 1991, 'Heterochrony, life history and Neandertal morphology', *American Journal of Physical Anthropology. Supplement* 12, p. 164.

349   M. Hess, M &McCarthy, R 2008, 'Were Neanderthals tongue-tied?' Seventh Annual Meeting of the American Association of Physical Anthropologists, Columbus, Ohio, 9 April.

350   McCarthy, R, Hammond, A, Yates, F & Lieberman, P 2008, 'Voices out of the past: synthesizing Neanderthal speech', Seventh Annual Meeting of the American Association of Physical Anthropology, Columbus, Ohio, 9 April.

351   Milstein, M 2008, 'Neandertals Had Big Mouths, Gaped Widely', *National Geographic News*, 2 May.

352   Shea, JJ 2004, 'The Middle Paleolithic of the East Mediterranean Levant', *Journal of World Prehistory* 17 (4), pp.313–394.

353   Pettitt, PB 2002, 'The Neanderthal dead: exploring mortuary variability in Middle Palaeolithic Eurasia', *Before Farming* 1 (4), pp.1–19.

354   Bourguignon, L, Sellami, F, Deloze, V, Sellier-Segard, N, Beyries, S, & Emery-Barbier, E 2002, 'L'habitat moustérien de « La Folie » (Poitiers, Vienne): synthèse des premiers résultats) *Paléo* 14, pp.29–48.

355   Cushing, BS, Martin, JO, Young, LJ & Carter, CS 2001, 'The Effects of Peptides on Partner Preference Formation Are Predicted by Habitat in Prairie Voles', *Hormones and Behavior* 39, pp.48–58.

356   File, SE, Zangrossi, Jr H, Sanders, FL, & Mabbutt, PS 1993, 'Dissociation between behavioral and corticosterone responses on repeated exposures to cat odor', *Physiology and Behaviour* 54, pp.1109–1111.

357 Cheney, DL & Seyfarth, RM 2007, *Baboon Metaphysics: The Evolution of a Social Mind*, University of Chicago Press, 2007.

358 Knudsen, HK et al. 2005, 'A Changed America? The Effects of September 11th on Depressive Symptoms and Alcohol Consumption', *Journal of Health and Social Behavior* 46 (3), pp.260–273.

359 Bossolo, L & Bergantino, D 2002, 'Many Americans Still Feeling Effects of September 11th; Are Reexamining Their Priorities in Life'. *American Psychological Association*, 11 February.

360 Serre, D, Langaney, A, Chech, M, Teschler-Nicola, M, Paunovic, M et al. 2004, 'No evidence of Neandertal mtDNA contribution to early modern humans', *PLoS Biology* 2, pp.313–317.

361 Smith, CI et al. 2003, 'The thermal history of human fossils and the likelihood of successful DNA amplification', *Journal of Human Evolution* 45, pp.203–217.

362 McCown, TD, Keith, A 1939, *The stone age of Mount Carmel, Vol. II, the fossil human remains from the Levalloiso-Mousterian*, Clarendon Press, Oxford.

363 Corruccini, RS 1992, 'Metrical reconsideration of the Skhul IV and IX and Border Cave 1 Crania in the context of modern human origins', *American Journal of Physical Anthropology* 87, 433–445.

364 Clark, GA, & Lindly, J 1989, 'Modern human origins in the Levant and Western Asia: the fossil and archeological evidence', *American Anthropologist* 91, pp.962–985.

365 Trinkaus, E & Shipman, P 1993, *The Neandertals: Changing the Image of Mankind*, Knopf, New York, p.248.

366 Corruccini, RS 1992, 'Metrical reconsideration of the Skhul IV and IX and Border Cave 1 Crania in the context of modern human origins'. *American Journal of Physical Anthropology* 87, pp.433–445.

367 Stefan, V, & Trinkaus, E 1998, 'Discrete trait and dental morphometric affinities of the Tabun 2 mandible', *Journal of Human Evolution* 34, pp.443–468.

368 Quam, RM & Smith, FH 1999, 'A Reassessment of the Tabun C2 Mandible', in Akazawa, T, Aoki, K, Bar-Yosef, O (eds), *Neandertals and Modern Humans in Western Asia*, Springer, p.417.

369 Arensburg, B & Belfer-Cohen, A 1998, 'Sapiens and Neanderthals: Rethinking the Levantine Middle Paleolithic Hominids', in Akazawa, et al. (eds), *Neanderthals and Modern Humans in Western Asia*, Plenum Press, New York, p.319.

370 Ibid p320.

371 Trinkaus, E & Shipman, P 1993, *The Neandertals: Changing the Image of Mankind*, Knopf, New York, p.289.

372 Bulyginal, E & Gunz, P 2008, 'Mousterian children from Teshik-Tash and Staroselie: a 3D geometric morphometric analysis' Seventy-Seventh Annual Meeting of the American Association of Physical Anthropologists, Columbus, Ohio, 9 April.

373 Volterra, V 1931, 'Variations and fluctuations of the number of individuals in animal species living together, in *Animal Ecology*, McGraw-Hill, Translated from 1928 edition by R N Chapman.

374 Abrams, PA 2000, 'The Evolution of Predator-Prey Interactions: Theory and Evidence', *Annual Review of Ecology and Systematics* 31, pp.79–105.

375 Grant, PR & Grant, BR 2002, Unpredictable evolution in a 30-year study of Darwin's finches, *Science* 296, pp.707–711.

376 Shea, JJ 2003b, 'Neandertals, Competition, and the Origin of Modern Human Behavior in the Levant', *Evolutionary Anthropology* 12, pp.173–187.

377 Shea, JJ 2005, 'The Middle Paleolithic of the Levant', in Kuhn, SL & Hovers, E (eds), *Transitions Before the Transition: Evolution and Stability in the Middle Paleolithic and Middle Stone Age*, Springer, p.205.

378 Shea, JJ 2003b, 'Neandertals, Competition, and the Origin of Modern Human Behavior in the Levant', *Evolutionary Anthropology* 12, pp.173–187.

379 Tomsky J 1991, *Das Mittelpaläolithikum im Vordern Orient*, Dr Ludwig Reichert Verlag, Wiesbaden.

380 Hovers, E 2006, 'Neandertals and Modern Humans in the Middle Paleolithic of the Levant: what kind of interaction?' in Conard, E (ed.) , *When Neandertals and Modern Humans Met*, pp.65–85, Kerns Verlag, Tübingen.

381 Shea, JJ 2003b, 'Neandertals, Competition, and the Origin of Modern Human Behavior in the Levant', *Evolutionary Anthropology* 12, pp.173–187.

382 Holliday, TW 2000, 'Evolution at the crossroads: modern human emergence in Western Asia', *American Anthropologist* 102, pp.54–68.

383 Steegmann, AT, Cerny FJ, & Holliday, TW 2002, 'Neandertal cold adaptation: physiological and energetic factors', *American Journal of Human Biology* 14, pp.566–583.

384 Lieberman, DE 1998, 'Neandertal and EMH mobility patterns: comparing archaeological and anatomical evidence', in Akazawa T, Aoki K, Bar-Yosef O, (eds), *Neandertals and modern humans in western Asia*, Plenum Press, New York, pp.263–276.

385 Kaufman, D 1999, *Archaeological Perspectives on the Origins of Modern Humans: A View from the Levant*, Bergin & Garvey, Westport, CT.

386 Kaufman, D 2001, 'Comparisons and the case for interaction among Neanderthals and EMHs in the Levant', *Oxford Journal of Archaeology* 20, pp.219–240.

387 Shea, JJ 2003, 'Neandertals, Competition, and the Origin of Modern Human Behavior in the Levant', *Evolutionary Anthropology* 12, pp.173–187.

388 Lahr, MM & Foley, R 1994, 'Multiple dispersals and modern human origins', *Evolutionary Anthropology* 3, pp.48–60.

389 Macaulay, V et al. 2005, 'Single, rapid coastal settlement of Asia revealed by analysis of complete mitochondrial genomes', *Science* 308, pp.1034–1036.

390 Gagneux, P et al. 1999, 'Mitochondrial sequences show diverse evolutionary histories of African hominoids', *Science* 96 (9), 27 April, pp.5077–5082.

391 Gagneux, P quoted in Dye, L 1999, 'We dodged extinction', ABC News web site. www.rpi.edu/~eglash/eglash.dir/ethnic.dir/race/chimps/chimps.htm

392 Gagneux, P et al. 1999, 'Mitochondrial sequences show diverse evolutionary histories of African hominoids', *Science* 96 (9) 27 April, pp.5077–5082.

393 Wood, B quoted in Dye, L 1999, 'We dodged extinction', ABC News web site. www.rpi.edu/~eglash/eglash.dir/ethnic.dir/race/chimps/chimps.htm

394 Kaessmann, H, Wiebe, V, Weiss, G, Pääbo, S 2001, 'Great ape DNA sequences reveal a reduced diversity and an expansion in humans', *Nature Genetics* 27, pp.155–156.

395 Fischer, A, Pollack, J, Thalmann, O, Nickel, B, Pääbo, S 2006, 'Demographic history and genetic differentiation in apes', *Current Biology* 16, pp.1133–1138.

396 Yu, N, Jensen-Seaman, MI, Chemnick, L, Ryder, O, Li, WH 2004, 'Nucleotide diversity in gorillas', *Genetics*, 166, pp.1375–1383.

397 Reich, DE et al. 2001, 'Linkage disequilibrium in the human genome', *Nature* 411, pp.199–204.

398 Ibid.

399 Simon, WL, Sulston, JE & Goodfellow, PN 1995, 'Sequence Variation of the Human Y Chromosome', *Nature* 378, 379–380.

400 Marth, G et al. 2003, 'Sequence variations in the public human genome data reflect a bottlenecked population history', *Proceedings of the National Academy of Sciences USA* 100 (1), 7 January, pp.1376–381.

401 Harpending, H & Rogers, A 2000, 'Genetic perspectives on human origins and differentiation', *Annual Review of Genomics and Human Genetics* 1, pp.361–385.

402 Reich, DE et al. 2001, 'Linkage disequilibrium in the human genome', *Nature* 411, pp.199–204.

403 Shea, JJ 2003b, 'Neandertals, Competition, and the Origin of Modern Human Behavior in the Levant', *Evolutionary Anthropology*, 12, pp.173–187.

404 Cott, HB 1940, *Adaptive Coloration in Animals*, Methuen, London.

405 Abrams, PA 2000, 'The Evolution of Predator-Prey Interactions: Theory and Evidence', *Annual Review of Ecology and Systematics* 31, pp.79–105.

406 Tinbergen, N 1951/1989, *The study of instinct*, Oxford University Press.

407 Smith, SM 1977, 'Coral-snake pattern recognition and stimulus generalisation by naive great kiskadees (Aves: Tyrannidae)', *Nature* pp.265, pp.535–536.

408 Smith, SM 1977, 'Coral-snake pattern recognition and stimulus generalisation by naive great kiskadees (Aves: Tyrannidae)', *Nature* 265, pp.535–536.

409 Newman, R 1970, 'Why man is such a sweaty and thirsty naked animal: a speculative review', *Human Biology* 42, pp.12–27.

410 Amaral, LQ do 1996, 'Loss of body hair, bipedality and thermoregulation', Comments on recent papers in the *Journal of Human Evolution*, *Journal of Human Evolution* 30, pp.357–366.

411 Schultz, AH 1931, 'The density of hair in primates', in *Human Biology* 3, pp.303–321.

412 Wade, N 2006, *Before the Dawn: Recovering the Lost History of Our Ancestors*, The Penguin Press, New York.

413 Darwin, C 1871, *The Descent of Man and Selection in Relation to Sex*, John Murray, London.

414 Harris, JR 2006, 'Parental selection: A third selection process in the evolution of human hairlessness and skin color', *Medical Hypotheses* 66, pp.1053–1059

415 Hardy, AC 1960, 'Was man more aquatic in the past?' *New Scientist* 7, pp.642–645.

416 Morgan, E 1982, *The Aquatic Ape*, Stein and Day, New York.

417 Langdon, JH 1997, 'Umbrella hypotheses and parsimony in human evolution: a critique of the Ape Hypothesis', *Journal of Human Evolution* 33 (4), pp.479–94.

418 Pagel, M & Bodmer, W 2003, 'A naked ape would have fewer parasites', *Proceedings of the Royal Society* 270, Biology Letters Supplement 1 / 7 August, S117–S119.

419 Wheeler, P 1984, 'The evolution of bipedality and loss of functional body hair in humans', *Journal of Human Evolution* 13, pp.91–98.

420 Johnson Jr, AE 1998, 'Lower Than the Angels: The Human Evolutionary Journey', Internet paper.

421 Kreger, D 2001, 'Human thermoregulation and hair loss', www.modernhumanorigins/com.

422 Amaral, LQ 1996, 'Loss of body hair, bipedality and thermoregulation', Comments on recent papers in the *Journal of Human Evolution*, *Journal of Human Evolution*, 30 (4), pp.357–366.

423 Kreger, D 2001, 'Human thermoregulation and hair loss', www.modernhumanorigins/com.

424 Murdock, G P & Provost, C 1973, 'Factors in the division of labor by sex: a cross-cultural analysis', *Ethnology* 12, pp.203–225.

425 Basow, SA 1991, 'The hairless ideal: Women and their body hair', *Psychology of Women Quarterly* 15, pp.83–96.

426 Tiggemann, M, & Kenyon, S J 1998, 'The hairlessness norm: The removal of body hair in women', *Sex Roles* 39, pp.873–885.

427 Toerien, M, Wilkinson, S & Choi, PYL 2005, 'Body Hair Removal: The 'Mundane' Production of Normative Femininity', *Sex Roles* 52, (5/6), March.

428 Cooper, W 1971, *Hair: Sex society symbolism*, Aldus Books, London.

429 Pawlowski, B 1998, 'Why are human newborns so big and fat?' *Human Evolution* 13 (1), pp.65–72.

430 Hey, EN & Katz, G 1970, 'The optimum thermal environment for naked babies'. *Arch. Dis. Child.* 45, pp.328–334.

431 Kittler, R, Kayser, M & Stoneking, M 2003, 'Molecular Evolution of Pediculus humanus and the Origin of Clothing', *Current Biology* 13, 19 August, pp.1414–1417.

432 Kittler, R, Kayser, M & Stoneking, M 2004, 'Erratum for Kittler et al. Current Biology 13 (16) 1414–1417.' *Current Biology* 14, p.2309, 29 December.

433 Lovejoy, CO 2005, 'The natural history of human gait and posture, Part 1, Spine and pelvis', *Gait and Posture* 21, pp.95–112

434 McDougall, I, Brown, FH & Fleagle, JG 2005, 'Stratigraphic placement and age of modern humans from Kibish, Ethiopia', *Nature* 433, pp.733–736.

435 Trinkaus, E 1983, *The Shanidar Neandertals*, Academic, New York.

436 Tattersall, I 2006, 'Neanderthal Skeletal Structure and the Place of Homo neanderthalensis in European Hominid Phylogeny', *Human Evolution.*

437 Trevathan, W, Smith, EO & McKenna, JJ 1999, *Evolutionary Medicine*, Oxford University Press, US, p.333.

438 Badcock, C 1991, *Evolution and Human Behavior*, Basil Blackwell, p.181.

439 Singh, D 1993, 'Adaptive significance of female physical attractiveness: Role of waist-to-hip ratio', *Journal of Personality and Social Psychology* 65, pp.293–307.

440 Goehring, J 1999, 'Modern Standards of Beauty: Nature or Nurture? An Evolutionary Perspective', *Evolutionary Psychology*, www.evoyage.com/Evolutionary%20Feminism/ModernStandardsBeauty.htm.

441 Tovee, MJ, Mason, SM, Emery, JL, McClusky, SF & Cohen-Tovee, EM 1997, 'Supermodels: stick insects or hour glasses?' *Lancet* 350, pp.474–1475.

442 Perrett, David I, et al. 1999, 'Symmetry and Human Facial Attractiveness', *Evolution and Human Behavior* 20 (5) September, pp.295–307.

443 Fernández-Carriba, S, Loeches, Á, Morcillo, A & Hopkins, WD 2002, 'Asymmetry in facial expression of emotions by chimpanzees', *Neuropsychologia* 1395, pp.1–11.

444 Schwartz, JH & Tattersall, I 2000, 'The human chin revisited: what is it and who has it?' *Journal of Human Evolution* 38, pp.367–409.

445 Kobayashi, T 1987, 'Ethological Hypothesis on the Origin of the Handsome Type Face in Humans', *Journal of Ethology* 5, pp.1–5.

446 Ibid.

447 Wrangham, R & Peterson, D 1997, *Demonic Males: Apes and the Origins of Human Violence*, Mariner Books, p.119.

448 Glassner, B 1988, *Bodies*, Putman, New York, p.107.

449 Epstein, CF 1986, *Deceptive Distinctions: Sex Gender and the Social Order*, Yale University Press, New Haven, Conn.

450 Halliday, T 1980, *Sexual Strategy*, Oxford University Press, p.144.

451 Daly, M, Wilson, M & Weghorn, S J 1982, 'Male sexual jealousy', *Ethology and Sociobiology* 3, pp.11–27.

452 Todd, J & Dewhurst, K 1955, 'The Othello syndrome: a study in the psychopathology of sexual jealousy', *Journal of Nervous and Mental Disease* 122, pp.367–374.

453 Cobb, J 1979, 'Morbid jealousy', *British Journal of Hospital Medicine* 21, pp.511–518.

454 Dell, S 1985, *Murder into Manslaughter*, Oxford University Press, Oxford.

455 Trinkaus, E & Shipman, P 1993, *The Nean-dertals: Changing the Image of Mankind*, Knopf, New York.

456 Stringer, C & Gamble, C 1993, *In Search of the Neanderthals*, Thames and Hudson.

457 Hrdy, SB 1979, 'Infanticide among animals: A review, classification, and examination of the implications for the reproductive strategies of females', *Ethology and Sociobiology* 1, pp.13–40.

458 Watts, DP 1989, 'Infanticide in Mountain Gorillas: New cases and a Reconsideration of the Evidence', *Ethology* 81, pp.1–18.

459 Barnard, GW, Vera, H, Vera, M I, & Newman, G 1982, 'Till death do us part: A study of spouse murder', *Bulletin of the American Association of Psychiatry and Law* 10, pp.271–280.

460 Wilson, M & Daly, M 1993, 'Spousal Homicide Risk and Estrangement', *Violence and Victims* 8 (1), pp.3–16.

461 Daly, M & Wilson, M 1988, 'Evolutionary Social Psychology and Family Homicide', *Science* 242, pp.5219–5240.

462 Morton, M 2003, *The Lover's Tongue, A merry romp through the language of love and sex*, Insomniac Press, p.186.

463 Etcoff, N 1999, *Survival of the Prettiest: The Science of Beauty*, Doubleday, p.187.

464 Matsumoto-Oda, A & Kasuya, E 2005, 'Proximity and estrous synchrony in Mahale chimpanzees', *American Journal of Primatology* 66 (2), pp.159–166.

465 Allott, R 1992, 'Evolutionary aspects of love and empathy', *Journal of Social and Evolutionary Systems* 15, (4), pp.353–370.

466 Ibid.

467 Ibid.

468 Goodall, J 1986, *The chimpanzees of Gombe: patterns of behavior*, The Belknap Press of Harvard University Press, Cambridge, Mass.

469 Ibid.

470 Emanuele, E, Politi, P, Bianchi, M, Minoretti, P, Bertona, M & Geroldi, D 2006, 'Raised plasma nerve growth factor levels associated with early-stage romantic love', *Psychoneuroendocrinology* 31, (3), pp.288–94.

471 Muller, M & Wrangham, R 2001, 'The reproductive ecology of male hominids', in Ellison, P (ed.) , *Reproductive Ecology and Human Evolution*, Aldine de Gruyter, New York.

472 Gordon, J 2004, 'Nighttime fears in children: Origins, frequency, content and severity', doctoral dissertation, Clayton, Victoria, Australia, Monash University.

473 Bauer, DH 1976, 'An exploratory study of developmental changes in children's fears', *Journal of Child Psychology and Psychiatry* 17, pp.69–74.

474 Muris, P, Merckelbach, H, Ollendick, TH, King, NJ & Bogie, N 2001, 'Children's nighttime fears: Parent–child ratings of frequency, content, origins, coping behaviors and severity', *Behaviour Research and Therapy* 39, pp.13–28.

475 Gordona, J, King, N, Gullone, E, Murisc, P & Ollendick, TH 2007, 'Nighttime fears of children and adolescents: Frequency, content, severity, harm expectations, disclosure, and coping behaviours', *Behaviour Research and Therapy* 45, pp.2464–2472.

476 King, N, Ollendick, TH, & Tonge, B J 1997, 'Children's nighttime fears', *Clinical Psychology Review* 17, pp.431–443.

477 Muris, P, Merckelbach, H, Meesters, C, & Van Lier, P 1997a, 'What do children fear most often?', *Journal of Behavior Therapy and Experimental Psychiatry* 28, pp.263–267.

478 Bauer, DH 1976, 'An exploratory study of developmental changes in children's fears', *Journal of Child Psychology and Psychiatry* 17, pp.69–74.

479 Slee, PT & Cross, DG 1989, 'Living in the nuclear age: An Australian study of children's and adolescents' fears', *Journal Child Psychiatry and Human Development* 19, (4), pp.270–278.

480 Mukhametov, LM, Supin, AY, Polyakova, IG 1977, 'Interhemispheric asymmetry of the electroencephalographic sleep patterns in dolphins', *Brain Res* 134, pp.581–584.

481 Rattenborg, NC, Lima, SC & Amlane, CJ 1999, 'Half-awake to the risk of predation', *Nature*, 4, (397), pp.397–398.

482 Davies, SJM & Valla, FR 1978, 'Evidence for the domestication jof the dog 12,000 ago in the Nutufian of Israel', *Nature* 276, pp.608–610.

483 Nobis, G 1979, 'Der älteste Haushund lebte vor 14,000 Jahren', *UMSHAU* 19, p.610.

484 Olsen, SJ 1985, *Origins of the Domestic Dog, The Fossil Record*, University of Arizona Press.

485 Ibid.

486 Thurston, ME 1996, *The Lost History of the Canine Race*, Andrews & McMeel, p 4.

487 Germonpre, M, Sablin, M, Stevens, R, Hedges, R, Hofreiter, M, Stiller, M & Jacnickedesprese, V 2008, 'Fossil dogs and wolves from Palaeolithic sites in Belgium, the Ukraine and Russia: osteometry, ancient DNA and stable isotopes', *Journal of Archaeological Science*.

488 Wayne, RK, Lehman, N, Allard, MW & Honeycutt, RL 1992, 'Mitochondrial DNA variability of the gray wolf: genetic consequences of population decline and habitat fragmentation', *Conservation Biology* 6, pp.559–569.

489 Nowak, R 1992, 'Wolves: The great travelers of evolution', *International Wolf* 2 (4), pp.3–7.

490 Vila, C et al. 1997, 'Multiple and Ancient Origins of the Domestic Dog', *Science* 276.

491 Birdsell, JB 1972, *Human Evolution: An Introduction to the New Physical Anthropology*, Rand-McNally, Chicago, p.232.

492 Lovejoy, CO 1981, 'The Origin of Man', *Science*, 211, pp.343.

493 Williamson, et al 2007, 'Localizing Recent Adaptive Evolution in the Human Genome', *PLoS Genetics* 3 (6).

494 Ehmsen, J, Poon, E, & Davies, K 2002, 'The dystrophin-associated protein complex', *Journal of Cell Science* 115, pp.2801–2803.

495 Trinkaus, E & Churchill, SE 1999, 'Diaphyseal Cross-sectional Geometry of Near Eastern Middle Palaeolithic Humans: The Humerus', *Journal of Archaeological Science* 26, pp.173–184

496 Weidenreich, F 1945, 'The brachycephalization of recent mankind', *Southwestern Journal of Anthropology* 1, pp.1–54.

497 Frayer, DW 1980, 'Sexual Dimorphism and Cultural Evolution in the Late Pleistocene and Holocene of Europe', *Journal of Human Evolution* 9, pp.399–415.

498 Goodkin, K, Antoni, MH & Blaney, PH 1986, 'Stress and hopelessness in the promotion of cervical intraepithelial neoplasia in invasive squamous cell carcinoma of the cervix', *J Psychosomatic Res* 30 (1), pp.67–76.

499 Ader, R 1982, *Psychoneuroimmunology*, Academic Press, cited in: Grossarth-Maticek, R, 'Interpersonal repression as a predictor of cancer', *Social Science and Medicine* 16, pp.493–8.

500 Fox, BH 1978, 'Premorbid psychological factors as related to cancer incidence', *Journal of Behavioural Medicine* 1, pp.45–133.

501 Borysenko, JZ 1982, 'Behavioural-physiological factors in the development and management of cancer', *General Hospital Psychiatry* 4, pp.69–74.

502 *Marine Mammal Inventory Report* (MMIR), 2000, National Marine Fisheries Service (NMFS) USA.

503 Lorenz, K, & Tinbergen, N 1938, 'Taxis und Instinkthandlung in der Eirollbewegung der Graugans', *Zeitschrift für Tierpsychologie* 2, pp.1–29.

504 Tinbergen, N 1951, *The Study of Instinct*, Oxford University Press, New York.

505 Crick, F 1970, 'Central Dogma of Molecular Biology', *Nature* 227 (August), pp.561–3.

506 Darwin, C 1872, *The Expression of the Emotions in Man and Animals*, John Murray.

507 Darwin, C 1873, 'Inherited Instinct', *Nature*, 13 February, vii, p.281.

508 Darwin, C 1868, *The Variation of Animals and Plants under Domestication, vol. ii*, p.75.

509 Smith, JM 1975, *The Theory of Evolution*, 3rd Edition, Penguin, Harmondsworth.

510 Sober, E 1984, *The nature of selection: evolutionary theory in philosophical focus*, The MIT Press, pp.101–107.

511 Cosmides, L, & Tooby, J 2000, 'Evolutionary Psychology and the Emotions', in Lewis, M & Haviland-Jones, JM (eds), *Handbook of Emotions*, 2nd Edition, Guilford.

512 Vendramini, D 2005, 'Noncoding DNA and the Teem theory of inheritance,emotions and innate behaviour', *Medical Hypotheses* 64 (3), pp.512–519.

513 Vendramini, D 2005, 'A second evolutionary process moderates the evolution of emotions and behaviour in metazoans', *The Second Evolution* website, www.thesecondevolution.com/paper1behaviour.pdf.

514 Vendramini, D 2005, 'The Teem theory of nonMendelian inheritance', *The Second Evolution* website, www.thesecondevolution.com/paper5dna.pdf.

515 Crick, F 1970, 'Central Dogma of Molecular Biology', *Nature* 227 (August), pp.561–563.

516 Gibson, EJ & Walk, RD 1960, 'The visual cliff,' *Scientific American* 202, pp.64–71.

517 Matlin, MW & Foley, HJ 1997, *Sensation and Perception* (4th Edition), Allyn and Bacon, p.448.

518 Marais, EN 1939, *My Friends the Baboons*, Methuen & Co. Ltd, London.

519 Sapolsky, RM 2004, 'Social status and health in humans and other animals', *Annual Review of Anthropology* 33, pp.393–418.

520 Segerstrom, SC, & Miller, GE 2004, 'Psychological stress and the human immune system: a meta-analytic study of 30 years of inquiry', *Psychological Bulletin* 130, pp.601–630.

521 Engh, AL et al. 2005, 'Behavioural and hormonal responses to predation in female chacma baboons (Papio hamadryas ursinus)', *Proc Biol Sci.* 273 (1587), pp.707–712.

522 Lundin, T 1984, 'Morbidity following sudden and unexpected bereavement', *British Journal of Psychiatry* 144, pp.84–88.

523 Darwin, C 1871, *The Descent of Man*, Chapter V—On the Development of the Intellectual and Moral Faculties, John Murray, London.

524 Campbell, J with Moyers, B1991, *The Power of Myth*, Anchor, p.123.

525 Phillips, T, Barnard, C, Ferguson, E & Reader, T 2008, 'Do humans prefer altruistic mates? Testing a link between sexual selection and altruism towards non-relatives', *British Journal of Psychology* 99 (4), pp.555–572.

526 Fromm, E 1973, *The Anatomy of Human Destructiveness*, Henry Holt and Co, p.212.

527 Rummel R J, 1994, Death By Government, Transaction Publishers, 1994, New Brunswick, N.J.

528 Knight, C, Studdert-Kennedy, M & Hurford, JR 2000, 'Language: A Darwinian Adaptation?' in Knight, C, Studdert-Kennedy, M & Hurford, JR (eds), *The Evolutionary Emergence of Language: Social Function and the Origins of Linguistic Form*, Cambridge University Press, Cambridge.

529 Noble, J 2000, 'Cooperation, Competition and the Evolution of Prelinguistic Communication', in Knight, C, Studdert-Kennedy, M & Hurford, JR (eds), *The Evolutionary Emergence of Language: Social Function and the Origins of Linguistic Form*, Cambridge University Press, Cambridge.

530 Bickerton, D 1990, *Language and Species*, University of Chicago Press, Chicago.

531 Ruhlen, M 1994, *On the Origin of Languages: Tracing the Evolution of the Mother Tongue*, Stanford University Press, Stanford.

532 Noble, W & Davidson, I 1996, *Human evolution, language and mind*, Cambridge University Press, Cambridge.

533 Lieberman, P, Fecteau, S, Theoret, H, Garcia, RR et al. 2007, 'The Evolution of Human Speech: Its Anatomical and Neural Bases / Comments / Reply', *Current Anthropology* 48, (1).

534 Ibid. p.39.

535 Davidson, I & Noble, W 1989, 'The archaeology of perception', *Current Anthropology* 30, pp.125–55.

536 Mellars, PA, 1989, 'Major issues in the emergence of modern humans', *Current Anthropology* 30, pp.349–85.

537 Noble, W & Davidson, I 1996, *Human evolution, language and mind*, Cambridge University Press, Cambridge.

538 Shea, JJ 2006, 'The origins of lithic projectile point technology: evidence from Africa, the Levant, and Europe', *Journal of Archaeological Science* 33, pp.823–846.

539 Hughes, SS 1998, 'Getting to the point: evolutionary change in prehistoric weaponry', *Journal of Archaeological Method and Theory* 5, pp.345–408.

540 Bar-Yosef, O 2000, 'The Middle and Early Upper Paleolithic in southwest Asia and neighboring regions', in Bar-Yosef, O, Pilbeam, D (eds), *The Geography of Neandertals and Modern Humans in Europe and the Greater Mediterranean*, Peabody Museum of Archaeology and Ethnology, Cambridge, MA, Bulletin No. 8, pp.107–156.

541 Shea, JJ 2006, 'The origins of lithic projectile point technology: evidence from Africa, the Levant, and Europe', *Journal of Archaeological Science* 33, pp.823–846.

542 Bergman, CA 1981, 'Point types in the Upper Palaeolithic sequence at Ksar Akil, Lebanon', in Cauvin, J & Sanlaville, P (eds), Pr´ehistoire du Levant, *Comptes rendus de l'Académie des sciences*, Paris, 319–330.

543 Bergman, C, & Newcomer, MH 1983, 'Flint arrowhead breakage: Examples from Ksar Akil, Lebanon', *Journal of Field Archaeology* 10, pp.238–243.

544 Shea, JJ 2006, 'The origins of lithic projectile point technology: evidence from Africa, the Levant, and Europe', *Journal of Archaeological Science* 33, p.839.

545 Churchill, SE 2002, 'Of assegais and bayonets: reconstructing prehistoric spear use', *Evolutionary Anthropology*. 11, pp.185–186.

546 Kortlandt, A 2002, 'Neanderthal anatomy and the use of spears', *Evolutionary Anthropology* 11, pp.183–184.

547 Mellars, P 1996, *The Neanderthal legacy: An archaeological perspective from Western Europe*, Princeton University Press, Princeton.

548 Shea, JJ, 'Spear Points from the Middle Paleolithic of the Levant', *Journal of Field Archaeology* 15, p.441–450.

549 Marean, CW & Assefa, Z 1999, 'Zooarchaeological evidence for the faunal exploitation behavior of Neandertals and EMHs', *Evolutionary Anthropology* 8, pp.22–37.

550 Shea, JJ 2006, 'The origins of lithic projectile point technology: evidence from Africa, the Levant, and Europe', *Journal of Archaeological Science* 33, pp.823–846.

551 Stiner, MC, Munro, ND & Surovell, TA 2000, 'The tortoise and the hare: small game use, the broad spectrum revolution, and Paleolithic demography', *Current Anthropology* 41, pp.39–73.

552 Valladas, H, Clottes, J, Geneste, J-M, Garcia, MA, Arnold, M, Cachier, H & Tisnérat-Laborde, N 2001, 'Palaeolithic paintings: Evolution of prehistoric cave art', *Nature* 413, (479).

553 Byrne, R W & A Whiten (eds), 1988, *Machiavellian Intelligence: Social expertise and the evolution of intellect in monkeys, apes and humans*, Claredon Press, Oxford.

554 Simmons, R 2002, *Odd Girl Out: The Hid-den Culture of Aggression in Girls*, Harcourt Books.

555 Fausto Sterling, A 1992, *Myths of Gender; Biological Theories about Women and Men*, Basic Books, New York, p.269.

556 Levin, M 1988, *Feminism and Freedom*, Trans-action Publishers, New Brunswick, New Jersey, pp.82–88.

557 Toussaint, L, & Webb JR 2005, 'Gender differences in the relationship between empathy and forgiveness', *Journal of Social Psychology* 145 (6), pp.673–85.

558 Junaid, KA & Fellowes, S 2006, 'Gender Differences in the Attainment of Motor Skills on the Movement Assessment Battery for Children', *Physical & Occupational Therapy in Pediatrics: A Quarterly Journal of Developmental Therapy* 26 (1,2), pp.5–11.

559 Synk, DJ 1983, 'The Effect of Sex on General Aptitude Test Battery Validity and Test Scores', Paper presented at the Annual Meeting of the American Psychological Association, 91st, Anaheim, CA, August 26–30.

560 Soffer, O 2004, 'Recovering Perishable Technologies through Use Wear on Tools: Preliminary Evidence for Upper Paleolithic Weaving and Net Making', *Current Anthropology* 45, pp.407–418.

561 Jones, CB 2005, *Behavioral Flexibility in Primates: Causes and Consequences*, Springer, p.116.

562 Bar-Yosef, O 1998, 'On the nature of transitions: The Middle to Upper Palaeolithic and the Neolithic revolution', *Cambridge Archeological Journal* 8, pp.141–163.

563 Klein, RG 2000, 'Archaeology and the evolution of human behavior', *Evolutionary Anthropology* 9, pp.7–36.

564 Bar-Yosef, O 2002, 'The Upper Palaeolithic revolution', *Annual Review of Anthropology* 31, pp.363–393.

565 Kuhn, SL, Stiner, MC, Reese, DS & Gulec E 2001, 'Ornaments of the earliest Upper Paleolithic: new insights from the Levant', *Proc Natl Acad Sci.* 98 (13), pp.7641–6.

566 Shea, JJ 2003, 'The Middle Paleolithic of the East Mediterranean Levant', *Journal of World Prehistory* 17 (4), pp.313–394.

567 Bar-Yosef, O 2002, 'The Upper Palaeolithic revolution', *Annual Review of Anthropology* 31, pp.363–393.

568 Kuhn, SL, Stiner, MC & Güleç E 1999, 'Initial Upper Palaeolithic in south-central Turkey and its regional context: a preliminary report', *Antiquity* 73, pp.505–517.

569 Martof, BS et al. 1980, *Amphibians and Reptiles of the Carolinas and Virginia*, University of North Carolina Press, Chapel Hill.

570 Stanyon, R, Consigliere, S & Morescalchi, MA 1993, 'Cranial capacity in hominid evolution', *Journal Human Evolution* 8 (3), pp.205–216.

571 Holliday, TW 2002, 'Body size and postcranial robusticity of European Upper Paleolithic hominins', *Journal of Human Evolution* 43(4), pp.513–528.

572 Formicola, V 2003, 'More is not always better: Trotter and Gleser's equations and stature estimates of Upper Paleolithic European samples', *Journal of Human Evolution*, 45, 3, September, 239–244.

573 Olweus, D, Mattsson, A, Schalling, D, Low, H 1980, 'Testosterone, aggression, physical, and personality dimensions in normal adolescent males', *PsychosomaticMedicine* 42, pp.253–269

574 Cleckley, HM 1941,*The Mask of Sanity*, Revised Edition, (1982), Mosby Medical Library.

575 Wrangham, R & Peterson, D 1997, *Demonic Males: Apes and the Origins of Human Violence*, Mariner Books.

576 Guilaine, J, Zammit, J 2004, *The Origins of War: Violence in Prehistory*, Blackwell Publishing Professional.

577 LeBlanc, S, Register, KE 2003, *Constant Battles: The Myth of the Peaceful, Noble Savage*, St Martins Press, NY.

578 Martin, D 1998, *Troubled Times: Violence and Warfare in the Past*, Routledge.

579 Darwin, C 1871, *The Descent of Man*, Chapter V—On the Development of the Intellectual and Moral Faculties, John Murray, London.

580 Mellars, P 2006, 'Archeology and the Dispersal of Modern Humans in Europe: Deconstructing the "Aurignacian,"' *Evolutionary Anthropology* 15, pp.167–182.

581 Kozlowski, JK 2004, 'Early Upper Paleolithic Levallois-derived industries in the Balkans and in the middle Danube basin.' *Anthropologie* 43, pp.289–306.

582 Bar-Yosef, O 2000, 'The Middle and early Upper Paleolithic in southwest Asia and neighbouring regions', in Bar-Yosef, O, and Pilbeam, D, (eds), *The geography of Neandertals and modern humans in Europe and the Greater Mediterranean*, Peabody Museum of Harvard University, Cambridge, pp.107–156.

583 Tostevin G 2003, 'A quest for antecedents: a comparison of the terminal Middle Paleolithic and the early Upper Paleolithic of the Levant', In: Goring-Morris N, Belfer-Cohen A, Editors, 2003, More than meets the eye, Oxford: Oxbow Books, 54–67.

584   Shea, JJ 2001, 'The Middle Paleolithic: Early
      Modern Humans and Neandertals in the
      Levant', *Near Eastern Archaeology*, 64 (1/2),
      pp.38–64.

585   Shea, JJ 2001, 'Modern Human Origins and
      Neanderthal Extinctions in the Levant',
      Athena Review 2, (4).

586   Schwarcz, HP & Rink, WJ 1998, 'Progress
      in ESR and U-series Chronology of the Le-
      vantine Paleolithic', in Akazawa et al. (ed.),
      *Neandertals and Modern Humans in Western
      Asia*, Plenum Press, New York.

587   Belmaker, M 2008, 'Mesowear analysis of
      ungulate diet during MIS 4–3 in the Levant:
      Implications for extinction of the Neander-
      thals', Seventy-Seventh Annual Meeting of
      the American Association of Physical An-
      thropologists, 9 April, Columbus, Ohio.

588   Cavalli-Sforza, L & Feldman, MW 2003,
      'The application of molecular genetic ap-
      proaches to the study of human evolution',
      Nature Genetics 33, pp.266 – 275.

589   Karafet, TM et al. 1999, 'Ancestral Asian
      source(s) of new world Y-chromosome
      founder haplotypes', *The American Journal of
      Human Genetics* 64, pp.817–831.

590   Olivieri, A, et al. 2006, 'The mtDNA Legacy
      of the Levantine Early Upper Palaeolithic in
      Africa', *Science* 314 (5806), pp.1767–1770.

591   Macaulay, V, et al. 1999, 'The emerging tree
      of West Eurasian mtDNAs: a synthesis
      of control-region sequences and RFLPs',
      The American Journal of Human Genetics 64,
      pp.232–249.

592   Van Peer, P & Vermeersch, M 1990, 'Middle
      to Upper Palaeolithic Transition: the Evi-
      dence for the Nile Valley', in *The Emergence
      of Modern Humans: An Archaeological Perspec-
      tive*, Mellars, P (ed.) , Edinburgh University
      Press, Edinburgh, pp.139–159.

593   Olivieri, A, et al. 2006, 'The mtDNA Legacy
      of the Levantine Early Upper Palaeolithic in
      Africa', *Science* 314 (5806), pp.1767–1770.

594   Ibid.

595   Mellars, PA 1992, 'Archaeology and the
      population-dispersal hypothesis of modern
      human origins in Europe', *Phil. Trans. R. Soc.
      Lond. B Biol Sci* 337, pp.225–234.

596   Bar-Yosef, O 2000, 'The Middle and the
      Early Upper Palaeolithic in Southwest Asia
      and Neighboring Regions', in Bar-Yosef,
      O & Pilbeam, D (eds), *The Geography of
      Neandertals and Modern Humans in Europe
      and the Greater Mediterranean*, pp.107–156,
      Peabody Museum Bulletin 8, Cambridge,
      Massachusetts.

597   Kozlowski, JK 2004, 'Early Upper Paleo-
      lithic Levallois-derived industries in the
      Balkans and in the middle Danube basin',
      Anthropologie 43, pp.289–306.

598   Bar-Yosef, O 2000, 'The Middle and early
      Upper Paleolithic in southwest Asia and
      neighbouring regions', in Bar-Yosef O, Pil-
      beam D, (eds), *The Geography of Neandertals
      and Modern Humans in Europe and the Greater
      Mediterranean*, pp.107–156, Peabody Mu-
      seum Bulletin 8, Cambridge, Massachusetts.

599   Mellars, PA 1992, 'Archaeology and the
      population-dispersal hypothesis of modern
      human origins in Europe. *Phil. Trans. R. Soc.
      Lond. B Biol Sci* 337, pp.225–234.

600   Tattersall, I, Schwartz, JH 1999, 'Hominids
      and hybrids: The place of Neanderthals in
      human evolution', *Proceedings of the National
      Academy of Sciences U S A* 96, pp.7117–7119.

601   Bocquet-Appel, J-P, & Demars PY 2000,
      'Neanderthal contraction and modern hu-
      man colonization of Europe', *Antiquity* 74,
      (285), pp.544–552.

602   Trinkaus, E & Shipman, P 1993, *The Nean-
      dertals: Changing the Image of Mankind*, Knopf,
      New York

603   Ovchinnikov, I, Gotherstrom, A, Romano-
      va, G, Kharitonov, V, Liden, K, Goodwin,
      W 2000, 'Molecular analysis of Neanderthal
      DNA from the northern Caucasus', *Nature*
      404, pp.490–493.

604   Smith, F, Trinkaus, E, Pettitt, P, Karavanic´,
      I, Paunovic´, M 1999, 'Direct radiocarbon
      dates for Vindija G1 & Velika Peina Late
      Pleistocene hominid remains', *Proceedings of
      the National Academy of Sciences U S A* 96,
      pp.12281–12286.

605   Harrold, F 1989, 'Mousterian, Chatelper-
      ronian and early Aurignacian in western
      Europe: Continuity or discontinuity?', in
      Mellars, P & Stringer, C (eds), *The Human
      Revolution: Behavioural and Biological Perspectives
      on the Origins of Modern Humans*, Edinburgh
      University Press, Edinburgh, pp.677–713.

606   Lévêque, F & Vandermeersch, B 1980,
      'Découverte de restes humains dans un
      niveau castelperronien à Saint-Césaire,
      (Charente-Maritime)', *CR Acad Sci Paris* 291,
      pp.187–189

607   Hublin, J-J, Spoor, F, Braun, M, Zonneveld,
      F & Condemi, S 1996, 'A late Neanderthal
      associated with Upper Palaeolithic artifacts',
      Nature 381 (16 May), pp.224–226.

608   Gravina, B, Mellars, P, & Bronk, RC 2005,
      'Radiocarbon dating of interstratified
      Neanderthal and early modern human oc-
      cupations at the Chatelperronian type-site',
      Nature 483, pp.51–56.

609   Mellars, P, Gravina, B & Ramsey, CB 2007
      'Confirmation of Neanderthal/modern
      human interstratification at the Chatelper-
      ronian type-site', *Proceedings of the National
      Academy of Sciences USA* 104, (9), pp.3657–
      3662.

610 Hublin, J-J, Spoor, F, Braun, M, Zonneveld, F & Condemi, S 1996, 'A late Neanderthal associated with Upper Palaeolithic artifacts', *Nature* 381, pp.224–226.

611 Trinkaus, E, Ruff, CB, Churchill, SE & Vandermeersch, B 1998, 'Locomotion and body proportions of the Saint-Césaire 1 Châtelperronian Neandertal', *Proceedings of the National Academy of Sciences USA* 95, pp.5836–5840.

612 White, R 1982, 'Rethinking the Middle-Upper Paleolithic transition', *Current Anthropology* 23, pp.169–92.

613 White, R 1992a, 'Beyond art: Toward an understanding of the origins of material representation in Europe', *Annual Review of Anthropology* 21, pp.407– 431 .

614 Taborin, Y 2002, 'Les objets de parure et les curiosa', in Schmider, B, (ed.) *L'Aurignacien de la grotte du Renne, Les fouilles d'André Leroi-Gourhan à Arcy-sur-Cure (Yonne)*, Paris, Gallia Préhistoire Supplément, XXXIV, pp. 251–256.

615 White, R 2002, 'Observations technologiques sur les objets de parure', in Schmider, B (Ed), *L'Aurignacien de la grotte du Renne, Les fouilles d'André Leroi-Gourhan à Arcy-sur-Cure (Yonne)*, Paris, Gallia Préhistoire Supplément XXXIV, pp.257–266.

616 Demars, PY & Hublin, JJ 1989, 'La transition Neandertaliens/hommes de type moderne en Europe occidentale: Aspects paleontologiques et culturels', in Otte, M (ed.) *L'homme de Neandertal, vol. 7, L'extinction*, pp.23–37, Likge: ERAUL.

617 Dobson, JE 1998, 'The iodine factor in health and evolution', *Geographical Review* 88(1), pp.1–28.

618 Zilhao, J & d'Errico, F 1999, 'The chronology and taphonomy of the earliest Aurignacian and its implications for the understanding of Neandertal extinction', *Journal of World Prehistory* 13, pp.1–68.

619 Smith FH, 1984, 'Fossil hominids from the Upper Pleistocene of Central Europe and the origin of modern Europeans', in Spencer, F, (Ed) *The origins of modern humans: A world survey of the fossil evidence*, Alan R Liss, New York, pp.137–210.

620 Stringer, C 2002, 'Modern human origins: progress and prospects', *Phil. Trans. R. Soc. Lond. B* 357, pp.563–579.

621 Trinkaus, E 2006, 'Late Neandertals & Early Modern Humans: Biology, Behavior and Population Dynamics', *Terra Nostra; 150 Years of Neanderthal Discoveries*, 21–26 July, 2006, Bonn, Germany, Congress, pp.74–83.

622 Jolly, CJ 2001, 'A proper study for mankind: Analogies from the Papionin monkeys and their implications for human evolution', *American Journal of Physical Anthropology* 116, (33), pp.177–204.

623 Brauer, G 2008, 'The Origin of Modern Anatomy: By Speciation or Intraspecific Evolution?' *Evolutionary Anthropology* 17, pp.22–37.

624 Smith, FH, Falsetti, AB & Donnelly, SM 1989, 'Modern human origins', *Yearbook of Physical Anthropology* 32, pp.35–68.

625 Wolpoff, MH, Xinzhi, W & Thorne, AG 1984, 'Modern Homo sapiens origins: a general theory of hominid evolution involving the fossil evidence from east Asia', in Smith, FH & Spencer, F (eds), *The Origins of Modern Humans: A World Survey of the Fossil Evidence*, pp.411–483, Alan R Liss, New York.

626 Serre, D et al 2004, 'No evidence of Neandertal mtDNA contribution to early modern humans', *PLoS Biol.* 2, pp.0313–0317.

627 Krings, M et al. 2000, 'A view of Neanderthal genetic diversity', *Nature Genetics* 26, pp.144–146.

628 Caramelli, D, Lalueza-Fox, C, Vernesi, C, Lari, M, Casoli, A et al. 2003, 'Evidence for a genetic discontinuity between Neandertals and 24,000-years-old anatomically modern Europeans', *Proceedings of the National Academy of Sciences USA* 100, pp.6593–97.

629 Krings, M, Stone, A, Schmitz, RW, Krainitzki, H, Stoneking, M et al. 1997, 'Neandertal DNA sequences and the origin of modern humans', *Cell* 90, pp.19–30.

630 Weaver, TD & Roseman, CC 2008, 'New Developments in the Genetic Evidence for Modern Human Origins', *Evolutionary Anthropology* 17, pp.69–80

631 Krings, M, Stone, A, Schmitz, RW, Krainitzki, H, Stoneking, M, Pääbo, S 1997, 'Neandertal DNA sequences and the origin of modern humans', *Cell* 90, pp.19–30.

632 Duarte, C, Maurício, J, Pettitt, PB, Souto, P, Trinkaus, E, van der Plicht, H & Zilhão, J 1999, 'The early Upper Paleolithic human skeleton from the Abrigo do Lagar Velho (Portugal) and modern human emergence in Iberia', *PNSS* 96 (13), pp.7604–7609.

633 Tattersall, I & Schwartz, JH 1999, Commentary: 'Hominids and hybrids: The place of Neanderthals in human evolution', *Proceedings of the National Academy of Sciences USA* 96, pp.7117–7119.

634 Trinkaus, E & Zilhao, J 1999, 'A Correction to the Commentary of Tattersall and Schwartz Concerning the Interpretation of the Lagar Velho 1 Child', www.ipa.min-cultura.pt/docs/eventos/lapedo/lv-faq_corr.html

635 Voisin, Jean-Luc, 2006, 'New interpretation for Neandertal extinction', Poster; Terra Nostra Conference: '150 years of Neanderthal discoveries; Early Europeans—Continuity & Discontinuity', 21–26 July, 2006, Bonn, Germany, p.140.

636 Brownmiller, S 1975, *Against Our Will: Men, Women, and Rape*, Simon and Schuster.

637 Finlayson, C 2004, *Neanderthals and Modern Humans: An Ecological and Evolutionary Perspective*, Cambridge University Press, Cambridge.

638 Finlayson, C et al. 2006, 'Late survival of Neanderthals at the southernmost extreme of Europe', *Nature*, published online 13 September.

639 Wendt, H 1963, *Op zoek naar de eerste mens*, de Haan, Zeist.

640 Bigelow, R 1969, *The Dawn Warriors: Man's Evolution towards Peace*, Little, Brown, Boston.

641 Gat, A 1999, 'Social organization, group conflict and the demise of Neanderthals', *Mankind Quarterly* 39, (4), pp.437–54.

642 Birdsell, JB 1972, *Human Evolution: An Introduction to the New Physical Anthropology*, Rand-McNally, Chicago.

643 Tattersall, I 1995, *The Fossil Trail: How We Know What We Think We Know about Human Evolution*, Oxford University Press, New York, p.202.

644 Boule, M 1912, *Les hommes fossiles*, Masson, Paris.

645 Cioffi-Revilla, C 1996, 'Origins and evolution of war and politics', *International Studies Quarterly* 40, pp.1–22.

646 Diamond, J 1992, *The Third Chimpanzee: The Evolution and Future of the Human Animal*, Harper Collins, New York, p45.

647 Richards, G 1987, *Human Evolution: An Introduction for the Behavioural Sciences*, Routledge & Kegan Paul, London.

648 Schaefer, U 1957, 'Homo neanderthalensis, (King), 1. Das Skelet aus dem Neandertal', *Z. Morphol. Anthropol.* 48, pp.268–97.

649 Trinkaus, E 1983, *The Shanidar Neandertals*, Academic, New York.

650 Trinkaus, E 1985, 'Pathology and the posture of the La Chapelle-aux-Saints Neandertal', *American Journal of Physical Anthropology* 67, pp.19–41.

651 Berger, TD & Trinkaus, E 1995, 'Patterns of trauma among the Neandertals', *Journal of Archaeological Science* 22 (66), pp.841–852.

652 Rand M, & Strom, K 1997, 'Violence-related Injuries in Hospital Emergency Departments Spec'. *Rep. Publ. NCJ, – 156921*, Washington, DC. US Dept. Justice Bur. Justice Stat.

653 Walker, PL 2001, 'A Bioarchaeological Perspective on the History of Violence', *Annual Review of Anthropology*, 30, pp.573–596.

654 Eldrege, N 1997, *Dominion*, University of California Press, P.86.

655 Finlayson, C, 2004, *Neanderthals and Modern Humans: An Ecological and Evolutionary Perspective*, Cambridge University Press.

656 Milliken, S 2007, 'Neanderthals, Anatomically Modern Humans, and 'Modern Human Behaviour' in Italy', *Oxford Journal Of Archaeology*, 26, (4), pp.331–358.

657 Ibid. p.3.

658 Milliken, S 1999, 'The earliest occupation of Italy', *Accordia Research Papers* 7, pp.7–36.

659 Tzedakis, PC, Hughen, KA, Cach, I & Harvati, K 2007, 'Placing late Neanderthals in a climatic context', *Nature* 449, pp.206–208.

660 Harvati, K 2007, 'New evidence on the role of climate in Neanderthal extinction', *Eureka Alert*.

661 Banks, WE, d'Errico, F, Peterson, AT, Kageyama, M, Sima, A, et al. 2008, 'Neanderthal Extinction by Competitive Exclusion', *PLoS ONE* 3, (12).

662 Stringer, CB, Finlayson, JC, R N E Barton, RNE, Fernández-Jalvo, Y, Cáceres, I, Sabin, RC, Rhodes, EJ, Currant, AP, Rodríguez-Vidal, J, Giles-Pacheco, F & Riquelme-Cantal JA 2008 'Neanderthal exploitation of marine mammals in Gibraltar', *Proceedings of the National Academy of Sciences USA* 2008 105, pp.14319–14324.

663 Biraben, J-N 2003, 'The rising numbers of humankind', *Population and Societies*, 394, pp.1–4.

664 Renfrew, C 2001, 'Commodification and Institution in Group-Oriented and Individualizing Societies', in W G Runciman (ed.) , *The Origin of Human Social Institutions*, Oxford University Press, Oxford, p.93.

665 Jablonski, NG & Chaplin, G 2000, 'The evolution of human skin coloration', *Journal of Human Evolution* 39, pp.57–106.

666 Pearce, N et al. 2004, 'Genetics, race, ethnicity, and health', *British Medical Journal* 328, pp.1070–1072.

667 Witherspoon, D J et al. 2007, 'Genetic Similarities Within and Between Human Populations' *Genetics* 176, pp.351–359.

668 Pawlowski, B, Dunbar, RIM & Lipowicz, A 2000, 'Evolutionary fitness: Tall men have more reproductive success', *Nature* 403 (156).

669 Mueller, J 1984, 'Underestimating the Enemy Caused Defeat', in Dudley, W & Bender, D (eds), *The Vietnam War: Opposing Viewpoints*, Greenhaven Press, pp.66–69.

670 Kutler, G 2007, 'US Military Fatalities in Iraq in Perspective: Year 4', *Orbis* 51 (3), pp.511–527.

671 Inbar, E 2007, 'How Israel Bungled the Second Lebanon War', *Middle East Quarterly*, Summer, pp.57–65.

672 Eibl-Eibesfeldt, I 1979, *The Biology of Peace and War*, Viking Press, NY.

673 Vencl, S 1999, 'Stone Age warfare', in Carman J, Harding A (eds), *Ancient warfare, archaeological perspectives*, Sutton Publishing, Ltd, Phoenix Mill, pp.57–73.

674 Schulting R & Wysocki, M 2005, 'An assessment of the evidence for cranial trauma in the British Neolithic', *Proceedings of the Prehistoric*, 71, pp.107–138.

675 Schulting, RJ & Wysocki, M 2002, 'Cranial trauma in the British earlier Neolithic', *Past* 41, pp.4–6.

676 Thorpe, N 2000, 'Origins of war: Mesolithic conflict in Europe', *British Archeology* 52, pp.9–12.

677 Frayer, D 1997, 'Ofnet: evidence for a Mesolithic massacre', in Frayer DW, (ed.), *Troubled times: violence and warfare in the past*, Gordon and Breach Publishers, Amsterdam, pp.181–216.

678 Keeley, LH 1997, 'Frontier Warfare in the Early Neolithic', in *Troubled Times*, Miller, D & Frayer, D (eds), pp.303–319, Gordon and Breach, Australia.

679 Bracha, HS, Yoshioka, DT, Masukawa, NK & Stockman, DJJ 2005, 'Evolution of the human fear-circuitry and acute sociogenic pseudoneurological symptoms: The Neolithic balanced-polymorphism hypothesis', *Journal of Affective Disorders* 88, pp.119–129.

680 LeBlanc, SA, Register, KE 2003, *Constant Battles: The Myth of the Peaceful, Noble Savage*, St Martin's Press, New York, p.3.

681 Schultz, AH 1949, 'Sex Differences in the Pelves of Primates', *American Journal of Physical Anthropology* 7, pp.401–424.

682 Leutenegger, W 1972, 'Functional Aspects of Pelvis Morphology of Simian Primates', *Journal of Human Evolution* 3, pp.201–222.

683 Trevathan, WR 1987, *Human Birth: An Evolutionary Perspective*, Aldine de Gruyter, Hawthorne, NY.

684 Trevathan, WR 1996, 'The Evolution of Bipedalism and Assisted Birth', *Medical Anthropology Quarterly*, New Series 10 (2), The Social Production of Authoritative Knowledge in Pregnancy and Childbirth, pp.287–290.

685 Gibbons, A 1996, 'Homo erectus in Java: a 250,000-year anachronism', *Science*, 274 (5294), pp.1870–1874.

686 Pearce, RH & Barbetti, M 1981, 'A 38,000-year-old archaeological site at Upper Swan, Western Australia', *Archaeology in Oceania* 16, pp.173–178.

687 O'Connella, JF & Allen, J 2004, 'Dating the colonization of Sahul (Pleistocene Australia–New Guinea): a review of recent research', *Journal of Archaeological Science* 31, pp.835–853.

688 Thorne, AG & Macumber, PG 1972, 'Discoveries of Late Pleistocene man at Kow Swamp', *Nature* 238, pp.316–319.

689 Stone, T, & Cupper, ML 2003, 'Last Glacial Maximum ages for robust humans at Kow Swamp, southern Australia', *Journal of Human Evolution* 45, pp.1–13.

690 Brown, P, Sutikna, T, Morwood, MJ, Soejono, RP, Jatmiko, Saptomo, EW & Due, RA 2004, 'A new small-bodied hominin from the late Pleistocene of Flores, Indonesia', *Nature* 431, pp.1055–61.

691 Morwood, MJ et al. 2004, 'Archaeology and age of a new hominin from Flores in eastern Indonesia', *Nature* 431, pp.1087–91.

692 Falk, D et al. 2007, 'Brain shape in human microcephalics and Homo floresiensis', *Proceedings of the National Academy of Sciences* 104 (7), pp.2513.

693 Miller, GH, Magee, JW, Johnson, BJ, Fogel, ML, Spooner, NA, McCulloch, MT & Ayliffe, L 1999, 'Pleistocene extinction of Genyornis newtoni: Human impact on Australian megafauna', *Science* 283, pp.205–208.

694 Flannery, T & Roberts, RG 1999, 'Late Quaternary extinctions in Australasia', in MacPhee, RDE (ed.), *Extinctions in Near Time: Causes, Contexts and Consequences*, Plenum, New York, pp.239–256.

695 Grayson, DK 2001, 'The archaeological record of human impacts on animal populations', *Journal of World Prehistory* 15, pp.1–65.

696 Eller, E 2001, 'Estimating relative population sizes from simulated data sets and the question of greater African effective size', *American Journal of Physical Anthropology* 116, pp.1–12.

697 Spencer, H 1892/1895, *The Principles of Ethics*, Williams & Norgate London; Appleton, New York.

698 Darwin, C 1874, *The Descent of Man*, Chapter II, (2nd Edition 1887, p.64).

699 Monod, J 1971/1975, *Chance and Necessity: An Essay on the Natural Philosophy of Modern Biology*, Knopf, New York.

700 Bigelow, R 1975, The role of competition and cooperation in human aggression, in Nettleship, MA, Givens, RD & Nettleship, A (eds), *War, its causes and correlates*, Mouton, The Hague, pp. 235–61.

701 Pitt, R 1978, 'Warfare and hominid brain evolution', *Journal of Theoretical Biology* 72 (3), pp.551–75.

702 Alexander, RD 1979, *Darwinism and Human Affairs*, University of Washington Press, Seattle.

703 Rummel, RJ 1994, *Death By Government*, Transaction Publishers, New Brunswick, NJ.

704 Stanton, GH 1998, *The Eight Stages of Genocide: How Governments Can Tell When Genocide Is Coming and What They Can Do To Stop It*, Woodrow Wilson Center Press.

705 Shaw, PR, & Wong, Y 1989, *Genetic Seeds of Warfare: Evolution, Nationalism, and Patriotism*, Routledge, p.78

706 Williamson, SH, Hubisz, MJ, Clark, AG, Payseur, BA, Bustamante, CD et al. 2007, 'Localizing Recent Adaptive Evolution in the Human Genome', *PLoS Genetics* 3 (6).

707 Ibid.

708 Voight, BF, Kudaravalli, S, Wen, X & Pritchard, JK 2006, 'A Map of Recent Positive Selection in the Human Genome', *PLoS Biology* 4 (3).

709 Lamason, RL, Mohideen, M, Mest, JR, Wong, AC, Norton, HL, et al. 2005, 'SLC24A5, a putative cation exchanger, affects pigmentation in zebrafish and humans', *Science* 310, pp.1782–1786.

710 Frost, P 2006, 'European hair and eye color: A case of frequency-dependent sexual selection?' *Evolution and Human Behavior* 27(2), pp.85–103.

711 Baumeister, FA, Egger, J, Schildhauer, MT, Stengel-Rutkowski, S 1993, 'Ambras syndrome: delineation of a unique hypertrichosis universalis congenita and association with a balanced pericentric inversion (8), (p11.2; p22)', *Clinical Genetics* 44 (3), pp.121–128.

712 Bennike, P 2008, *Evidence for trauma in earlier Neolithic Denmark, Conference: Neolithic violence in a European perspective*, School of Archaeology, University of Oxford, 14–15 March.

713 Walker, PL 2001, 'A bioarchaeological perspective on the history of violence', *Annual Review of Anthropology* 30, Academic Research Library, pp.573–596.

714 Knauft, BM 1987, 'Reconsidering violence in simple human societies', *Current Anthropology* 28, 457–498.

715 Robb, J 1997, 'Violence and gender in early Italy', in Martin, DL, Frayer, DW, (eds), *Troubled times: violence and warfare in the past*, Gordon and Breach, Amsterdam, pp.111–144.

716 Walker, PL 2001, 'A bioarchaeological perspective on the history of violence', *Annual Review of Anthropology* 30, pp.573–596.

717 Villa, P & Courtin, J 1991, 'Cannibalism in the Neolithic', *Nature* 351, pp.613–614.

718 Villa, P et al. 1986, 'Cannibalism in the Neolithic', *Science* 233 (4762), pp.431–437.

719 Angel, JL 1974, 'Patterns of fracture from Neolithic to modern times', *Anthropol/Kozlemenyek* 18, pp.9–18.

720 Robb, J 1997, 'Violence and gender in early Italy', in Martin DL, Frayer DW (eds), *Troubled times: violence and warfare in the past*, Gordon and Breach, Amsterdam, pp.111–144.

721 Heider, K 1970, *The Dugum Dani: A Papuan culture in the highlands of West New Guinea*, Aldine Transaction.

722 Chagnon, NA 1983, *Yanomamo: The Fierce People*, CBS College Publishing, New York, NY.

723 Robarchek, C & Robarchek, C 1997, *Waorani: The Contexts of Violence and War*, Harcourt Brace College Publishers.

724 Neill, D 2007, 'Review: Cortical evolution and human behaviour', *Brain Research Bulletin* 74, pp.191–205.

725 Barbas, H 2000, 'Connections underlying the synthesis of cognition, memory and emotion in primate prefrontal cortices', *Brain Research Bulletin* 52, pp.319–330.

726 Dehaene, S & Changeux, J-P 2005, 'Ongoing spontaneous activity controls access to consciousness: a neural model for inattentional blindness', *PLoS Biol.* 3, (e141).

727 Neill, D 2007, 'Review: Cortical evolution and human behaviour', *Brain Research Bulletin* 74, pp.191–205.

728 Smith, AD 1987, *The Ethnic Origins of Nations*, Blackwell.

729 Banks, M 1996, *Ethnicity: Anthropological Constructions*, Routledge, p.151.

730 McGuire, WJ, McGuire, CV, Child, P & Fujioka, T 1978, 'Salience of ethnicity in the spontaneous self-concept as a function of one's ethnic distinctiveness in the social environment', *Journal of Personality and Social Psychology* 36 (5), pp.511–20.

731 Eriksen, TH 2001, *Small places, large issues, An introduction to social and cultural anthropology* (2nd Ed.), London, p.261.

732 Alexander, RD 1971, 'The Search for an Evolutionary Philosophy of Man', *Proceedings of the Royal Society of Victoria (Melbourne)* 84, pp.99–120.

733 Bairoch, P 1988, *Cities and Economic Development: From the Dawn of History to the Present*, University of Chicago Press, Chicago.

734 Kelly, RL 1995, *The Foraging Spectrum: Diversity in Hunter-Gatherer Lifeways*, Smithsonian Institution, Washington.

735 Barnard, A J, (ed.) 2004, *Hunter-gatherers in history, archaeology and anthropology*, Berg.

736 Johnson, A & Earle, T 1987, *The Evolution of Human Societies: From Foraging Group to Agrarian State*, Stanford University Press.

737 Childe, VG 1936, *Man Makes Himself*, Watts and Co, London.

738 Hayden, B 1990, 'Nimrods, piscators, pluckers, and planters: the emergence of food production', *Journal of Anthropological Archaeology* 9, pp.31–69.

739 Fernandez-Armesto, F 2001, *Food: A History*, Macmillan, London.

740 Harlan, JR 1995, *The Living Fields: Our Agricultural Heritage*, Cambridge University Press, Cambridge.

741 Smith, BD 1995, *The Emergence of Agriculture*, Scientific American Library, New York.

742 Hayden B, 1990, 'Nimrods, piscators, pluckers, and planters: the emergence of food production.', *Journal of Anthropological Archaeology* 9, pp.31–69.

743 Weisdorf, J 2005, *From Foraging to Farming: Explaining the Neolithic Revolution*, Institute of Economics, University of Copenhagen, Blackwell Publishing.

744 Smith, VL 1975, 'The Primitive Hunter Culture, Pleistocene Extinction, and the Rise of Agriculture', *Journal of Political Economy* 83, pp.727–755.

745 Hayden, B 1990, 'Nimrods, piscators, pluckers, and planters: the emergence of food production', *Journal of Anthropological Archaeology* 9, pp.31–69.

746 Locay, L 1989. 'From Hunting and Gathering to Agriculture', *Economic Development and Cultural Change* 37, pp.737–756.

747 Morand, OF 2002, *Evolution Through Revolutions: Growing Populations and Changes in Modes of Production*, University of Connecticut.

748 Weisdorf, JL 2003b, *Stone Age Economics: The Origins of Agriculture and the Emergence of Non-Food Specialists*, Discussion Paper No. 03–34, University of Copenhagen.

749 Wade, N 2006, *Before the Dawn: Recovering the Lost History of Our Ancestors*, The Penguin Press, New York, p.125.

750 North, DC & Thomas, RP 1977, 'The First Economic Revolution', *Economic History Review* 30, pp.229–241.

751 Greg Wadley & Angus Martin, 1993, 'The origins of agriculture – a biological perspective and a new hypothesis', *Australian Biologist* 6, pp.96–105.

752 Cohen, MN 1989, *Health and the rise of civilization*, Yale University Press, New Haven.

753 Cohen, M N 1977, 'Population pressure and the origins of agriculture: an archaeological example from the coast of Peru', in Reed, CA (ed.) , *The origins of agriculture*, Mouton, The Hague.

754 MacNeish, RS 1974, 'Reflections on my search for the beginnings of agriculture in Mexico', in Willey, GR (Ed), *Archaeological researchers in retrospect*, University Press of America, Washington, DC, pp.207–234.

755 Kenyon, KM 1957, *Digging Up Jericho*, Ernest Benn, London, pp.261–62.

756 McKeown, T 1988, *The Origin of Human Disease*, Blackwell Publishers Ltd, Oxford, pp.233.

757 Black, FL 1975, 'Infectious diseases in primitive societies', *Science* 187, pp.515–518.

758 Wade, N 2006, *Before the Dawn: Recovering the Lost History of Our Ancestors*, The Penguin Press, New York, p.124.

759 Lee, R B & DeVore, I 1968, 'Problems in the study of hunters and gatherers,' in Lee, RB & DeVore, I (eds), *Man the hunter*, Aldine, Chicago.

760 Cohen, M N, 1977. 'Population pressure and the origins of agriculture: an archaeological example from the coast of Peru', in Reed, CA, (ed.), *The origins of agriculture*, Mouton, The Hague.

761 Peterson, J 1998, 'The Natufian Hunting Conundrum: Spears, Atlatls, or Bows? Musculoskeletal and Armature Evidence', *International Journal of Osteoarchaeology* 8, pp.378–380.

762 Evans, RK, & Rasson, JA 1984, 'Ex Balcanis Lux? Recent Developments in Neolithic and Chalcolithic Research in Southeast Europe', *American Antiquity* 49 (4), pp.713–741.

763 Tringham, R 1971, *Hunters, Fishers and Farmers of Eastern Europe: 6000–3000 BC*, Hutchinson University Library, London.

764 Cronk, L 1999, *That Complex Whole: Culture and the Evolution of Human Behavior*, Westview Press.

765 McCullough, DW (ed.) 1998, *Chronicles of the Barbarians*, Times Books.

766 Finnane, M 2001, "Payback', Customary Law and Criminal Law in Colonised Australia', *International Journal of the Sociology of Law*, 29 (4) December, pp.293–310.

767 Watson, L 1995, *Dark Nature: A Natural History of Evil*, Hodder and Stoughton, p.145.

768 Conard, NJ 2003, 'Palaeolithic ivory sculptures from southwestern Germany and the origins of figurative art', *Nature* 426 (18), p.25.

769 Lefkowitz, M 1993, *Seduction and rape in Greek myth, Consent and coercion to sex and marriage in ancient and medieval societies*, Laiou, AE (ed.), Washington, DC, Dumbarton Oaks Research Library and Collection.

770   Robson, E 1997, 'Bestiality and bestial rape in Greek myth', in *Rape in antiquity: Sexual Violence in the Greek and Roman worlds*, Deacy, S & Pierce, KF, Duckworth, London, pp.65–96.

771   Batra, R 1994, *Wild Men in the Looking Glass: The Mythic Origins of European Otherness*, The University of Michigan Press, Ann Arbor.

772   Bernheimer, R 1952, *Wild Men in the Middle Ages: A Study in Art, Sentiment and Demonology*, Harvard University Press, Cambridge, Massachusetts.

773   Campbell, J 1949, *The Hero with a Thousand Faces*, Bollingen Foundation Inc.

774   Campbell, J 1987, *The Masks of God: Primitive Mythology*, Penguin Books.

775   Stookey, L 2004, *Thematic Guide to World Mythology*, Greenwood Press, p.8.

776   Quoted in Carroll, RT, 'Bigfoot [aka Abominable Snowman of the Himalayas, Mapinguari (the Amazon), Sasquatch, Yowie (Australia) and Yeti (Asia)]', *Skeptical Inquirer*, Internet paper.

777   Almas (Cryptozoology), Wikipedia, http://en.wikipedia.org/wiki/Almas_28cryptozoology29 downloaded 2 April, 2008.

778   Barmanou, Wikipedia, http://en.wikipedia.org/wiki/Barmanour downloaded 2 April, 2008.

779   Moehau, Wikipedia, http://en.wikipedia.org/wiki/Moehau, downloaded 2 April, 2008.

780   Bigfoot, Wikipedia. http://en.wikipedia.org/wiki/Sasquatch Downloaded 2nd April, 2008

781   Nguoi Rung, Wikipedia. http://en.wikipedia.org/wiki/Nguoi_Rung Downloaded 2nd April, 2008

782   Tjutjuna. Wikipedia, http://en.wikipedia.org/wiki/Chuchunaa. Downloadedd 2nd April, 2008

783   Orang Mawas, Wikipedia, http://en.wikipedia.org/wiki/Orang_Mawas Downloaded, 2nd April, 2008

784   Maricoxi, Wikipedia. http://en.wikipedia.org/wiki/Maricoxi Downloaded 2nd April, 2008

785   Neff, D 2001, 'Nearly Two Decades Later, Ariel Sharon Is Indicted For Sabra and Shatila War Crimes. Special Report', Washington Report on Middle East Affairs, August/September 2001, p.9.

786   Golub, S 1989, *Periods: From Menarche to Menopause*, Sage Publications, London, pp.38–43.

787   Cohen, P quoted in Goleman, D 1989, 'Pioneering Studies Find Surprisingly High Rate Of Mental Ills in Young', New York Times, 10 January.

788   Darwin, C 1859, Personal correspondence to L Jenyns Ilkley, Yorkshire, 13 November.

789   Armstrong, JS 1997, 'Peer Review for Journals: Evidence on Quality Control, Fairness, and Innovation', *Science and Engineering Ethics* 3, pp.63–84.

790   Kuhn, TS 1962, *The Structure of Scientific Revolutions*, University of Chicago Press, Chicago.

791   Mahoney, M 1977, 'Publication prejudices: An experimental study of confirmatory bias in the peer review system', Cognitive Therapy and Research 1, pp.161–175.

792   Darwin, C 1859, *The Origin of Species*, Random House Edition, 1993,'Conclusion' p.639.

793   Plaut, M 2004, 'Profile: Uganda's LRA rebels', BBC News, Friday, 6 February, online web site: http://news.bbc.co.uk/2/hi/africa/3462901.stm.

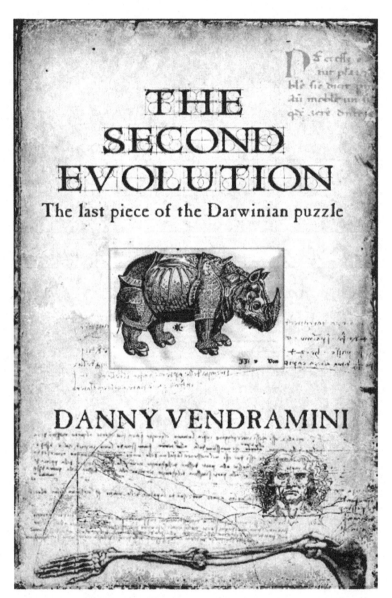

Watch out for *The Second Evolution*, Danny Vendramini's forthcoming book on Teem theory.
Find out more at www.thesecondevolution.com

"We've been called the 'third chimpanzee'. Instead, Vendramini
asks: Why are we such a distinctively odd primate species—
anatomically, behaviourally, and beset by dark atavistic fears?
His thesis that intensive predation by Neanderthals enforced rapid,
protective, evolutionary changes offers innovative insight into the
many things about 'us' that we might otherwise take for granted.
A well-argued case to be answered."

Professor Tony McMichael, Australian National University

Put aside everything you thought you knew about Neanderthals. Evolutionary detective Danny Vendramini's meticulous research shows they were not docile omnivores, but savage, cannibalistic carnivores: the 'apex predators' of the stone age. And everything else—including humans—was their prey.

Vendramini's Neanderthal predation theory argues that the evolution of modern humans—including our unique physiology, sexuality and human nature–is the result of systematic long-term sexual predation and cannibalism by Eurasian Neanderthals.

Neanderthal predation theory is one of those groundbreaking concepts that revolutionises scientific thinking. It represents a quantum leap in our understanding of human origins.

"Sometimes it takes an outsider to cut through the most intractable problems in science. That is what Vendramini's approach offers the reader in his daring claims about the interactions between humans and their most famous evolutionary relatives, the Neanderthals." Professor Iain Davidson, Australian Studies, Harvard University, Emeritus Professor of Archaeology, University of New England

"Danny Vendramini presents a truly unique and innovative picture of the role of Neandertal predation in human evolution... Vendramini pulls together countless different threads of scientific evidence to re-cast Neandertals as "apex predators", proverbial "wolves with knives" who were effective rivals with our ancestors... It has been a long time since I read a book about human evolution that I enjoyed so much." Professor John Shea, Stony Brook University, New York

Danny Vendramini has had successful careers as a theatre director, international award-winning film director and scriptwriter. Since 1999, he has devoted his attention to theoretical biology, specialising in the evolution of behaviour and human origins. He lives in Sydney and is married to the writer, Rosie Scott.

kardoorairpress

Made in the USA
Las Vegas, NV
07 February 2024

85383911R00214